ALAN ROGERS SELECT

EUROPE

over 400 of the best campsites across Europe

alan rogers

full page listings
easy-to-use maps
comprehensive writeups

Compiled by: Alan Rogers Travel Ltd

Editorial & Production
Editor: Robin Fearn - enquiries@alanrogers.com
Production & Cartography: Robert Baker
Visual Design: Ben Tully

Advertising
UK Sales: Jo Smethurst - jo@alanrogers.com
Europe Sales: Minou Gurmeet - minou@alanrogers.com

European Advertising Agencies
France: ICCS International Tourism Promotions - info@iccsfrance.com
Spain: Servicios Turisticos Heinze Latzke S.A. - info@servitur-heinze.com
Portugal: Roteiro Lda - info@roteiro-campista.pt
Belgium & Netherlands: CampingMedia - jos@campingmedia.info
Rest of Europe: Straver E-Marketing Projecten - info@cornelstraver.nl

Alan Rogers Travel
Chief Operating Officer: Chris Newey
Finance Manager: Alison Harris
IT Manager: Roland Greenstreet

Special thanks to Campsite Assessors
John & Margaret Corrall, Paul & Jill Bate-Jones,
Pete Lowen & Ann Cazenave, Mike Annan

Cover Photograph
Château de l'Epervière - Page 132
By Thomas Lambelin, www.lambelin.com

Published by: Alan Rogers Travel Ltd,
Spelmonden Old Oast, Goudhurst, Kent TN17 1HE
www.alanrogers.com

52nd edition - February 2020
ISBN 978-1-909057-94-4

Printed in Great Britain by Stephens & George Print Group

Stay in touch alanrogers.com/signup

Contact us alanrogers.com/contact

facebook.com/alanrogerstravel

twitter.com/alanrogers

instagram.com/alanrogerstravel

Welcome

to the 52nd edition

Alan Rogers Guides were first published over 50 years ago. Since Alan Rogers published the first campsite guide that bore his name, the nature of European campsites has changed immeasurably.

Back in 1968 many campsites, though well established, were still works in progress having been converted from farms and orchards in the post-war years. Of course, there were fewer to choose from than today, and the quality levels varied hugely.

Over the 52 years since the first edition of the Alan Rogers guide, the quality of most campsites has evolved in leaps and bounds. In terms of today's facilities, infrastructure, technology and accommodation types, there is very little comparison with what was on offer half a century ago.

Since 1968 we at Alan Rogers have developed longstanding relationships with many campsites. We have worked with different generations of campsite owners and shared with many of them the trials and tribulations along the way. Typically, campsite owners are a hardy breed, passionate about their campsite and ever keen to show it and their region off to every visitor.

The Alan Rogers guides have always aimed to celebrate the variety, recognise the quality and salute the unique (check out our annual awards on pages 10–11). So read on and find the perfect campsite for your next holiday, whatever type of campsite that may be.

Whether you're an old hand in terms of camping and caravanning or are contemplating your first trip, a regular Alan Rogers reader or a new convert, we wish you well in your travels and some pleasurable 'armchair touring' in the meantime!

28

number of sites featured in our first guide that are still on our website

434

number of guides we've published since 1968

8,000+

number of campsite that we feature on our website

*"Alan Rogers considers that the greatest degree of comfort is obtained by using organised camping sites and, more especially, by using **only the best** of these sites. Alan Rogers' Selected Sites for Caravanning and Camping in Europe 1968 enables you to do just this."*

Alan Rogers
1918 - 2000

1918 Alan Rogers is born in Warwickshire.

1939 Rogers works as a wireless telegrapher for the RAF during World War Two.

1948 After the war, Rogers devoted much of his leisure time to his twin passions of rallying and caravanning. He spent long periods over the summer with his wife Ruth exploring newly founded continental campsites and collecting information on these sites.

1967 Work begins on compiling his first official guide to camping. It goes on sale the following year.

1986 Rogers retires. He continues inspecting campsites until the mid 1990s.

2001 Aged 81, Alan passes away. His legacy lives on through the annual guides that bear his name.

Alan Rogers

in search of 'only the best'

There are many thousands of campsites across Europe of varying quality: this guide contains impartially written reports on over 400, including many of the very finest, in 19 countries. Are there more? Yes, of course, and in countries not included in this book. Online at alanrogers.com you'll find details of many more - over 8,000 campsites.

Put simply, a guide like this can never be exhaustive. We have had to make difficult editorial decisions with the aim of providing you with a selection of the best, rather than information on all – in short, a more selective approach.

We are mindful that people want different things from their choice of campsite so we try to include a range of campsite 'styles' to cater for a wide variety of preferences: from those seeking a small peaceful campsite in the heart of the countryside, to visitors looking for an 'all singing, all dancing' site in a popular seaside resort.

Those with more specific interests, such as sporting facilities, cultural events or historical attractions, are also catered for. The size of the site, whether it's part of a chain or privately owned, should make no difference in terms of quality. The key is that it should be 'fit for purpose' in order to shine and stand out.

If a campsite can identify and understand what kind of campsite it sets out to be, and who it wants to attract, then it can enhance its kerb appeal by developing with that in mind.

By way of example, a lakeside campsite with credentials as a serious windsurfing centre should probably offer equipment for hire, secure storage for customers' own kit, courses and tuition, meteorological feeds and so on.

A campsite in the heart of the Loire Valley might offer guided excursions to local châteaux, weekly tastings of regional wine and cheese, suggested walking or cycling itineraries to local châteaux with entry discounts and so on.

Whatever style of campsite you're seeking, we hope you'll find some inspiration here.

Country

Alan Rogers reference code and on-site information including accommodation count, pitch count, GPS coordinates, Postcode and campsite address.

Campsite Name

Campsite contact information

Opening dates

A description of the site in which we try to give an idea of its general features - its size, its situation, its strengths and its weaknesses. This section should provide a picture of the site itself with reference to the facilities that are provided and if they impact on its appearance or character. We include details on approximate pitch numbers, electricity (with amperage), hardstandings etc. in this section as pitch design, planning and terracing affect the site's overall appearance. Similarly, we include a reference to pitches used for caravan holiday homes, chalets, and the like.

Lists more specific information on the site's facilities and amenities and, where available, the dates when these facilities are open (if not for the whole season).

Below we list 'Key Feautres.' These are features we think are important and make the site individual.

- Beach nearby
- Dogs allowed
- Open all year
- Fishing
- Watersports
- Golf

This is a QR code. You can scan it with your smartphone and it will take you directly to the campsite listing on our website. Download a QR code app for your phone and try it!

How to use

this guide

The layout of this edition is similar to our 2018 anniversary edition Europe guide but different from previous editions. We still aim to provide comprehensive information, written in plain English in an easy to use format, but a few words of explanation regarding the content may be helpful.

Toilet blocks Typically, toilet blocks will be equipped with WCs, washbasins with hot and cold water and hot shower cubicles. They will have all necessary shelves, hooks, plugs and mirrors. There will be a chemical toilet disposal point, and the campsite will provide water and waste-water drainage points and bin areas.

Shop Basic or fully supplied, and opening dates.

Bars, restaurants, takeaway facilities and entertainment: We try hard to supply opening and closing dates (if other than the campsite opening dates) and to identify if there are discos or other entertainment.

Swimming pools These might vary from a simple, conventional swimming pool to an elaborate complex with multiple pools and waterslides. Opening dates, charges and levels of supervision are provided where we have been notified. There is a regulation whereby Bermuda shorts may not be worn in swimming pools (for health and hygiene reasons). It is worth ensuring that you do take 'proper' swimming trunks with you.

Leisure facilities For example, playing fields, bicycle hire, organised activities and entertainment.

Dogs If dogs are not accepted, or restrictions apply, we state it here. If planning to take a dog, or other pet, we recommend you check in advance.

Opening dates Campsites can, and sometimes do alter these dates before the start of the season, often for good reasons. If you intend to visit shortly after a published opening date, or shortly before the closing date, it is wise to check that it will actually be open at the time required. Similarly, some sites operate a restricted service during the low season, only opening some of their facilities (e.g. swimming pools) during the main season. Again if you are at all doubtful, it is wise to check.

Sometimes, campsite amenities may be dependent on there being enough customers on-site to justify their opening. Some campsites may not be fully ready by their stated opening dates – grass may not all be cut or perhaps only limited sanitary facilities open. At the end of the season, they also tend to close down some facilities and generally wind things down.

We usually give an overview of the pitches, including an approximate quantity. This figure may vary year on year so is rarely absolute.

Awards 2019

by Alan Rogers and the Caravan and Motorhome Club

Launched in 2004, our awards have a broad scope and before committing to our winners, we carefully consider more than 2,000 campsites featured in the Alan Rogers guides and the Caravan and Motorhome Club 'Venture Abroad' program, taking into account comments from our site assessors, our head office team and, of course, our members & readers.

For the 2019 there were nine categories including two new categories, each with a winner and a highly commended runner-up.

Overall Winners 2019

Alan Rogers	PO8202	Turiscampo Algarve	Portugal	p380
CAMC	FR72030	Château de Chanteloup	France	p108

Progress Award 2019

This award reflects the hard work and commitment undertaken by particular site owners to improve and upgrade their site.

Winner	FR85680	Camping le Pin Parasol	France	p117
Runner-up	FR17856	Huttopia Chardons Bleu	France	p123

Welcome Award 2019

This award takes account of sites offering a particularly friendly welcome and maintaining a friendly ambience throughout readers' holidays.

Winner	DE31970	Eifel-Camp	Germany	p214
Runner-up	FR88120	Au Clos de la Chaume	France	p101

Eco Award 2019 NEW

Our Environmental Award acknowledges campsites which are emphasising care of the environment, possibly with features which are unique and cannot be found elsewhere.

Winner	FR41100	Camping les Saules	France	p113
Runner-up	AU0265	Park Grubhof	Austria	p18

Dog Award 2019 NEW

This award is made for sites which are particularly good for your four-legged friend.

Winner	IT62750	Fornella Camping	Italy	p289
Runner-up	CR6765	Camping Kovacine	Croatia	p50

Seaside Award 2019

This award is made for sites which we feel are particularly suitable for a really excellent seaside holiday.

Winner	FR66150	Les Criques de Porteils	France	p178
Runner-up	CR6782	Zaton Holiday Resort	Croatia	p53

Country Award 2019

This award contrasts with our seaside award and acknowledges sites which are attractively located in delightful, rural locations.

Winner	NL6449	Resort de Arendshorst	Netherlands	p351
Runner-up	ES90600	Camping Peña Montañesa	Spain	p439

All Year Award 2019

This award acknowledges sites which are open all year round.

Winner	ES83900	Vilanova Park	Spain	p422
Runner-up	ES87530	Caravaning La Manga	Spain	p433

Family Site Award 2019

Many sites claim to be family friendly but this award acknowledges the sites we feel to be the very best in this respect.

Winner	FR30290	Domaine de Massereau	France	p171
Runner-up	NL5970	Camping De Paal	Netherlands	p331

Small Campsite Award 2019

This award acknowledges excellent small campsites (fewer than 150 pitches) which offer a friendly welcome and top quality amenities throughout the season to their guests.

Winner	FR24740	Domaine des Mathevies	France	p158
Runner-up	IT66081	La Valle Agricampeggio	Italy	p301

Alpine mountains >

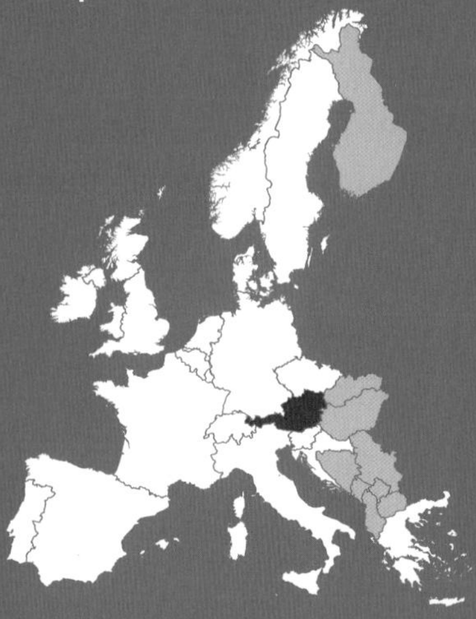

Capital Vienna
Currency Euro (€)
Language German
Time Zone CET (GMT+1)
Telephone Code 00 43

Tourist Website
austria.info/uk

Climate Temperate, moderately hot summers, cold winters and snow in the mountains.

Shops Varied. Generally 9am to 6.30pm Mon-Fri and 9am to 5pm Sat.

Banks 8am or 9am to 3pm Mon-Fri. City and smaller branches' hours may differ.

Accessible Travel Generally well catered for in cities and larger towns. Most attractions and services offer assistance but it is certainly not universal.

Travelling with children
Programs are usually organised for children over the summer period. Many lakes have supervised beach areas. Many museums in Vienna are free for under 18s. Restaurants will have children's menus or prepare smaller portions.

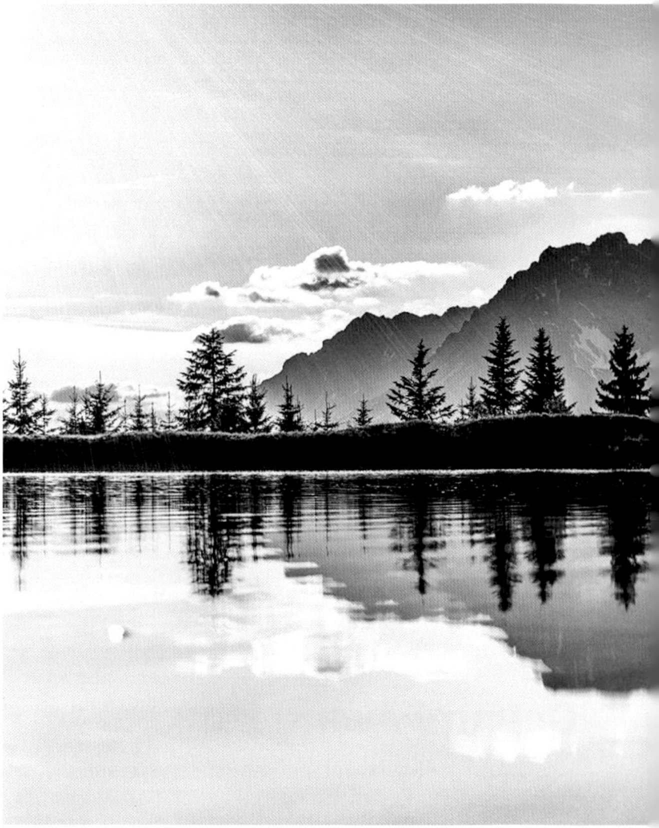

See campsite map page

472

Public Holidays New Year's Day, Epiphany, Easter Monday, Labour Day (1 May), Ascension, Whit Monday, Corpus Christi, Assumption, National Day (26 Oct), All Saints, Conception, Christmas Day, Boxing Day.

Motoring Visitors using Austrian motorways and 'A' roads must display a Motorway Vignette on their vehicle as they enter Austria. Failure to have one will mean a heavy, on-the-spot fine. Vignettes are obtained at all major border crossings into Austria and at larger petrol stations. All vehicles above 3.5 tonnes maximum permitted laden weight are required to use a small device called the 'GO Box'.

Environmental Policies Austria has implemented Low Emission Zones in many of its major cities but these currently only affect heavy duty vehicles. Austria has one of the highest recycling rates in the world. Metal, plastic, glass, paper and cardboard are widely recycled.

View all campsites in Austria
alanrogers.com/austria

Austria

Austria is primarily known for two contrasting attractions: the capital Vienna with its cathedral, wine bars and musical events, and the skiing and hiking resorts of the Alps. It is an ideal place to visit all year round, for the Easter markets, winter sports and the many cultural and historical attractions, as well as the breathtaking scenery.

The charming Tirol region in the west is easily accessible and popular with tourists who flock to its ski resorts in winter. In the summer it is transformed into a verdant landscape of picturesque valleys dotted with wildflowers, a paradise for walkers.

Situated in the centre are the Lake District, and Salzburg, city of Mozart, with its wealth of gardens, churches and palaces. Vienna's iconic Ferris wheel is a must for taking in the beautiful parks and architecture from 200 ft.

The neighbouring provinces of Lower Austria, Burgenland and Styria, land of vineyards, mountains and farmland are off the tourist routes, but provide good walking territory. Further south, Carinthia enjoys a mild, sunny climate and is dominated by crystal clear lakes and soaring mountains. There are numerous monasteries and churches, and the cities of Villach and Klagenfurt, known for its old square and attractive Renaissance buildings.

Alan Rogers Code: AU0075
2 accommodations
150 pitches
GPS: 47.64061, 12.32404
Post Code: A-6344

Walchsee, Tirol

Terrassencamp Sudsee

www.alanrogers.com/au0075
info@terrassencamping.at
Tel: 053 745 339
www.terrassencamping.at

Open (Touring Pitches):
All year.

Located on the shores of the enchanting Walchsee lake, Ferienpark Terrassencamping Süd-See is a terraced campsite with excellent panoramic views of the lake and Kaisergebirge mountains beyond. As well as 150 touring pitches, the site has two apartments available to rent. Lakeside pitches tend to be reserved for tourers, with the upper terraces taken up by seasonal/permanent caravans. Almost all pitches are hardstanding and shade is generally sparse. Walchsee is the only lake in the Austrian Tyrol to permit waterskiing, and being relatively small and shallow, the water temperature average 23°C from May to September. The lake also hosts an aqua fun park on the Eastern shore, including a giant inflatable 'iceberg' ideal for hot summer afternoons with the kids.

Max 2 dogs allowed. WiFi throughout. BBQ Permitted. Chemical toilet disposal point. Laundry with washers/dryers. Fresh bread available. Small shop. Snack bar (seasonal) Takeaway (seasonal) Restaurant. Bicycle hire. SUP hire, Gas available. Fishing permitted and boat launch available. Large children's playground. 6 pitches available for larger/American style motorhomes.

Key Features

- Open All Year
- Pets Accepted
- Disabled Facilities
- Play Area
- Bar/Restaurant
- Skiing
- Bike Hire
- Fishing

Scan me for more information.

Alan Rogers Code: AU0065
10 accommodations
170 pitches
GPS: 47.46196, 11.90713
Post Code: A-6233

Kramsach, Tirol

www.alanrogers.com/au0065
info@camping-seehof.com
Tel: 053 376 3541
www.camping-seehof.com

Open (Touring Pitches):
All year.

Camping Seehof

Camping & Appartements Seehof is a family run site and excellent in every respect. It is situated in a marvellous sunny and peaceful location on the eastern shores of the Reintalersee. The site's comfortable restaurant has a terrace with lake and mountain views and serves local dishes as well as homemade cakes and ice cream. The site is in two areas: a small one next to the lake is ideal for sunbathing, the other larger one adjoins the excellent sanitary block. There are 170 pitches, 140 of which are for touring (20 tent pitches), served by good access roads and with 16A electricity (Europlug) and TV points; 100 pitches are fully serviced, with more being upgraded every year. Seehof provides an ideal starting point for walking, cycling and riding (with a riding stable nearby) and skiing in winter. The Alpbachtal Seenland Card is available without cost at reception and allows free bus transport and free daily entry to many worthwhile attractions in the region.

The sanitary facilities are first class and include ten bathrooms to rent for private use. Baby room. Facilities for disabled visitors. Dog shower. Washing machine and dryer. Ski room. Motorhome services. Small shop. Good value restaurant. Playground. Bicycle hire. Fishing. WiFi over site (charged). Apartments to rent. Renovated fitness and play rooms.

Key Features

- Open All Year
- Pets Accepted
- Disabled Facilities
- Play Area
- Bar/Restaurant
- Skiing
- Bike Hire
- Fishing

Scan me for more information.

Alan Rogers Code: AU0165
70 pitches
GPS: 47.26382, 11.32622
Post Code: A-6020

Innsbruck, Tirol

www.alanrogers.com/au0165
info@kranebitterhof.at
Tel: 051 227 9558
www.kranebitterhof.at

Open (Touring Pitches):
All year.

Camping Kranebitterhof

Camping Innsbruck Kranebitterhof is set on steep terraces and is easily reached from the A12. Being only 5 km. West of Innsbruck it is suitable for overnight stays, as well as a base from which to visit the city. The 70 level pitches are 80 to 120 sq.m. and all have 16A electricity, water and wastewater connections, and their terracing and southerly aspect make the most use of the sunshine, allowing unobstructed views of the valley and mountains. A large, two-storey, air-conditioned sanitary block is at the top of the site. Lower down are the reception, further WCs (including disabled facilities), the Italian bar/restaurant and shop, all housed in a modern building with large glass windows. Although near the autobahn, railway and airport the site is not particularly noisy. A bus service passes close to the site and the Innsbruck card, available to purchase at reception, allows free public transport, including a sightseeing tour and free museum entry. During the winter there is plenty of skiing within 5 km. and in summer lots of touring. A look through the information brochures in reception will show that this region has a lot to offer the visitor.

Two heated sanitary facilities, large block at top of the site and smaller one in the reception building. Free hot showers, three family shower rooms, one with a bath. Facilities for disabled visitors in the lower block. Kitchen with hotplates, dishwashing and laundry. Small shop (bread can be ordered). Italian restaurant, bar. Play area. WiFi over site (free). Bicycle hire.

Key Features

- OPEN 365 Open All Year
- Pets Accepted
- Disabled Facilities
- Play Area
- Bar/Restaurant
- Skiing
- Bike Hire

Scan me for more information.

Alan Rogers Code: AU0160
1 accommodations
160 pitches
GPS: 47.33993, 12.80914
Post Code: A-5700

Zell am See, Salzburg

www.alanrogers.com/au0160
zell@seecamp.at
Tel: 065 427 2115
www.seecamp.at

Open (Touring Pitches):
All year.

Seecamp Zell am See

The Zeller See, delightfully situated in the south of Salzburg province and near the start of the Grossglocknerstrasse, is ideally placed for enjoying the splendid southern Austrian countryside. Seecamp is right by the water, less than two kilometres from the town of Zell and with fine views to the south end of the lake. Stretching along the waterfront, the site has 160 good level, mainly grass-on-gravel pitches of average size, 147 with 16A electricity. About half have water, drainage and TV connections. Units can be close together in peak season. Good English is spoken. A large, modern building in the centre, houses the amenities. The lake is accessible for watersports, including windsurfing, canoeing and sailing schools. An activity programme for adults includes rafting, canoeing, mountain biking, water-skiing and hiking.

Excellent, heated sanitary facilities include facilities for disabled visitors and a baby room. Washing machines, dryers and irons. Motorhome services. Bar, restaurant and takeaway (all 20/12-Easter; Mother's day-October). Shop. Play area. Play room. Fishing. Bicycle hire. Canoe/kayak hire. Topi Club and summer entertainment for children. Activity programme. Winter ski packages and free ski bus. Glacier skiing possible in summer. Free WiFi.

Key Features

- Open All Year
- Pets Accepted
- Disabled Facilities
- Play Area
- Bar/Restaurant
- Skiing
- Bike Hire
- Fishing

Scan me for more information.

Alan Rogers Code: AU0265
10 accommodations
200 pitches
GPS: 47.57427, 12.70602
Post Code: A-5092

St Martin bei Lofer, Salzburg

Park Grubhof

www.alanrogers.com/au0265
home@grubhof.com
Tel: 065 888 2370
www.grubhof.com

Open (Touring Pitches):
All Year

Park Grubhof is a beautifully laid out, level and spacious site set in the former riding and hunting park of the 14th-century Schloss Grubhof. The 200 touring pitches, all with 12-16A electricity, have been carefully divided into separate areas for different types of visitor – dog owners, young people, families and groups, and a quiet area. There are 167 very large pitches (at least 120 sq.m), all with electricity, water and drainage, many along the bank of the Saalach river. Although new, the central building has been built in traditional Tirolean style using, in part, materials hundreds of years old reclaimed from old farmhouses. The result is most attractive. On the ground floor you will find reception, a cosy café/bar, a restaurant and a small shop, and on the first floor, a deluxe sauna, beauty and wellness suite, two apartments and a relaxation room.

Three attractive, modern sanitary units constructed of wood and glass provide excellent facilities. Large family bathrooms (free with certain pitches, to rent in winter). Washing machine, dryer and drying gallery. Gym upstairs (€5 membership). Recreation and conference room and a small library. Saunas, steam bath and massage. Ski and canoe storage room. Motorhome services. Luxury dog shower. Shop, restaurant and bar. Adventure-style playground. Youth room. Playroom. Watersports. Cabins to rent. Hotel and B&B accommodation. WiFi throughout (charged).

Key Features

- Pets Accepted
- Disabled Facilities
- Play Area
- Bar/Restaurant
- Skiing
- Bike Hire
- Fishing

Scan me for more information.

Alan Rogers Code: AU0210
100 pitches
GPS: 47.49370, 13.34700
Post Code: A-5023

Salzburg

www.alanrogers.com/au0210
office@camping-nord-sam.com
Tel: 0662 66 04 94
www.camping-nord-sam.com

Open (Touring Pitches):
10 April - 11 Oct. & Selected Dec. Dates

Camping Nord-Sam

The centrally-located campsite on the outskirts of the city of Salzburg has been managed by the Lex family for the past 60 years. Only 700 metres from the motorway exit "Salzburg Nord", it is not only the perfect place to stay while passing through, but for leisure and recreational holidays as well. With its approximately 100 pitches, this well-maintained campsite, set amongst lush greenery and blooming flowers is the ideal starting point for the 3.5 km distant city. It is also suitably located for day trips to the Salzkammergut (lake district), the Ice Caves, the Salt Mines and many more sights. A bus stop and bike path to the city centre are right on the doorstep. The complex is equipped with a swimming pool, newly-renovated sanitary facilities with free showers, washing machine & dryer, new toddler playground, bike rental, kiosk with basic food, cafeteria and Wi-Fi. A restaurant (150m) and supermarket (300m) are also nearby.

One big sanitary block equipped with toilets, showers, washing- and drying machines. Cafeteria. Mini market. Ticket counter. Outdoor pool. Bicycle hire. Information point. Bus stop on the doorstep. Hiking path. Bicycle path. WiFi (charged).

Key Features

- Pets Accepted
- Swimming Pool
- Play Area
- Bar/Restaurant
- Bike Hire

Scan me for more information.

Alan Rogers Code: AU0450
34 accommodations
248 pitches
GPS: 46.63184, 13.44654
Post Code: A-9620

Hermagor, Carinthia

www.alanrogers.com/au0450
camping@schluga.com
Tel: 342 822 760
www.schluga.com

Open (Touring Pitches):
10 May - 20 September

Naturpark Schluga

Naturpark Schluga Seecamping is pleasantly situated on a natural wooded hillside. It is about 300 m. from a small lake with clean water, where the site has a beach of coarse sand and a large grassy meadow where inflatable boats can be kept. There is also a small bar and a sunbathing area for naturists, although this is not a naturist site. Around 250 pitches for touring units are on individual, level terraces, many with light shade and all with 8/16A electricity (adaptors are required on some pitches, and can be collected from outside reception). There are 154 pitches that also have water, drainage and satellite TV. A further 47 pitches are occupied by a tour operator, and there are also mobile homes for rent. English is spoken.

Four heated modern toilet blocks are well constructed, with some washbasins in cabins and family washrooms to rent. Facilities for disabled campers. Washing machines and dryer. Motorhome services. Shop (20/5-10/9). Restaurant/bar by entrance and takeaway (all 20/5-10/9). Heated outdoor pool with toddler pool. Playground. Room for young people and children. Films. Kiosk and bar with terrace at beach. Surf school. Pedalo and canoe hire. Aqua jump and Iceberg. Pony rides. Bicycle hire. Weekly activity programme with mountain walks and climbs. Internet point. WiFi over site (charged).

Key Features

- Pets Accepted
- Disabled Facilities
- Swimming Pool
- Play Area
- Bar/Restaurant
- Bike Hire

Scan me for more information.

Alan Rogers Code: AU0332
9 accommodations
45 pitches
GPS: 48.22778, 14.57912
Post Code: A-4332

Au an der Donau, Upper Austria

www.alanrogers.com/au0332
info@camping-audonau.at
Tel: 072 625 3090
www.camping-audonau.at

Open (Touring Pitches):
1 April - 30 September.

Camping Au an der Donau

You can be sure of a friendly welcome, in English, at this attractive site on the Danube cycle route. Reception, bar, restaurant and flowered terrace are located on the dam top from where there are views of the Danube and surrounding countryside – an ideal place to try out the local drink, cider, and home-smoked trout. The 45 touring pitches are in a protected area behind the dam, all with 13A electricity. A separate area accommodates 30 tents; each area has its own well maintained sanitary facility. The pitches are grassy and separated by hedges. This is a small, well-organised site where a lot of thought and work has been put in by the two owners. Although the camping area is comfortable and attractive with landscaping, flowers and a small lake, most visitors will spend their time either enjoying the views from the restaurant terrace or touring in the region.

Two modern sanitary units with hot water, free controllable showers and facilities for disabled visitors. Laundry room with washing machine and dryer. Motorhome services. Small bar (1/5-15/9). Restaurant (1/4-30/9) serving local specialities (breakfast and fresh bread available). Playground. Regular entertainment on site's own stage. Access to Danube beach and small motorboat to hire. Small boat (Tille) on lake (free). Bicycle hire. Barbecue and campfire areas. Tourist information in reception. Free WiFi over site.

Key Features

- Pets Accepted
- Disabled Facilities
- Play Area
- Bar/Restaurant
- Bike Hire
- Fishing

Scan me for more information.

Alan Rogers Code: AU0360
29 accommodations
271 pitches
GPS: 46.58800, 14.62700
Post Code: A-9141

Eberndorf, Carinthia

www.alanrogers.com/au0360
fkkurlaub@rutarlido.at
Tel: 434 236 2262
www.rutarlido.at

Open (Touring Pitches):
All year.

Naturisten Rutar Lido

Rutar Lido FKK Naturist See-Camping is affiliated to the International Naturist Federation and is in a peaceful location adjacent to both open countryside and forested hills. The 365 pitches (around 300 for touring units) are either on an open area of grass marked out by low hedges or in a more established area of pine trees. There are 10A electrical connections throughout, and some pitches have dedicated water and waste points. One area is set aside for those with dogs. There are three lakes on the site, one for swimming and dinghies, two for those who enjoy fishing. The area around the lakes has been left to nature with many wildflowers and other plants creating colour and interest. A feature of the site, there are no less than six swimming pools, two being indoors. These are both heated, as are two of the others. Membership of the INF is not a requirement; however, visitors are expected to comply with their rules and ideals. Children are allowed, but adults and seniors mostly use the site.

Four sanitary blocks with some private cabins and free controllable showers. Facilities for disabled visitors. Laundry facilities. Well stocked small supermarket (1/4-30/9). Two bar/restaurants (one all year). Outdoor pools (1/4-30/9). Indoor pools (all year). Two saunas. Play area, club and activities for children (July/Aug). Fitness room. Disco. Bowling alley. Live music evenings and dances (high season). Small chapel. Fishing. WiFi (charged).

Key Features

- Naturist Site
- Open All Year
- Pets Accepted
- Disabled Facilities
- Swimming Pool
- Play Area
- Bar/Restaurant
- Fishing

Scan me for more information.

Alan Rogers Code: AU0543
21 accommodations
140 pitches
GPS: 47.10760, 14.13953
Post Code: A-8861

St. Georgen am Kreischberg, Steiermark

Camping Olachgut

www.alanrogers.com/au0543
office@olachgut.at
Tel: 035 322 162
www.olachgut.at

Open (Touring Pitches):
All year.

Based on a working farm, Camping Olachgut is located in the Murau-Kreischberg region of Austria. Taking a keen interest in ecological matters, the site has won various eco-awards from both the Austrian and European governments. The site is especially suited to those requiring accessible accommodation with adapted bathing facilities and accommodation available. Horse riding is particularly popular at this site, with lessons available for everyone, from beginner upwards. Pitches are marked out and many have shade.

Horse riding school. Children's playground with trampoline. Entertainment program in high season. Sauna. Fishing available. Ski hire. Fresh bread available. Restaurant. Gas available. Laundry with Washer/Dryer. Accessible bathing facilities. Family toilet facilities. BBQ's allowed. Max. 2 dogs allowed. WiFi throughout.

Key Features

- Open All Year
- Pets Accepted
- Disabled Facilities
- Play Area
- Bar/Restaurant
- Skiing
- Fishing
- Horse Riding

Scan me for more information.

Alan Rogers Code: AU0546
6 accommodations
25 pitches
GPS: 47.02200, 14.95508
Post Code: A-8584

Hirschegg, Steiermark

www.alanrogers.com/au0546
info@camping-hirschegg.at
Tel: 031 412 201
www.camping-hirschegg.at

Open (Touring Pitches):
All year.

Camping Hirschegg

Located 900 meters above sea level, Camping Hirschegg can be found on the edge of the village of the same name in Western Styria. This small and straightforward campsite only has 60 pitches, 25 of which are dedicated to tourers, many with electrical hookups. The site is well maintained by the owners, with clean and tidy sanitary facilities. The nearby lake can be used for fishing and swimming in the summer and is used for ice skating in the winter (Ice skates and ice hockey sticks for rent at the campsite.) Foraging is encouraged, particularly in the autumn months when mushrooms and lingonberries can be found in the woods.

Fishing and lake swimming nearby. Ski hire nearby. Games room available. No entertainment program. Breakfasts available on request. Laundry with Washing Machine. Max. 2 dogs allowed. BBQs permitted. Free WiFi in reception.

Key Features

- Open All Year
- Pets Accepted
- Skiing
- Fishing

Scan me for more information.

Alan Rogers Code: AU0020
14 accommodations
94 pitches
GPS: 47.14256, 9.92589
Post Code: A-6751

Braz, Vorarlberg

Walch's Camping

www.alanrogers.com/au0020
info@landhauswalch.at
Tel: 055 522 8102
www.landhauswalch.at

Open (Touring Pitches):
All year excl. 2-26 November.

Walch's Camping & Landhaus is found in the Vorarlberg region of Western Austria. The site has 94 marked out pitches, mostly without shade. The reception building houses a small shop, laundry, toilet facilities and ski/boot room, while the upper floor has a small wellness centre, comprising of a Finnish style sauna and solarium. The campsite is rightly proud that up to 80% of their energy is generated through geothermal activity. Attractions include the nearby ski resorts of Montafon and Golm, the Fohrenburg brewery and the Milka chocolate factory.

Excellent accessible facilities. Fishing nearby. Easy access to ski slopes. Ski hire available. Children's playground and indoor play-room. Wellness centre with Sauna, steam bath and solarium. Breakfast available (seasonal) Fresh bread available. Small shop. Gas available. Laundry with washer/dryer. Boot/Ski room. BBQs allowed. WiFi throughout.

Key Features

- Pets Accepted
- Disabled Facilities
- Play Area
- Skiing

Scan me for more information.

Groenerei Canal, Bruges >

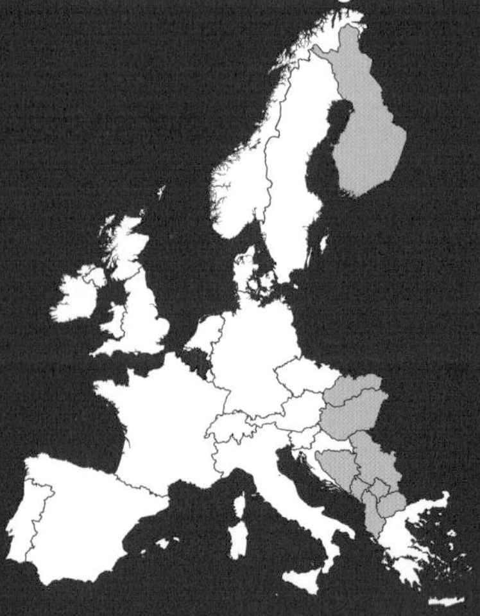

Capital Brussels
Currency Euro (€)
Language French in the south, Flemish in the north, German in the east.
Time Zone CET (GMT+1)
Telephone Code 00 32

Tourist Website
belgiumtheplaceto.be

Climate Temperate, similar to Britain. Cool, damp winters and mild summers.

Shops Varied. Generally 10am to 6.30pm Mon-Sat.

Banks 8.30am to 3.30pm on weekdays and some also on Saturday morning.

Accessible Travel Most public areas and services are suitable for wheelchair users and less able individuals. Transport is well equipped.

Travelling with Children
Many cities have museums and other attractions that run activity days and programs for children. Entrance fees for many attractions are reduced for those under 12. In much of Flanders there are special rates for young people under 26.

See campsite map page

473

Public Holidays New Year's Day, Easter Monday, Labour Day, Ascension, Whit Monday, National Day (21 Jul), Assumption, All Saints, Armistice Day, Christmas Day. Some essential and government services may also be closed on King's Day (15 Nov).

Motoring For cars with a caravan or trailer, motorways are toll free except for the Liefenshoek Tunnel in Antwerp. Maximum permitted overall length of vehicle/trailer or caravan combination is 18m. Blue Zone parking areas exist in most major cities. Parking discs can be obtained from police stations, garages, and some shops.

Environmental Policies Belgium has enforced Low Emission Zones in all of its major cities. This affects all motor vehicles. Stickers are not required but you will need to register your vehicle, prior to arriving, if you plan to drive in or through a major city. Metal, plastic, glass, paper and cardboard are widely recycled.

View all campsites in Belgium
alanrogers.com/belgium

Belgium

A small country divided into three regions, Flanders in the north, Wallonia in the south and Brussels the capital. Belgium is rich in scenic countryside, culture and history, notably the great forest of Ardennes, the historic cities of Bruges and Ghent, and the western coastline with its long sandy beaches.

Brussels is at the very heart of Europe and is a must-see destination with its heady mix of shops, bars, nightlife, exhibitions and festivals – a multi-cultural and multi-lingual city that is a focal point of art, fashion and culture.

In the French-speaking region of Wallonia lies the mountainous Ardennes, home to picturesque villages rich in tradition and folklore. It is a favourite of nature-lovers and walkers who enjoy exploring its many castles and forts. The safe, sandy beaches on the west coast run for forty miles. The cosmopolitan resort of Ostend with its yacht basin and harbour offers year-round attractions including a carnival weekend and a Christmas market, and the myriad seafood restaurants will suit every taste. Bruges is Europe's best-preserved medieval city, crisscrossed by willow-lined canals, where tiny cobbled streets open onto pretty squares. After visiting the many museums and art galleries, why not sample some of the delicious chocolate for which the city is famous.

Alan Rogers Code: BE0578
616 accommodations
120 pitches
GPS: 51.28318, 3.05753
Post Code: B-8420

West Flanders, Flanders

Camping Ter Duinen

www.alanrogers.com/be0578
info@campingterduinen.be
Tel: 050 413 593
kampeerverblijfparkterduinen.be

Open (Touring Pitches):
15 March - 15 October.

Ter Duinen is a large, seaside holiday site with 120 touring pitches and over 700 privately owned static holiday caravans. The pitches are laid out in straight lines with tarmac access roads, and the site has three toilet blocks with token-operated showers. Other than a bar, small shop, playground and a playing field, the site has few other facilities, but it is only a 600 m. walk to the sea, and next door to the site is a large sports complex with a sub-tropical pool and several sporting facilities. Opportunities for riding and hiring bikes are close by. De Haan is famous for its Belle Epoque buildings and the English cottage-style houses. Access to the beach is via a good woodland footpath through the sand dunes. There is a main road and tramway to cross, but there are designated pedestrian crossings. The site is surrounded by lush woods and has numerous beautiful cycling paths to Bruges, Blankenberge and Ostend which are worth a day trip. You can also visit the polygonal Fort Napoleon and enjoy a drink/meal in their restaurant.

Three modern toilet blocks have good fittings, washbasins in cubicles (hot and cold water) and showers (€ 1.20). Baby bath. Facilities for disabled visitors. Laundry facilities with two washing machines and a dryer, irons and ironing boards. Motorhome services. Shop. Snack bar and takeaway. Internet room (charged).

Key Features

- Pets Accepted
- Disabled Facilities
- Play Area
- Bar/Restaurant

Scan me for more information.

Alan Rogers Code: BE0555
45 accommodations
137 pitches
GPS: 51.18448, 3.10445
Post Code: B-8490

West Flanders, Flanders

www.alanrogers.com/be0555
info@kleinstrand.be
Tel: 050 811 440
www.kleinstrand.be

Open (Touring Pitches):
All Year

Recreatiepark Klein Strand

In a convenient location just off the A10 motorway and close to Bruges, this site is in two distinct areas divided by an access road. The main part of the site offers a lake with a marked off swimming area, a sandy beach, water slides and boating (no fishing). The touring section has 137 large pitches on flat grass separated by well trimmed hedges; all have electricity and access to water and drainage. Some leisure facilities for children are provided on this part of the site, along with a spacious bar and snack bar with takeaway (seasonal). The main site with all the privately owned mobile homes is closer to the lake, so has most of the amenities. These include the main reception building, restaurants, bar, minimarket, and sports facilities.

Single modern, heated, toilet block includes good sized showers (charged) and vanity style washbasins. Baby room. Basic facilities for disabled campers. Washing machines and dryer. Additional toilet facilities with washbasins in cubicles are located behind the touring field reception building (open July/Aug). Motorhome services. Bar and snack bar. Play area. Fun pool for small children. In main park: European and Chinese restaurants, bar and snack bar, takeaways (all year). Shop (Easter-end Aug). Tennis courts and sports field. Water ski school; water ski shows (Sundays in July/Aug). Bicycle hire. WiFi throughout (free).

Key Features

- Open All Year
- Pets Accepted
- Disabled Facilities
- Play Area
- Bar/Restaurant
- Bike Hire
- Fishing

Scan me for more information.

Alan Rogers Code: BE0580
80 pitches
GPS: 51.20692, 3.26294
Post Code: B-8310

West Flanders, Flanders

www.alanrogers.com/be0580
info@campingmemling.be
Tel: 050 355 845
www.brugescamping.be

Open (Touring Pitches):
All Year

Camping Memling

This traditional site is ideal for visiting Brugge (or Bruges). The 120 marked pitches (80 for touring caravans, 20 hard standing) are on level grass, with gravel roads and trees and hedges providing some shade. Electricity (10A) is available to all pitches. There is a separate area for 40 small, two-person tents. Bars, restaurants, local shops and supermarkets are within walking distance. Brugge itself has a network of cycleways, and for those on foot, a bus stops near the campsite and runs into the centre. Reservation from May to September is recommended. Visitors with large units should always telephone in advance to ensure an adequate pitch. There is no restaurant on-site, but there are several to choose from in the centre of Sint-Kruis. As well as visiting Brugge, historical Ghent is just 40 minutes drive away. The international port of Zeebrugge and the town of Blankenberge are within 17 km. of the site if you are looking for a day out at the coast with sandy beaches and the usual amenities of a seaside resort.

A new toilet block provides washbasins (open and in cabins) and spacious showers. Laundry with washing machine and dryer. New reception room with self check-in, coffee vending machine, TV and piano. WiFi over site (free). Dogs are not accepted in July/ Aug.

Key Features

- Open All Year
- Pets Accepted
- Disabled Facilities

Scan me for more information.

Alan Rogers Code: BE0650
221 accommodations
75 pitches
GPS: 51.30513, 4.58622
Post Code: B-2960

Antwerp, Flanders

Floreal Het Veen

www.alanrogers.com/be0650
info@campinghetrietveen.nl
Tel: 036 361 327
www.campinghetrietveen.nl

Open (Touring Pitches):
All year.

Floreal Het Veen can be found 20 km. North of Antwerp in a woodland area, with many sports facilities. There are around 300 marked pitches (approximately 75 for touring units) on level grass, most with some shade and 10A electricity (long leads in some places) and also six hardstandings. Amenities include an indoor sports hall (hourly charge), while tennis courts, football, basketball and softball are outside. There are also three playgrounds for children and an entertainments program in the main season. Good cycling and walking opportunities exist in the area, with a canal running alongside the site. French, Dutch, English, German are all spoken.

Three spacious toilet blocks include a few washbasins in cubicles (only two are close to touring pitches). Facilities for disabled visitors. Laundry facilities. Motorhome services. Shop. Restaurant, bar, café and takeaway (daily July/Aug. weekends only at other times). Tennis. Badminton. Boules. Playgrounds and children's entertainment (seasonal) Fishing. Canoeing. Bicycle hire. WiFi (free). Wooden chalets to rent. Max 1 Dog allowed (on a lead) BBQ's permitted.

Key Features

- Open All Year
- Pets Accepted
- Disabled Facilities
- Play Area
- Bar/Restaurant
- Bike Hire
- Fishing

Scan me for more information.

Alan Rogers Code: BE0660
12 accommodations
71 pitches
GPS: 51.35757, 4.95896
Post Code: B-2300

Antwerp, Flanders

www.alanrogers.com/be0660
info@baalsehei.be
Tel: +32 14 448 470
www.baalsehei.be

Open (Touring Pitches):
16 January - 15 December.

Camping Baalse Hei

The Campine is an area covering three quarters of the Province of Antwerp, noted for its nature reserves, pine forests, meadows and streams and is ideal for walking and cycling, while Turnhout itself is an interesting old town. Baalse Hei, a long established, friendly site, has 469 pitches including a separate touring area of 71 large grass pitches (all with 16A electricity, TV connections and shared water point), thoughtfully developed with trees and bushes. Cars are parked away from, but near the pitches. Large motorhomes can be accommodated (phone first to check availability). There is also accommodation to rent.

Three toilet blocks provide hot showers on payment (€ 0.50), some washbasins in cabins and facilities for disabled visitors. Dishwashing (hot water € 0.20). Launderette. Motorhome services. Shop (1/4-30/9). Café/restaurant (daily 1/4-30/9, w/ends only other times, closed 16/11-25/1). Breakfast served in high season. Club/TV room. Lake swimming. Fishing. Tennis. Boules. Volleyball. Basketball. Adventure play area. Bicycle hire. English is spoken. Overnight pitches for vehicles under 3.5t. In low season reception opens for limited hours (14.00-17.00). WiFi throughout (free).

Key Features

- Pets Accepted
- Disabled Facilities
- Play Area
- Bar/Restaurant
- Bike Hire
- Fishing

Scan me for more information.

Alan Rogers Code: BE0780
9 accommodations
70 pitches
GPS: 51.02852, 5.59813
Post Code: B-3660

Limburg, Flanders

www.alanrogers.com/be0780
receptie@wilhelmtell.com
Tel: 089 810 014
www.wilhelmtell.com

Open (Touring Pitches):
All year.

Camping Wilhelm Tell

Wilhelm Tell is a family run site that caters particularly well for children with its indoor and outdoor pools and lots of entertainment throughout the season. There are 128 pitches with 70 available for touring units, some separated, others on open fields and 60 electricity connections (10A). The super bar/restaurant has access for wheelchair users. The owner has an extraordinary attitude towards his customers and tries to ensure they leave satisfied and want to return. For example, in his restaurant, he says 'it serves until you are full.' The Limburg region is a relaxing area with much to do, including shopping and touring the historic towns with a delightful choice of food and drink!

Toilet facilities are adequate, but might be under pressure in high season. Facilities around the pool supplement at busy times. Baby room in reception area. Two en-suite units for disabled visitors. Laundry facilities. Motorhome services. Fridge hire. Bar/restaurant and snack bar (times vary acc. to season). Outdoor heated pool with slide and wave machine (July/Aug) and indoor pool (all year), both well supervised. Play area. WiFi. No charcoal barbecues.

Key Features

- Open All Year
- Pets Accepted
- Disabled Facilities
- Swimming Pool
- Play Area
- Bar/Restaurant
- Bike Hire

Scan me for more information.

Alan Rogers Code: BE0760
24 accommodations
244 pitches
GPS: 51.17343, 5.53902
Post Code: B-3950

Limburg, Flanders

www.alanrogers.com/be0760
info@goolderheide.be
Tel: 0032 89 469 640
www.goolderheide.be

Open (Touring Pitches):
1 April - 30 September

Goolderheide Familiepark

A large family holiday site with 900 individual pitches, Goolderheide has been owned and operated by the same family for many years and has an excellent pool complex and playgrounds. There are many seasonal and rental units, plus around 250 touring pitches with 6/10/16A electricity, all in a forest setting. The pitches are of variable size and access roads are quite narrow. The outdoor pool complex has two large pools (one of Olympic size), a slide and a paddling pool. There is also a fishing lake, and a lake with a small sandy beach. An enormous area is devoted to a comprehensive play area with a vast range of equipment.

Four sanitary buildings provide an ample supply of WCs and washbasins in cabins, but rather fewer preset showers. Family facilities. Two en-suite units for disabled visitors (key access). Laundry facilities. Dishwasher. Shop, bar and takeaway (daily in July/Aug, w/ends and public holidays in low season). Takeaway. Swimming pools. Tennis. Fishing. Boules. Minigolf. Play area and assault course. Extensive programme of activities (July/Aug).

Key Features

- Pets Accepted
- Disabled Facilities
- Swimming Pool
- Play Area
- Bar/Restaurant
- Bike Hire
- Fishing

Scan me for more information.

Alan Rogers Code: BE0590
15 accommodations
70 pitches
GPS: 50.79098, 3.92370
Post Code: B-9500

East Flanders, Flanders

www.alanrogers.com/be0590
gavers@oost-vlaanderen.be
Tel: 054 416 324
www.oost-vlaanderen.be

Open (Touring Pitches):
All year.

Camping De Gavers

Camping De Gavers is a modern, well organised holiday site in a peaceful location adjacent to a large sports complex, about 5 km. outside Geraardsbergen. A busy site in season, there is good security and a card-operated barrier. Most of the 428 grassy, level pitches are taken by seasonal pitches, but some 70 are left for touring units. Pitches are arranged on either side of surfaced access roads with some hedges and a few trees to provide shade in parts, with electricity available to all (long cables may be required). The site offers an extensive range of sporting activities and a full entertainment programme over a long season. This is an excellent site for water-based activities and would make a good stopover. Due to the extensive range of activities on offer, it becomes hectic in high season, so booking is advisable. Larger units may have difficulty with access, as the approach is either through a village with parked cars or over a narrow canal bridge.

Six modern, heated and well equipped sanitary buildings provide hot showers on payment (€ 0.50). Modern rooms for disabled visitors and babies. Launderette. Motorhome services. Shop (July/Aug). Restaurant and takeaway (all year). Cafeteria and bars (daily in summer, otherwise weekends). Heated indoor pool (all year). Outdoor pool (seasonal). Excellent playground. Tennis. Boules. Minigolf. Fishing. Sailing. Canoes, windsurfers, pedaloes, yachts and rowing boats for hire. Bicycle hire. Tourist train. Swimming and beach area at the lake. Climbing. Internet in reception.

Key Features

- Open All Year
- Pets Accepted
- Disabled Facilities
- Swimming Pool
- Play Area
- Bar/Restaurant
- Bike Hire
- Fishing

Scan me for more information.

Alan Rogers Code: BE0850
22 accommodations
55 pitches
GPS: 50.11128, 5.13376
Post Code: B-5580

Namur, Wallonia

www.alanrogers.com/be0850
info@leroptai.be
Tel: 084 388 319
www.leroptai.be

Open (Touring Pitches):
1 February - 31 December.

Camping Le Roptai

This family site in the heart of the Ardennes, within easy reach of Dinant and Namur, was established in 1932. In a rural wooded setting with its own adventure playground in the trees, it is a good site for an active holiday, especially in high season when there is a weekly programme including rock climbing, abseiling, mountain biking and potholing. There are 55 good sized, grassy, touring pitches on sloping ground, most with 6A electricity. A programme of activities is organised for adults and children in high season. Other amenities include a swimming pool, a well-stocked shop and a bar/snack bar. There are excellent footpaths around the site and the owner and staff will be pleased to recommend routes. The pretty little village of Ave is just 1 km. from le Roptai, and the larger village of Han-sur-Lesse is around 4 km. away. There is an evening market at Han, as well as world-famous caves. The village is also home to the interesting Maison de la Vie Paysanne.

Sanitary facilities below reception include an excellent suite for babies and disabled visitors. Five other blocks of varying styles are kept clean and offer basic facilities. Shop (1/7-31/8). Bar/snack bar with takeaway (1/7-31/8). Swimming pool and paddling pool (1/7-31/8). Play area. Activity programme (July/Aug). Bicycle hire. WiFi over part of site (charged). Mobile homes for rent.

Key Features

- Pets Accepted
- Disabled Facilities
- Swimming Pool
- Play Area
- Bar/Restaurant
- Bike Hire
- Golf

Scan me for more information.

Alan Rogers Code: BE0632
2 accommodations
47 pitches
GPS: 50.43916, 6.11793
Post Code: B-4950

Liège, Wallonia

www.alanrogers.com/be0632
info@campinganderegg.be
Tel: 080 679393
www.campinganderegg.be

Open (Touring Pitches):
April - October

Camping Anderegg

Camping Anderegg is an attractive, family-owned site in the village of Bruyeres in the Belgian Ardennes, close to the picturesque towns of Malmedy and Waimes. The grassy touring pitches (80-100sqm) are well laid out, separated by low hedges, and have 6A electricity. Trees shade some, others more open. A shallow, unfenced stream runs through the site, where children can play under supervision. There are miles of cycle routes in the area including the RAVeL Routes, extending 150 km along the former railway road and mountain. Electric bikes are available for hire locally, and the owners can provide maps with cycling and walking trails. Up to 4 dogs are allowed per pitch. This lovely, rural site is ideal for families who enjoy the great outdoors.

The modern, heated sanitary building is clean and has showers (coin operated), washbasins in cubicles and baby facilities. Situated by the entrance it may be a distance from some pitches. Small shop for basics (bread can be ordered in high season). Recreation room with books and games. Takeaway. Adventure play area and a smaller play area for younger children. Football field. Badminton court. WiFi throughout (charged). Jeu de boules. Darts

Key Features

- Pets Accepted
- Play Area

Scan me for more information.

Alan Rogers Code: BE0706
83 accommodations
404 pitches
GPS: 50.34838, 6.11990
Post Code: B-4770

Liège, Wallonia

www.alanrogers.com/be0706
info@campingoosheem.be
Tel: 080 349741
www.campingoosheem.be

Open (Touring Pitches):
All year.

Camping Oos Heem

Camping Oos Heem in the Ardennes region of Belgium is situated directly on the Vennbahn cycle track, 125 km of what was once the steam train route but which now offers an excellent way for cyclists to explore the region in the safety of a track not accessible to motor vehicles. The site is bordered by the forest, where action in both World Wars was intense and has much to offer the curious camper. The campsite is surrounded by undulating pine forests, being close to the highest peak in Belgium. Pitches are wooded, grassy and level for tourers or offering a range of glamping possibilities. There is a broad field which can accommodate up to 40 tents, popular with motorcyclists who are welcome (please note large groups of bikers only during low season). Families will particularly enjoy the range of activities provided both on the site and nearby. Ponies are brought in once a week for younger children to ride, and bikes can be hired on-site.

There is one central sanitary block with showers and a private bathing and changing facility for babies. Dishwashing area, clothes washing machine and dryer. Small shop, bar, restaurant and takeaway. Heated, covered pool and heated outdoor paddling pool. Games room with table tennis, table football and giant Connect-4. Football pitch, volleyball court. Supervised activities during high season, pony riding, bicycle hire. Wifi access in the bar area (free)

Key Features

- Open All Year
- Pets Accepted
- Swimming Pool
- Play Area
- Bar/Restaurant
- Skiing
- Bike Hire
- Horse Riding

Scan me for more information.

Alan Rogers Code: BE0710
46 accommodations
217 pitches
GPS: 49.58015, 5.54773
Post Code: B-6760

Luxembourg, Wallonia

www.alanrogers.com/be0710
info@collinederabais.be
Tel: 063 422 177
www.collinederabais.be

Open (Touring Pitches):
All year.

Floreal Colline de Rabais

Floreal Camping Colline de Rabais is a large site on a hilltop looking out over the surrounding wooded countryside. The Dutch owners offer a warm welcome and are slowly making improvements to the site while maintaining its relaxed atmosphere. There are around 220 pitches for touring units, all with 16A electricity (some long leads needed), plus 46 mobile homes and bungalows to rent and a few tour operator tents. Various activities are organised throughout the season. The adjacent forest is open to walkers and cyclists alike - you can just keep on going without seeing another person. The French border is only 10 km. to the south if you fancy a taste of France, whilst the Duchy of Luxembourg is about 30 km. to the east and its capital city is less than an hour's drive away. A similar distance to the northwest along country roads is the town of Bouillon, which has an interesting ruined castle and from where you can explore the green hillsides and valleys of the Ardennes and perhaps take a canoe trip along a section of meandering river.

Three toilet blocks, one modernised with shower/washbasin cubicles and an en-suite room for disabled visitors. Cleaning and maintenance can be variable and not all blocks are open in low season. Washing machines and dryers. Shop (seasonal). Bar/restaurant and takeaway (Apr-Oct). Small outdoor swimming pool (seasonal) with wood decking for sunbathing. Bicycle hire. Free WiFi over part of site.

Key Features

- Open All Year
- Pets Accepted
- Disabled Facilities
- Swimming Pool
- Play Area
- Bar/Restaurant
- Bike Hire

Scan me for more information.

Alan Rogers Code: BE0732
297 accommodations
290 pitches
GPS: 50.17600, 5.58600
Post Code: B-6980

Luxembourg, Wallonia

www.alanrogers.com/be0732
camping.laroche@florealgroup.be
Tel: 084 219 467
www.florealgroup.be

Open (Touring Pitches):
All year.

Floreal La Roche

Maintained to very high standards, this site is set in a beautiful wooded valley bordering the Ourthe river. Open all year, the site is located on the outskirts of the attractive small town of La Roche-en-Ardenne, in an area understandably popular with tourists. The site is large with 587 grass pitches (min. 100 sq.m), of which 290 are for touring units. The pitches are on level ground, and all have 10/16A electricity and water connections. Amenities on-site include a well-stocked shop, a bar, a restaurant and takeaway food. In the woods and rivers close by, there are plenty of opportunities for walking, mountain biking, rafting and canoeing. For children, there is a large adventure playground which is very popular, and during the summer entertainment programmes are organised.

Six modern, well maintained sanitary blocks provide washbasins (open and in cabins), free preset showers. Facilities for disabled visitors. Baby room. Washing machines and dryers (token from reception). Motorhome services. Well stocked shop (with fresh bread, pastries and newspapers in July/Aug). Bar, restaurant, snack bar and takeaway. At Camping Floreal 2: heated outdoor swimming pool (1/7-31/8). New wellness facilities with sauna and jacuzzi (all year). Professional entertainment team (during local school holidays). Sports field. Volleyball. Tennis. Minigolf. Pétanque. Dog shower. WiFi. Mobile homes to rent.

Key Features

- Open All Year
- Pets Accepted
- Disabled Facilities
- Swimming Pool
- Play Area
- Bar/Restaurant
- Skiing
- Fishing

Scan me for more information.

Alan Rogers Code: BE0810
10 accommodations
39 pitches
GPS: 49.87728, 5.56247
Post Code: B-6640

Luxembourg, Wallonia

www.alanrogers.com/be0810
campingasdl@tiscali.be
Tel: 061 255049
www.ecocamping.be

Open (Touring Pitches):
24 April - 5 September

Aux Sources De Lescheret

Aux Sources De Lescheret is a small natural campsite with modern facilities, situated in a beautiful natural park in the South Belgian Ardennes/Gaume at 18km from Bastogne. Featuring lots of greenery and three spring lakes for swimming, playing and fishing during hot summer days. Even during the busy periods, the site remains relatively quiet and has spacious pitches. A playground with trampoline and table tennis are available for the children, and there are hundreds of kilometres of walking and cycling trails from the site and in the surrounding area. There is much to do within a 1-hour drive, including kayaking and climbing. Abbeys, castles, caves, churches and museums are all nearby as are day trips to France, Luxembourg or Germany. Wooden wigwams, tent houses, tents and retro caravans are available for rent.

Motorhomes allowed, 2 hardstanding pitches available. Seasonal Guided walks. Small river beach. Natural swimming lake. WiFi is unreliable, connection with cable possible. Private washing cubicles and WC's (toilet paper not provided) Bar with pool table.Table tennis. Geocaching and archery. Breakfast and fresh bread available. Children's playground. Fishing on site. Laundry with washer and dryer. Chemical toilet disposal point (only bio toiletfluid). Max 3 Dogs permitted.

Key Features

- Pets Accepted
- Play Area
- Bar/Restaurant
- Fishing

Scan me for more information.

City of Dubrovnik >

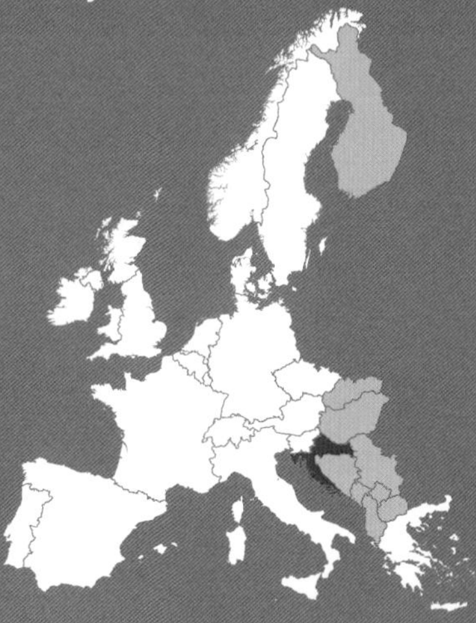

Capital Zagreb
Currency Kuna (Kn)
Language Croatian
Time Zone CET (GMT+1)
Telephone Code 00 385

Tourist Website
croatia.hr

Climate Warm, hot summers with temperatures of up to 40 degrees Celcius.

Shops Hours vary widely. In high-season 8am to 8pm weekdays and until 2pm or 3pm on Saturdays. Some shops take a break from 2pm to 5pm.

Banks 8am or 9am to 8pm weekdays and 7am or 8am to 1pm or 2pm Saturdays.

Accessible Travel Largely unequipped for less able travellers but improving. Public transport in larger cities is generally good.

Travelling with Children Beaches are safe. Many museums and historical attractions run activity trails. Child fees are applicable for under 9s. The dining scene is relaxed and many restaurants will offer a kids menu.

See campsite map page

474

Public Holidays New Year's Day, Epiphany, Easter Monday, Labour Day, Corpus Christi, Anti-Fascist Resistance Day (22 Jun), Statehood Day (25 Jun), Thanksgiving (5 Aug), Assumption, Independence Day (8 Oct), All Saints, Christmas Day, Boxing Day.

Motoring The road network has improved dramatically over the last few years. Roads along the coast can become heavily congested in summer and queues are possible at border crossings. Tolls are present on some motorways, bridges and tunnels. Cars towing a caravan or trailer must carry two warning triangles. It is illegal to overtake military convoys.

Environmental Policies Croatia currently has no Low Emission Zones in place although this could change. Recycling in Croatia is a little hit and miss however things are improving. Paper, plastic and glass can be recycled in some locations. Bottles and drink cans can be taken to deposit stations.

View all campsites in Croatia
alanrogers.com/croatia

Croatia

Croatia has developed into a lively and friendly tourist destination, while retaining the unspoilt beauty and character of its coastal ports, traditional towns and tiny islands with their secluded coves. Its rich history is reflected in its Baroque architecture, traditional festivals and two UNESCO World Heritage sites.

The most developed tourist regions in Croatia include the peninsula of Istria, where you will find the preserved Roman amphitheatre in Pula, the beautiful town of Rovinj with cobbled streets and wooded hills, and the resort of Umag, with a busy marina, charming old town and an international tennis centre. The coast is dotted with islands, making it a mecca for watersports enthusiasts, and there is an abundance of campsites in the area.

Further south, in the province of Dalmatia, Split is Croatia's second largest city and lies on the Adriatic coast. It is home to the impressive Diocletian's Palace and a starting point for ferry trips to the islands of Brac, Hvar, Vis and Korcula, with their lively fishing villages and pristine beaches. The old walled city of Dubrovnik is 150 km. south. A favourite of George Bernard Shaw, who described it as 'the pearl of the Adriatic,' it has a lively summer festival, numerous historical sights and a newly restored cable car to the top of Mount Srd.

Alan Rogers Code: CR6737
111 accommodations
588 pitches
GPS: 44.79780, 13.91366
Post Code: HR-52100

Premantura, Istria

Arena Camping Stupice

www.alanrogers.com/cr6737
arenastupice@arenacampsites.com
Tel: 052 575 111
www.arenacampsites.com

Open (Touring Pitches):
April - October

This quiet site, which offers superb views over the sea to the nearby islands, is situated in a delightful strip of coast on the Istrian peninsula near the small village of Premantura. Most of the site is covered with undulating, dense pinewood providing ample shade with a carpet of pine needles. There are nearly 1,000 pitches in total with 588 touring pitches in three sizes, mostly sloping, and some with sea views. A narrow pebble beach and flat rocks separate the sea from the site and provide a perfect place to relax and enjoy the view. Areas of water are netted off from motorsports, making them for safe swimming. There is boat launching with a marina as well as many sporting activities. For those who enjoy a sunny position, a small circular rocky spit of land approximately 500 m. in diameter extends from the site. Surrounded by water and enjoying excellent views, there is room for about 60 pitches, although with no shade or facilities on the spit (generally occupied by motorhomes).

The six toilet blocks, although old, were immaculately clean when we visited. Toilets are a mixture of Turkish and British style. Showers and free hot water. Washing machines. Good supermarket. Kiosk and several good small bars and grills. Minigolf. Modern playground. Activities for children and some live entertainment at the restaurant in high season. Rock and pebble beach. Marina, boat launching, jetty and scuba diving. Bicycle and beach buggy hire. Aquapark. Free WiFi over 80% of site.

Key Features

- Pets Accepted
- Disabled Facilities
- Beach Access
- Play Area
- Bar/Restaurant
- Bike Hire
- Fishing

Scan me for more information.

Alan Rogers Code: CR6715
763 accommodations
1719 pitches
GPS: 45.36707, 13.54716
Post Code: HR-52470

Umag, Istria

www.alanrogers.com/cr6715
camp.park.umag@istraturist.hr
Tel: 052 725 040
www.istracamping.com

Open (Touring Pitches):
Mid-April - End-September.

Camping Park Umag

This extensive site is very well planned in that just 60% of the 127 hectares is used for the pitches, resulting in lots of open space around the pitch area. It is the largest of the Istraturist group of sites. Of the 2,000 plus pitches, 1,700 are for touring units, all with 10A electricity. Some pitches have shade. There are also around 750 mobile homes, some of which are available to rent. Some noise is transmitted from the road alongside the site. The site is very popular with Dutch campers, and a friendly and happy atmosphere prevails, even during the busiest times. The very long curved beach is of rock and shingle with grassy sunbathing areas. There are many watersports on offer, and the swimming pool complex has four pools, cascades and fountains.

Ten toilet blocks (some newly renovated) include two bathrooms with deep tubs. Two blocks have children's WCs. Facilities for disabled visitors. Freshwater and wastewater points only at toilet blocks. Motorhome services. Range of shops and supermarket. Bars, snack bars and restaurant (musical entertainment some evenings) all open early morning to midnight (one until the small hours). Swimming pool complex. Tennis. Fishing (permit from Umag). Minigolf. Watersports. Massage. Entertainment and clubs for children of all ages. Barbecue area. WiFi (free in some areas).

Key Features

- Pets Accepted
- Disabled Facilities
- Beach Access
- Swimming Pool
- Play Area
- Bar/Restaurant
- Bike Hire
- Fishing

Scan me for more information.

Alan Rogers Code: CR6717
146 accommodations
280 pitches
GPS: 45.31536, 13.57581
Post Code: HR-52466

Novigrad, Istria

www.alanrogers.com/cr6717
camping@aminess.com
Tel: 052 858 690
www.aminess-campsites.com

Open (Touring Pitches):
Mid-March - Early November.

Camping Sirena

The site slopes towards the seafront and has two areas for 280 touring units, one set on uneven gravel under pine tree shade, the other to the left of the site is grassy without shade and borders a quarry, which can be noisy at times. All pitches have 10/16A electricity. A large number of permanent campers are housed at the back of the site. This leaves the seafront available for touring units, however, apart from the very front row of this area, views over the open sea are restricted due to overhanging trees and the parked caravans and motorhomes. Adjoining the site is a top-class hotel with a restaurant and children's playground that are reached through a small gate, as is the path leading to Novigrad.

Three comfortable, well maintained sanitary blocks with spacious showers and controllable free hot water. Bar and restaurant in adjoining hotel. Facilities for disabled visitors. Direct beach access. Sports centre. Activity and entertainment programme. Fishing. Bicycle hire. WiFi (charged.)

Key Features

- Pets Accepted
- Disabled Facilities
- Beach Access
- Play Area
- Bar/Restaurant
- Bike Hire
- Fishing

Scan me for more information.

Alan Rogers Code: CR6742
127 accommodations
708 pitches
GPS: 44.85972, 13.81450
Post Code: HR-52100

Pula, Istria

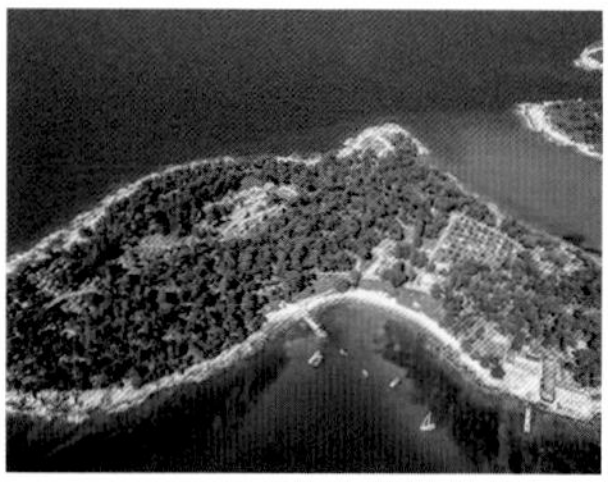

www.alanrogers.com/cr6742
arenastoja@arenacampsites.com
Tel: 052 387 144
www.arenacampsites.com

Open (Touring Pitches):
30 March - 4 November.

Arena Camping Stoja

Camping Stoja in Pula is an attractive and well-maintained site on a small peninsula and therefore almost entirely surrounded by the waters of the clear Adriatic. In the centre of the site is the old Fort Stoja, built in 1884 for coastal defence. Some of its buildings are now used as a toilet block/laundry, and the entertainment team uses its courtyard. The 700+ touring pitches here vary significantly in size (50-120 sq.m) and are marked by round, concrete, numbered blocks, separated by young trees. About half have shade from mature trees, and all are slightly sloping on grass and gravel. Pitches close to the pebble and rock beach have beautiful views of the sea and Pula. This site is an ideal base for visiting Pula, considered to be the capital of Istrian tourism and full of history, tradition and natural beauty, including a spectacular Roman amphitheatre.

Four toilet blocks with British style toilets, open plan washbasins with cold water only and controllable hot showers. Child size washbasins. Facilities for disabled visitors. Laundry and ironing service. Fridge box hire. Motorhome service point. Supermarket. Bar/restaurant. Miniclub and teen club. Bicycle hire. Water-skiing. Boat hire. Boat launching. Surfboard and pedalo hire. Fishing (with permit). Island excursions. Free WiFi throughout. No barbecues on pitches, communal areas provided.

Key Features

- Pets Accepted
- Disabled Facilities
- Beach Access
- Play Area
- Bar/Restaurant
- Bike Hire
- Fishing
- Sailing

Scan me for more information.

Alan Rogers Code: CR6729
1700 pitches
GPS: 45.14288, 13.60527
Post Code: HR-52450

Vrsar, Istria

www.alanrogers.com/cr6729
info@maistra.hr
Tel: 052 441 378
www.maistracamping.com/naturist-park-koversada-campsite-vrsar

Open (Touring Pitches):
Mid-April - End-September.

Naturist Park Koversada

According to history, the first naturist on Koversada was the famous adventurer Casanova. Today, Koversada is a first-class enclosed naturist camping holiday park with 1700 pitches, all with access to 10A electricity. The site splits it's camping between the mainland, and it's own island, which is only suitable for tents and is reached by a narrow bridge. This island also has its own restaurant and two toilet blocks. The pitches are of average size on grass and gravel ground and slightly sloping. Pitches on the mainland are numbered and partly terraced beneath mature pine and olive trees, some with sea views available. Pitches on the island are unmarked and have shade from mature trees. Between the island and the mainland is an enclosed, shallow section of water for swimming. A long beach surrounds the site, part sand, partly paved.

Seventeen toilet blocks provide British and Turkish style toilets, washbasins and controllable hot showers. Facilities for children and disabled visitors. Laundry service. Motorhome services. Supermarket. Kiosks with newspapers and tobacco. Several bars and restaurants. Tennis. Minigolf. Surf boards, canoes and kayaks for hire. Tweety Club for children. Live music. Sports tournaments. Internet access in reception and WiFi throughout (incl in price of pitch). Communal barbecue.

Key Features

- Naturist Site
- Pets Accepted
- Disabled Facilities
- Beach Access
- Play Area
- Bar/Restaurant
- Bike Hire
- Sailing

Scan me for more information.

Alan Rogers Code: CR6751
9 accommodations
160 pitches
GPS: 45.02244, 14.56179
Post Code: HR-51500

Krk, Kvarner

www.alanrogers.com/cr6751
info@camp-bor.hr
Tel: 051 221581
www.camp-bor.hr

Open (Touring Pitches):
Open all year.

Autocamp Bor

Located close to the centre of the City of Krk, famous for its 5th-century cathedral, Camping Bor features a high standard of accommodation, a couple of small swimming pools and a good quality restaurant, serving homegrown wine. The family-owned and run campsite, Autocamp Bor is only a couple of minutes walk from the main beaches, though you should be prepared for an uphill slog on the way back to the campsite. Facilities for the storage of vehicles are available. The ground can be hard and is somewhat sloping in places. Spread across terraces, shade can be limited on some pitches, but this is more than compensated by the views. Popular with the Dutch and Germans, this is a part of Europe which isn't visited as frequently as others by the Brits.

Dogs accepted (maximum 2 per pitch). Chemical waste disposal point. Hot & cold showers. Laundry available. Restaurant/bar with a good selection of food and drink available (seasonal). A small shop with a limited selection of goods. BBQ's permitted. Small children's playground. No entertainment program.

Key Features

- OPEN 365 Open All Year
- Pets Accepted
- Swimming Pool
- Play Area
- Bar/Restaurant

Scan me for more information.

Alan Rogers Code: CR6765
187 accommodations
952 pitches
GPS: 44.96346, 14.39747
Post Code: HR-51557

Cres, Kvarner

www.alanrogers.com/cr6765
campkovacine@kovacine.com
Tel: 051 573 150
www.camp-kovacine.com/en

Open (Touring Pitches):
19 March - 16 October.

Camping Kovacine

Camping Kovacine is located on a peninsula on the beautiful Kvarner island of Cres, just 2 km. from the town of the same name. The site has just under 1,000 pitches for touring units, most with 16A electricity (from renewable sources) and a water supply. On sloping ground, partially shaded by mature olive and pine trees, pitching is on the large, open spaces between the trees. From the waterside pitches there are far reaching views over the sea to the coast beyond. Kovacine is partly an FKK (naturist) site, which is quite common in Croatia, and has a pleasant atmosphere. The site has its own beach (Blue Flag), part concrete, part pebbles, and a jetty for mooring boats and fishing.

Seven modern, well maintained toilet blocks (water heated by solar power) with open plan washbasins (some cabins for ladies) and free hot showers. Private family bathrooms for hire. Facilities for disabled visitors and children. Laundry sinks and washing machine. Motorhome services. Electric car/scooter charging point. Car wash. Mini-marina and boat crane. Supermarket. Bar. Restaurant and pizzeria (May-16/10). Playground. Daily children's club. Evening shows with live music. Boat launching. Fishing. Diving centre. Motorboat hire. WiFi (free). Airport transfers.

Key Features

- Pets Accepted
- Disabled Facilities
- Beach Access
- Play Area
- Bar/Restaurant
- Bike Hire
- Fishing

Scan me for more information.

Alan Rogers Code: CR6752
93 accommodations
250 pitches
GPS: 45.09642, 14.84573
Post Code: HR-51252

Klenovica, Kvarner

Camping Klenovica

www.alanrogers.com/cr6752
camp.klenovica@luje.hr
Tel: 051 796 251
www.camp-klenovica.com

Open (Touring Pitches):
1 May - 30 September.

Camping Klenovica can be found around 20 km. South of the Crikvenica Riviera and is a well established seaside site with its own pebble beach. There are approximately 250 touring pitches, of varying sizes, the majority with electricity and some with water and drainage. Pitches are mostly shaded, and some are terraced with beautiful sea views. Several mobile homes are also available to rent. Boats can be moored at the site's small harbour (additional charge). On-site amenities include a popular restaurant, 'Ribarska Koliba Valentin', specialising in locally caught fish and a well-stocked supermarket. Klenovica itself is a pleasant small harbour in the bay of the same name. The town is located at the foot of the Velebit mountains, and Croatia's major winter sports region is only 40 km. away. Although Klenovica is a quiet spot with three or four pleasant restaurants, the larger resort of Crikvenica to the north, has a good selection of shops and restaurants, as well as lively nightlife.

Sanitary blocks with hot showers and facilities for children and disabled visitors. Laundry facilities. Shop. Bar/café. Self-service restaurant with pizzeria. Direct access to pebble beach. Play area. Mobile homes to rent. WiFi (free in reception and restaurant).

Key Features

- Pets Accepted
- Disabled Facilities
- Beach Access
- Swimming Pool
- Play Area
- Bar/Restaurant

Scan me for more information.

Alan Rogers Code: CR6916
448 accommodations
792 pitches
GPS: 43.69887, 15.87887
Post Code: HR-22000

Sibenik, Dalmatia

www.alanrogers.com/cr6916
camping@solaris.hr
Tel: 22 361 017
www.campingsolaris.com

Open (Touring Pitches):
12 April - 20 October.

Solaris Beach Resort

Solaris Camping is an extensive site situated on the coast some 90 km. South of Zadar and 6 km. from Sibenik. It forms part of the modern, well equipped Solaris holiday complex located right on the beach and surrounded by olive trees and a tall pine forest. The one-kilometre long concrete beach has steps that lead directly into the sea, and there is also a small pebbled cove. There are around 1,200 pitches with 792 level shady pitches for touring, all with 6A electricity. The complex offers numerous recreational facilities (many at extra cost) including bars and restaurants, shops, a disco, several swimming pools, an aqua pool, a seawater swimming pool, tennis, beach volleyball and fitness equipment. There is a supermarket, a souvenir shop, a restaurant and a beach bar. Guests can also book diving, sailing and windsurfing lessons. For the youngest guests, there is a mini-club and a water slide. For an additional fee, campers can also use the wellness centre at the nearby hotel.

The sanitary blocks have facilities for babies and disabled visitors. Motorhome services. Several restaurants, bars and an ice-cream kiosk. Indoor and outdoor swimming pools with slides (Aquapark). Sea swimming. Beach volleyball. Tennis. windsurfing, boat hire. Extensive entertainment program for all the family. Bicycle hire. Excursions to the Dalmatian coast. WiFi (charged). No open fire and charcoal barbecues.

Key Features

- Pets Accepted
- Disabled Facilities
- Beach Access
- Swimming Pool
- Play Area
- Bar/Restaurant
- Bike Hire
- Fishing

Scan me for more information.

Alan Rogers Code: CR6782
300 accommodations
1030 pitches
GPS: 44.23477, 15.16437
Post Code: HR-23232

Zaton, Dalmatia

Zaton Holiday Resort

www.alanrogers.com/cr6782
camping@zaton.hr
Tel: 023 280 215
zaton.hr

Open (Touring Pitches):
30 April - 30 September.

Zaton Holiday Resort is a modern family holiday park with a 1.5 kilometre private sandy beach. It is close to the historic town of Nin and just a few kilometres from the ancient city of Zadar. This park itself is more like a large village and has every amenity one can think of for a holiday on the Dalmatian coast. The village is divided into two areas separated by a public area with reception, bakery, shops, restaurant and a large car park, one for campers close to the sea, the other for a complex with holiday apartments. Zaton has 1,030 mostly level pitches for touring units, all with electricity, water and waste water.

Five modern and one refurbished toilet blocks with washbasins (some in cabins) and controllable hot showers. Child size washbasins. Family shower rooms. Facilities for disabled visitors. Outdoor grill station. Motorhome services. Car wash. Shopping centre. Restaurants (self-service one has breakfast, lunch and evening menus). Several bars and kiosks. Water play area for children. Heated outdoor swimming pools. Mini-car track. Riding. Tennis centre. Trim track. Scuba diving. Professional entertainment team. Teen club. Games hall. Beach extension with climbing pyramids. Live shows on stage by the beach. Free WiFi.

Key Features

- Pets Accepted
- Disabled Facilities
- Beach Access
- Swimming Pool
- Play Area
- Bar/Restaurant
- Bike Hire
- Horse Riding

Scan me for more information.

Prague at night >

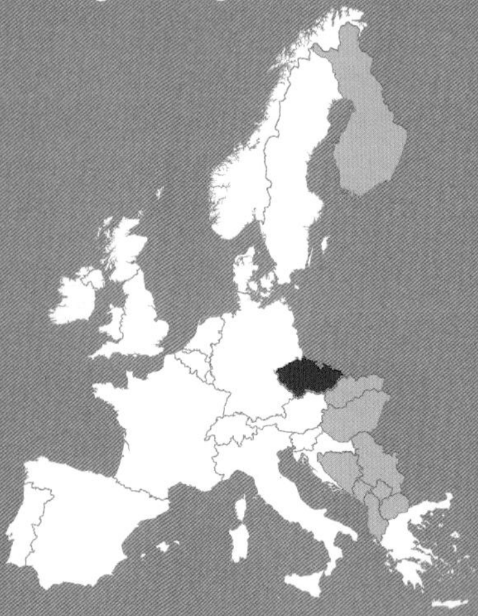

Capital Prague
Currency Czech Koruna (CZK)
Language Czech
Time Zone CET (GMT+1)

Telephone Code 00 420

Tourist Website
czechtourism.com

Climate Temperate oceanic climate with warm summers and cold, snowy winters.

Shops 9am to 6pm weekdays, some stores open 9am to 1pm on Saturday. Shopping centres have longer opening hours.

Banks 9am to 4pm weekdays, some 9am to 1pm Saturday.

Accessible Travel Behind when it comes to accessibility. Older buildings, including museums, are not well equipped. Transport in cities is improving.

Travelling with Children The country is becoming more child-friendly however, baby facilities remain rare. More often than not, restaurants will cater for children. Historical sights and attractions are partly geared towards kids. Child rates apply up to the age of 18.

See campsite map page

472

Public Holidays New Year's Day, Good Friday, Easter Monday, May Day (1 May), Liberation Day (8 May), St Cyril & St Methodius Day (5 Jul), Jan Hus Day (6 Jul), Statehood Day (28 Sep), Independence Day (28 Oct), Freedom & Democracy Day (17 Nov), Christmas Eve, Christmas Day, Boxing Day.

Motoring There is a good, well-signposted road network throughout the Republic and surfaces are generally good. An annual road tax is levied on all vehicles using Czech motorways and express roads, and a disc can be purchased at border crossings, post offices and petrol stations. Dipped headlights are compulsory throughout winter. Give way to trams and buses.

Environmental Policies Prague has set up a Low Emission Zone, which currently only affects heavy-duty vehicles. Recycling schemes differ across the Republic. In and around the capital black bins denote landfill waste, metal, plastic, glass, paper and cardboard are generally recycled.

View all campsites in Czech Republic
alanrogers.com/czech-republic

Czech Republic

The Czech Republic, once known as Bohemia, is a land of fascinating castles, romantic lakes and valleys, picturesque medieval squares and famous spas. It is divided into two main regions, Bohemia to the west and Moravia in the east.

Although small, the Czech Republic has a wealth of attractive places to explore. The historic city of Prague is the hub of tourist activity and a treasure trove of museums, historic architecture, art galleries and theatres, as well as the annual 17-day beer festival!

The beautiful region of Bohemia, known for its Giant Mountains, is popular for hiking, skiing and other sports. West Bohemia is home to three renowned spas: Karlovy Vary, Mariánské Lázne and Františkovy Lázne, which have developed around the hundreds of mineral springs which rise in this area, and offer a wide variety of restorative treatments.

Brno is the capital of Moravia in the east, lying midway between Prague, Vienna and Budapest. Visitors will admire its beautiful architecture, notably Mies van der Rohe's Villa Tugendhat. North of Brno is the Moravian Karst, where the underground Punkya River has carved out a network of caves, some open to the public and connecting with boat trips along the river.

Alan Rogers Code: CZ4590
41 accommodations
150 pitches
GPS: 50.61036, 15.60264
Post Code: CZ-54362

Vychodocesky, North Bohemia

www.alanrogers.com/cz4590
info@liscifarma.cz
Tel: 499 421 473
holiday-park-vrchlabi.cz

Open (Touring Pitches):
All year.

Holiday Park Lisci Farma

New owners took over this campsite in early 2019. The new ownership is good news as this used to be a truly excellent site and we're looking forward to seeing the further improvements they have promised. Considering its amenities, pitches and welcome Lisci Farma retains a pleasant Czech atmosphere. In the winter months, when local skiing is available, snow chains are essential. The 150 pitches (reduced from the previous 250) are relatively flat, although the terrain is slightly sloping and some pitches are terraced. There is shade, and some pitches have hardstanding. The site is well equipped for the whole family with its adventure playground offering trampolines for children, archery, beach volleyball. Russian bowling and an outdoor bowling court for older youngsters. A beautiful sandy, lakeside beach is 800 m. from the entrance.

Two dated but serviceable sanitary blocks near the entrance and another block next to the hotel include toilets, washbasins and spacious, controllable showers (on payment). Child size toilets and baby room. Toilet for disabled visitors. Sauna and massage. Launderette with sinks, hot water and a washing machine. Shop (15/6-15/9). Bar/snack bar with pool table. Games room. Swimming pool (6x12 m). Adventure-style playground on grass with climbing wall. Trampolines. Tennis. Minigolf. Archery. Russian bowling. Paragliding. Rock climbing. Bicycle hire. Entertainment programme. Excursions to Prague.

Key Features

- Open All Year
- Pets Accepted
- Disabled Facilities
- Swimming Pool
- Play Area
- Bar/Restaurant
- Skiing
- Bike Hire

Scan me for more information.

Alan Rogers Code: CZ4695
10 accommodations
180 pitches
GPS: 50.70430, 14.93898
Post Code: CZ-46352

Severocesky, North Bohemia

www.alanrogers.com/cz4695
camping2000@online.nl
Tel: 485 179 621
www.camping2000.com

Open (Touring Pitches):
15 April - 15 September.

Camping 2000

Created from pleasant farm buildings and the fields behind them, Camping 2000 is especially popular with Dutch visitors. It is a good base for exploring Northern Bohemia with Prague (90 km) and the Krkonose mountains (50 km) from a pleasant, rural location. Most of the pitches are of average size (up to 100 sq.m) and numbered, all with 6A electricity. There is little shade and cars parked on the pitches can make the curved rows feel a bit crowded during high season. Further off, there are a few pitches catering for larger units. The social heart of the site is a large barn with a bar and a takeaway serving pizzas and typical Dutch snacks. Outdoors, a terrace overlooks a paddling pool and a larger, circular swimming pool featuring a 48 m. waterslide.

Until an extra new block is built, in high season prefabricated units are used next to the main toilet block. Facilities for disabled visitors. Washing machine and dryer. Shop (July/Aug). Bar and takeaway (May-Sept). Swimming and paddling pools. Bicycle hire. TV room. Five wooden cottages (fully equipped) for hire. WiFi.

Key Features

- Pets Accepted
- Disabled Facilities
- Swimming Pool
- Play Area
- Bar/Restaurant
- Bike Hire

Scan me for more information.

Alan Rogers Code: CZ4555
5 accommodations
36 pitches
GPS: 50.61641, 16.22865
Post Code: CZ-54982

Kralovehradecky, East Bohemia

Mini Camping Aktief

www.alanrogers.com/cz4555
bert.mien@tiscali.cz
Tel: 491 582 138
www.aktief.cz

Open (Touring Pitches):
1 May - 1 October.

Camping Aktief is a small, rural site on the outskirts of the village of Vernerovice. The campsite is close to the Polish border, east of the Krkonose (Giant) Mountains. The spectacular rock formations of Adrspach and Teplice nad Metuji are close at hand. There are just 36 pitches (20 with 6A electricity), located in a tranquil and protected area with many fruit trees. From the campsite, there are good views around the surrounding rolling meadows and hills. The friendly Dutch owners have developed Camping Aktief as an important hiking centre. Plenty of other activities are also organised here, and detailed walking and cycle routes are available (in Dutch). The owners, Bert and Mien van Kampen, are happy to share their knowledge of the local area, including some good restaurants. They also organise special tours, including visits to a local brewery and glassworks. Bikes, mountain bikes and fishing equipment are available for hire on site. In peak season, a weekly barbecue is organised.

Modern toilet block with hot showers and underfloor heating. Sauna. Washing machine. Mobile home to rent. Accommodation in luxuriously converted farm buildings. Bicycle hire. WiFi (free).

Key Features

- Open All Year
- Skiing
- Bike Hire

Scan me for more information.

Alan Rogers Code: CZ4840
7 accommodations
120 pitches
GPS: 49.95145, 14.47517
Post Code: CZ-25241

Prague, Central Bohemia

www.alanrogers.com/cz4840
info@campingoase.cz
Tel: 241 932 044
www.campingoase.cz

Open (Touring Pitches):
8 May - 8 September.

Camping Oase Praha

Camping Oase Praha is an exceptional site, only five kilometres from Prague and with easy access. You can take the bus (from outside the site) or drive to the underground stop (ten minutes). The site has 120 pitches, all around 100 sq.m, with 6/12A electricity and 55 with water and drainage, on level, well-kept fields. The site is very well maintained and has just about everything one would expect, including an outdoor pool and an indoor pool with a separate paddling pool, a restaurant and a bar. Children can amuse themselves with trampolines, a playground, an indoor play area, volleyball and football field.

An outstanding toilet block includes washbasins, controllable showers and child-sized toilets. Facilities for disabled visitors. Family showers. Laundry facilities. Campers' kitchen with hob, fridge and freezer and dishwasher. Motorhome services. Shop (essentials). Bar and restaurant. Outdoor pool (9x15m) and separate paddling pool with slide (open July/Aug), heated indoor pool (10x4 m; all season). Jacuzzi with sauna and massage (30/4-15/9). Adventure-style playgrounds and covered miniclub. Trampolines. Football. Minigolf. TV and video. Board games. CCTV cameras. Barbecues are permitted. Internet point and WiFi (charged).

Key Features

- Pets Accepted
- Disabled Facilities
- Swimming Pool
- Play Area
- Bar/Restaurant

Scan me for more information.

Alan Rogers Code: CZ4655
4 accommodations
30 pitches
GPS: 49.94419, 12.72797
Post Code: CZ-35301

Zapadocesky, West Bohemia

Camping Stanowitz

www.alanrogers.com/cz4655
info@stanowitz.cz
Tel: 354 624 673
www.stanowitz.com

Open (Touring Pitches):
1 April - 31 October.

The town of Mariánské Lázne (better known among westerners as Marienbad) is an old-style health resort in the heart of Western Bohemia, a region full of historical and natural beauty. The town became popular as a spa resort between 1870 and the 1920s, with around 100 mineral springs. However, this is not the only reason to stay at Camp Stanowitz. This cosy, family size campsite has only 30 pitches, all with 10A electricity, in a slightly sloping, unmarked apple and plum orchard (look out for falling fruit in the Autumn) Drainage is good. The owner makes a real effort to show off his beautiful country to interested visitors and probably has more brochures than the average tourist office. Attached to the site is a pension and a small restaurant, which offers a limited menu, but receives positive reports from visitors.

Modern, heated toilet block with free hot showers. Washing machine. Restaurant/bar. Riding. Internet. Free WiFi. BBQ's permitted. Max 2 Dogs allowed. No children's entertainment program.

Key Features

- Pets Accepted
- Bar/Restaurant
- Skiing

Scan me for more information.

Alan Rogers Code: CZ4710
6 accommodations
140 pitches
GPS: 48.85583, 14.20850
Post Code: CZ-38208

Jihocesky, South Bohemia

www.alanrogers.com/cz4710
info@campingchvalsiny.nl
Tel: 380 739 123
www.campingchvalsiny.nl

Open (Touring Pitches):
17 April - 15 September.

Camping Chvalsiny

Camping Chvalsiny is Dutch-owned and has been developed from an old farm into real camping fields which are terraced and level. The pitches are of average size but look more substantial because of the open nature of the terrain, which also means there is little shade. Chvalsiny is a real family site, and children are kept occupied with painting, crafts and stories. Older youngsters take part in soccer, volleyball and rafting competitions. The location in the middle of the Blanky Les nature reserve, part of the vast Sumava forest, provides excellent opportunities for walking, cycling and fishing. It also has a rich culture and heritage. You can visit the charming UNESCO world heritage registered village of Cesky Krumlov with its impressive castle and scenic centre is the most important.

Modern, clean and well kept toilet facilities include washbasins in cabins and controllable showers (coin operated). Family showers and baby room. Laundry. Motorhome services. Kiosk (1/6-13/9) with bread and daily necessities. Snack bar (1/6-15/9). Lake swimming. Outdoor pool. Climbing equipment and swings. Crafts, games and soccer (July/Aug). Play attic. Recreation hall (used in bad weather and for film nights). Animal farm. Torches useful. WiFi (free).

Key Features

- Pets Accepted
- Swimming Pool
- Play Area
- Bar/Restaurant
- Fishing

Scan me for more information.

Alan Rogers Code: CZ4686
52 accommodations
100 pitches
GPS: 49.41296, 16.80847
Post Code: CZ-79862

Severocesky, North Moravia

Camping Baldovec

www.alanrogers.com/cz4686
info@baldovec.cz
Tel: 606 744 265
www.baldovec.cz

Open (Touring Pitches):
27 February - 31 December.

Camping Baldovec is in the Moravian Karst region, a few kilometres from the abyss known as the Macocha Gorge, the largest of its kind in Europe. It lies in the Valley of the White Water, surrounded by deep forests and unspoiled nature. There are 100 good sized pitches on slightly sloping grass or hard ground. Some areas have low terracing. The Baldovec restaurant, with an outdoor terrace, offers a wide range of foods. This is an ideal site for the active families seeking a good site to unwind after a busy day, having a meal in the restaurant or watching the evening family entertainment. Wellness centre complete with artificial caves, water world and massage room. Wide range of sporting activities including many marked cycling and hiking trails. The Lookout Tower on the Podvrsi Hill is one of the popular tourist destinations in the region and is very easily accessible from the parking lot at the Culture House.

Heated sanitary facilities. Washing machine and dryer. Snack bar, fresh bread (high season). Restaurant (all season). Small swimming pool and sunbathing area (1/6-30/9). Games room. Children's play area. Wellness centre. Climbing tower. Rope course. Tarzan Jump. Paintball. Archery. Tennis. Football. Volleyball. Slingshot. Multisports centre (floodlit). WiFi throughout (free). Accommodation to rent.

Key Features

- Pets Accepted
- Disabled Facilities
- Swimming Pool
- Play Area
- Bar/Restaurant
- Skiing
- Bike Hire

Scan me for more information.

Alan Rogers Code: CZ4890
14 accommodations
40 pitches
GPS: 49.03980, 17.79993
Post Code: CZ-68771

Jihomoravsky, South Moravia

www.alanrogers.com/cz4890
info@eurocamping.cz
Tel: 604 236 631
www.eurocamping.cz

Open (Touring Pitches):
1 May - 30 September.

Eurocamping Bojkovice

This family site in Bojkovice, close to the Slovak border and with views across the valley to the white castle Novy Svetlo, is attractive and well managed. It is on hilly ground with tarmac access roads connecting the 40 pitches. These are all for touring units on grassy fields taking six or eight units. Mostly on terraces in the shade of mature birch trees, all have 6A electricity. A footpath connects the three toilet blocks which offer a more than adequate provision. It also leads to the bar/ restaurant and the centrally located outdoor pool. There is no entertainment programme, but we were told that children and teenagers enjoy their stay here. At the reception you may borrow a map with extensive tourist information about the local area.

Three good toilet blocks (one refurbished) are clean and include British style toilets, open washbasins and controllable hot showers (free). Washing machine. Campers' kitchen. Bar/ restaurant with open-air terrace (breakfast and dinner served, open 1/7-30/8). Outdoor swimming pool (15x8 m, unfenced). Fishing. Bicycle hire. WiFi.

Key Features

- Pets Accepted
- Swimming Pool
- Bar/Restaurant
- Bike Hire
- Fishing

Scan me for more information.

Nyhavn Canal, Copenhagen >

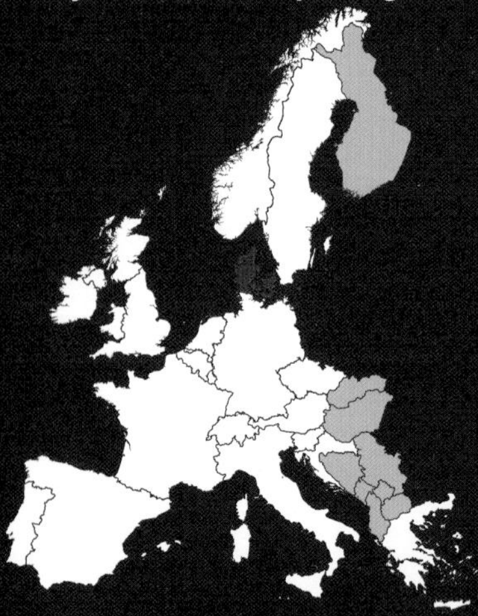

Capital Copenhagen
Currency Danish Krone (DKK)
Language Danish
Time Zone CET (GMT+1)
Telephone Code 00 45

Tourist Website
visitdenmark.com

Climate Generally mild although changeable throughout the year.

Shops Varied. Generally open from 10am to 6pm weekdays and until 4pm on Saturday. Some larger stores may be open Sunday. Supermarkets open from 8am to 9pm.

Banks 10am to 4pm weekdays.

Accessible Travel Access to buildings, transport and rural areas is improving but some areas are certainly not universally accessible yet.

Travelling with Children Very much tailored to children with a whole host of attractions from theme parks and zoos to family-friendly beaches. Entry to most museums is free. Many campsites have special programs for children during peak season.

See campsite map page

475

Public Holidays New Year's Day, Maundy Thursday, Good Friday, Easter Sunday, Easter Monday, Great Prayer Day, Ascension, Whitsunday, Whit Monday, Constitution Day (5 Jun), Christmas Eve (from noon), Christmas Day, Boxing Day.

Motoring Driving is much easier than at home as roads are much quieter. Driving is on the right. Do not drink and drive. Dipped headlights are compulsory at all times. Strong measures are taken against unauthorised parking on beaches, with on-the-spot fines.

Environmental Policies Low Emission Zones are in place in many large cities in Denmark; however these only apply to heavy-duty vehicles. Recycling is mainstream in Denmark, it was the first country in the world to implement recycling laws and targets in 1978. Metal, plastic, glass, paper and cardboard are widely recycled, and bottle deposit schemes can be found in some supermarkets.

View all campsites in Denmark
alanrogers.com/denmark

Denmark

Denmark offers a diverse landscape all within a relatively short distance. The countryside is green and varied with flat plains, rolling hills, fertile farmland, many lakes and fjords, wild moors and long beaches, interspersed with pretty villages and towns.

It is the easiest of the Scandinavian countries to visit, and distances are short so it is easy to combine the faster pace of the city with the tranquillity of the countryside and the beaches. It comprises the peninsula of Jutland and the larger islands of Zeeland and Funen, in addition to hundreds of smaller islands, many uninhabited.

Zeeland is home to the climate-friendly capital city, Copenhagen, with its relaxing waterside cafés, vibrant nightlife, Michelin star restaurants and the stunning Frederiksborg castle. Funen is Denmark's second-largest island, linked to Zeeland by the Great Belt Bridge.

Known as the Garden of Denmark, its gentle landscape is dotted with orchards and pretty thatched, half-timbered houses. It also has plenty of safe, sandy beaches. Jutland's flat terrain makes it ideal for cycling, and its long beaches are popular with windsurfers.

Alan Rogers Code: DK2020
65 accommodations
204 pitches
GPS: 54.93826, 8.79940
Post Code: DK-6270

Sønderjylland, Jutland

Møgeltønder Camping

www.alanrogers.com/dk2020
info@mogeltondercamping.dk
Tel: 74 73 84 60
mogeltondercamping.dk

Open (Touring Pitches):
All year.

This site is only five minutes' walk from one of Denmark's oldest villages and ten minutes' drive from Tønder with its well preserved old buildings and interesting pedestrian shopping street. A quiet family site, Møgeltønder is well maintained with 285 large, level, numbered pitches on grass, with electricity (10A), of which 204 are for tourers. They are divided up by shrubs and hedges. The site has an excellent outdoor heated swimming pool and children's pool, a good playground with zip wire, table tennis, bouncy cushion and a range of trolleys, carts and tricycles. There are two good free kitchens for campers' use, and fishing is available next to the site.

Two heated sanitary units include roomy showers (on payment), washbasins with either divider/curtain or in private cubicles, plus bathrooms for families and disabled visitors. Baby room. Two kitchens with hobs (free). Laundry. Motorhome services. Well stocked shop (bread ordered daily, seasonal). Outdoor heated swimming pool (10x5m) with chute and paddling pool (June-Sept). Minigolf. Playground. TV and games rooms. WiFi (charged).

Key Features

- OPEN 365 Open All Year
- Pets Accepted
- Disabled Facilities
- Swimming Pool
- Play Area

Scan me for more information.

Alan Rogers Code: DK2140
232 accommodations
612 pitches
GPS: 56.75082, 8.81580
Post Code: DK-7900

Viborg, Jutland

www.alanrogers.com/dk2140
jesperhus@jesperhus.dk
Tel: 96 70 14 00
www.jesperhus.dk

Open (Touring Pitches):
All year.

Jesperhus Camping

Jesperhus Feriecenter & Camping is a large, well organised and busy site with many leisure activities, adjacent to Blomsterpark (Northern Europe's largest flower park). This site has 612 numbered pitches, mostly in rows with some terracing, divided by shrubs and trees and with shade in parts. Many pitches are taken by seasonal, tour operator or rental units, so booking is advised for peak periods. Electricity (6A) is available on all pitches, and water points are in all areas. There are 300 pitches available with full services. With all the activities at this site, an entire holiday could be spent here regardless of the weather, although Jesperhus is also an excellent centre for touring.

Four good sanitary units are cleaned three times daily. Facilities include washbasins in cubicles or with divider/curtain, family and whirlpool bathrooms (on payment), suites for babies and disabled visitors. Free sauna. Superb kitchens and a fully equipped laundry. Supermarket (Seasonal). Restaurant. Bar. Café, takeaway. Pool complex with spa facilities. Bowling. Minigolf. Tennis. Go-karts and other outdoor sports. Children's 'Playworld.' Playgrounds. Pets corner. Golf. Fishing pond. Practice golf (3 holes).

Key Features

- Open All Year
- Pets Accepted
- Disabled Facilities
- Swimming Pool
- Play Area
- Bar/Restaurant
- Bike Hire
- Fishing

Scan me for more information.

Alan Rogers Code: DK2170
44 accommodations
460 pitches
GPS: 57.13333, 9.16667
Post Code: DK-9690

Nordjylland, Jutland

Klim Strand Camping

www.alanrogers.com/dk2170
ksc@klim-strand.dk
Tel: 98 22 53 40
www.klimstrand.dk

Open (Touring Pitches):
End-March - Mid-October.

A large family holiday site right beside the sea, Klim Strand is a paradise for children. It is a privately-owned site with a full complement of quality facilities, including a fire engine and trained staff! The site has 460 numbered touring pitches, all with electricity (10A), laid out in rows, many divided by trees and hedges, with shade in parts. Some 220 of these are extra-large (180 sq.m) and fully serviced with electricity, water, drainage and TV hook-up. On-site activities include an outdoor water slide complex, an indoor pool, tennis courts and pony riding (all free). A wellness spa centre including a pirate-themed indoor play hall is a recent addition.

Two good, large, heated toilet blocks are central, with spacious showers and some washbasins in cubicles. Separate room for children. Baby rooms. Bathrooms for families (some charged) and disabled visitors. Laundry. Well equipped kitchens and barbecue areas. TV lounges. Motorhome services. Pizzeria. Supermarket, restaurant and bar (all season). Pool complex. Wellness centre with sauna, solariums, whirlpool bath, fitness room and indoor play hall. TV rental. Play areas. Crèche. Bicycle hire. Cabins to rent. WiFi over part of site (charged).

Key Features

- Pets Accepted
- Disabled Facilities
- Beach Access
- Swimming Pool
- Play Area
- Bar/Restaurant
- Bike Hire
- Fishing

Scan me for more information.

Alan Rogers Code: DK2050
32 accommodations
230 pitches
GPS: 56.12409, 9.71037
Post Code: DK-8600

Århus, Jutland

www.alanrogers.com/dk2050
info@terrassen.dk
Tel: 86 84 13 01
www.terrassen.dk

Open (Touring Pitches):
End-March - Mid-September.

Terrassen Camping

If you are looking for a good quality family campsite with excellent views in the heart of the Danish lake district, then Terrassen Camping is for you. This family-run site arranged on terraces overlooking the lovely Lake Julso and the countryside is open and spacious and has many fruit trees dotted across the site. There are 230 touring pitches, many with outstanding views, all with electricity (16A). The solar-heated swimming pool with slides and paddling pool has a paved terrace and is well fenced. The large play areas with good quality equipment are suitable for toddlers up to younger teenagers. This is an excellent site from which to explore this picturesque area of Denmark. There is a warm welcome and real enthusiasm for making your holiday enjoyable.

Modern and spacious, heated sanitary unit with hot showers (on payment), family bathrooms and large baby room. Kitchens with hobs, ovens and microwaves. Laundry. All facilities are clean and well maintained. Motorhome services. Well stocked shop (seasonal). Takeaways from town (by arrangement). Swimming pool (seasonal) and sunbeds. Games/TV rooms with Internet. Adventure playground. Pets' corner. Covered barbecue. Canoe hire. WiFi (free). Bicycles and riding by arrangement.

Key Features

- Pets Accepted
- Disabled Facilities
- Swimming Pool
- Play Area
- Skiing

Scan me for more information.

Alan Rogers Code: DK2042
30 accommodations
125 pitches
GPS: 55.46346, 9.47339
Post Code: DK-6000

Vejle, Jutland

Kolding City Camp

www.alanrogers.com/dk2042
info@koldingcitycamp.dk
Tel: 75 52 13 88
www.koldingcitycamp.dk

Open (Touring Pitches):
All year.

Dancamps Kolding is on the main 170 road running from Christiansfeld to Kolding, so pitches near the entrance can be a little noisy. Further back, high bushes and trees protect you from the road noise. From the entrance it is only eight minutes by bus to the centre of the historic town of Kolding and, being so close to the city, this campsite does not have many amenities. There are 120 level, grass pitches, all for tourers and all with 6/10A electricity. Pitching is in several broad areas divided by high trees, although the pitches themselves are not separated. Access is off gravel roads. The main attraction of this site is a visit to Kolding with the Koldinghus, an ancient castle with fortress, the Legotøjsmuseet, a museum of 20th-century toys and a nurses' museum. Many people, especially from Sweden, stay on this site for one or two nights to visit Legoland, which is only 60 km. away.

Toilet facilities are old and have British style toilets, washbasins in cabins and controllable hot showers (DKR 2). Family shower rooms (charge). Baby room. Laundry with washing machines and dryers. Campers' kitchen. Motorhome services. Basics from reception. Playground. Minigolf. TV and games room. Torch useful. English is spoken. WiFi (charged).

Key Features

OPEN 365 Open All Year

Play Area

Scan me for more information.

Alan Rogers Code: DK2212
46 accommodations
250 pitches
GPS: 55.56000, 10.44000
Post Code: DK-5450

Fyn, Islands

www.alanrogers.com/dk2212
info@hasmarkcamping.dk
Tel: 64 82 62 06
hasmark.dk

Open (Touring Pitches):
28 March - 20 September.

Hasmark Strand Camping

In recent years the campsite has been completely redeveloped. There are around 250 touring pitches, with five grades of pitch available. Even the most basic (bronze/silver) pitches benefit from 10/16A electricity. Gold and silver pitches all have 16A electricity, water and drainage, and are surrounded by mature hedges. Platinum pitches have access to an exclusive new toilet block and are located next to the playgrounds, making them ideal for those with younger children. The 28 diamond pitches all have private bathroom facilities and the option to rent an extra family room, should you require it. Hasmark is constructed in Viking style and, right from the entrance, you might feel back in the Dark Ages with the Viking Borg that houses the reception, the Freja restaurant, and the Valhalla party hall, pizzeria and takeaway. Next to the Viking Borg is a new adventure playground with colourful Viking Castle and Viking Longship. The sandy beach is only 700 m. away.

Modern toilet blocks include toilets, washbasins in cabins and controllable hot showers (card operated). Family rooms with toilet, basin and shower. Facilities for disabled visitors. Platinum area blocks with luxury bathrooms. Laundry. Kitchen with attractive terrace. Well stocked shop. Restaurant and pizzeria with bar. Superplay area. Football field. Games and TV room. Fishing. Bicycle hire. Pets corner. Viking games. Live music and karaoke. WiFi (charged).

Key Features

- Disabled Facilities
- Swimming Pool
- Play Area
- Bar/Restaurant
- Bike Hire
- Fishing

Scan me for more information.

Alan Rogers Code: DK2335
7 accommodations
100 pitches
GPS: 55.70937, 11.84527
Post Code: DK-4070

Sjælland, Islands

www.alanrogers.com/dk2335
solbakken@solbakken-camping.dk
Tel: 51 32 94 67
www.solbakken-camping.dk

Open (Touring Pitches):
1 April - 31 August.

Solbakken Naturist Camp

Camping Solbakken is a seven-hectare naturist campsite bordering Isefjorden in Zealand, some 50 km. west of Copenhagen. A former apple orchard, it is divided into two areas, each with up to 50 touring pitches. These are mainly on level grass, with electricity and an open aspect. There are also seven cabins to rent. Campers have direct private access, via a pathway, down to the fjord and jetty. Swimming and rafting are very popular in warm weather as are low-key themed evenings and daytime games. There is a small kiosk and bakery on-site, and a larger supermarket is within walking distance. Naturism obligatory (weather dependant).

Sanitary blocks with hot showers and facilities for disabled visitors. Laundry room. Kitchen area. Shop. Swimming. Sauna. Games room. Play areas. Minigolf. Pétanque. Fjord access. Entertainment. Fishing. Bicycle hire. Communal barbecue. WiFi throughout (charged). Accommodation to rent.

Key Features

- Naturist Site
- Beach Access
- Play Area
- Bike Hire
- Fishing

Scan me for more information.

Alan Rogers Code: DK2260
15 accommodations
275 pitches
GPS: 55.80830, 12.53108
Post Code: DK-2850

Sjælland, Islands

www.alanrogers.com/dk2260
naerum@dcu.dk
Tel: 45 80 19 57
dcu.dk/dcu-camping-naerum

Open (Touring Pitches):
20 March - 18 October.

DCU Nærum Camping

Everyone arriving in Sjælland will want to visit 'wonderful, wonderful Copenhagen' but, like all capital cities, it draws crowds and traffic to match. This sheltered site is near enough to be convenient but distant enough to afford peace and quiet (apart from the noise of nearby traffic), and a chance of relaxing after sightseeing. The 275 touring pitches are in two areas – in wooded glades taking about six units each (mostly used by tents) or on more open meadows where electricity is available. Nærum, a Danish Camping Union site, is only 15 km. from the city centre and very near a suburban railway that takes you there.

Two toilet blocks, the one in the meadow area has been refurbished and includes partitioned washbasins. Good block at the reception can be heated and also provides a laundry and a campers' kitchen. Good facilities for babies and disabled campers. Four family bathrooms (free). Motorhome services. Reception and shop for basics (closed 12.00-14.00 and 22.00-07.00). Clubroom and TV. Barbecue. Adventure playground.

Key Features

- Pets Accepted
- Play Area

Scan me for more information.

Saint Emilion at sunrise >

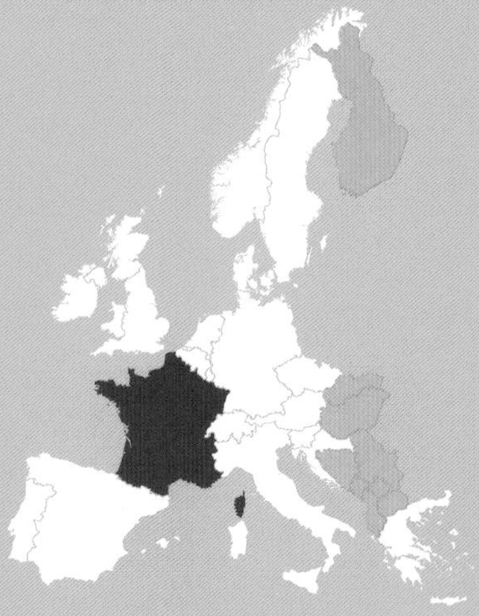

Capital Paris
Currency Euro (€)
Language French
Time Zone CET (GMT+1)
Telephone Code 00 33

Tourist Website
france.fr

Climate Temperate climate. Warmer in the south and east, wetter in the north and west and snowy in the mountains.

Shops Varied. In high-season 10am to noon and 2pm to 7pm Mon to Sat. Shops located in cities open longer.

Banks 9am to noon and 2pm to 5pm Mon to Fri or Tues to Sat.

Accessible Travel Efforts to improve accessibility are being made but the Paris metro is unusable for wheelchair users.

Travelling with Children Perhaps one of the most child-friendly countries in Europe, France has a good mix of cultural sights, historical monuments and other attractions. Each region has something different to offer. Most museums are free for under 18s.

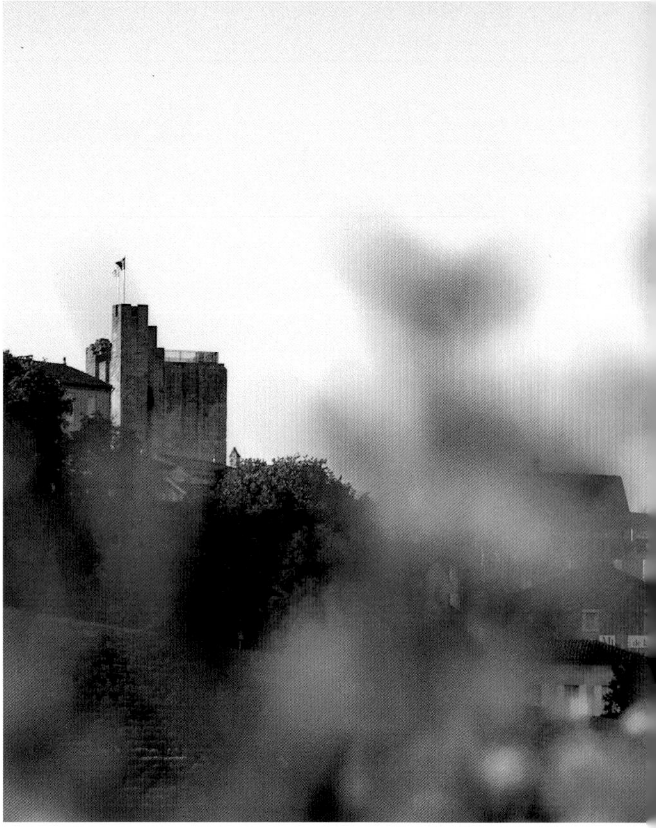

See campsite map pages

476 477 478

Public Holidays New Year's Day, Easter Monday, Labour Day (1 May), VE Day (8 May), Ascension, Whit Monday, Bastille Day (14 Jul), Assumption, All Saints, Armistice Day, Christmas Day. Good Friday and Boxing Day are only public holidays in Alsace and Moselle.

Motoring France has a comprehensive road system from motorways (Autoroutes), Routes Nationales (N roads), Routes Départmentales (D roads) down to purely local C class roads. Tolls are payable on the extensive autoroute network but are expensive, and are also payable on certain bridges.

Environmental Policies Some major cities have implemented Low Emission Zones. Some apply only to heavy-duty vehicles while others to all motor vehicles. Crit'Air stickers are mandatory and can be purchased through official websites. Recycling varies from region to region, but metal, plastic, glass, paper and cardboard are generally recycled.

View all campsites in France
alanrogers.com/france

France

From the hot sunny climate of the Mediterranean to the more northerly and cooler regions of Normandy and Brittany, with the Châteaux of the Loire and the lush valleys of the Dordogne, and the mountain ranges of the Alps, France offers holidaymakers a huge choice of destinations to suit all tastes.

France boasts every type of landscape imaginable, ranging from the wooded valleys of the Dordogne to the volcanic uplands of the Massif Central, the rocky coast of Brittany to the lavender-covered hills of Provence and snow-capped peaks of the Alps. The diversity of these regions is reflected in the local customs, cuisine, architecture and dialect.

Many rural villages hold festivals to celebrate the local saints and you can also find museums devoted to the rural arts and crafts of the regions. France has a rich cultural heritage with a wealth of festivals, churches, châteaux, museums and historical monuments to visit. The varied landscape and climate ensure many opportunities for outdoor pursuits from hiking and cycling, wind- and sand-surfing on the coast and rock climbing and skiing in the mountains. And no trip to France is complete without sampling the local food and wine.

Alan Rogers Code: FR29180
33 accommodations
80 pitches
GPS: 47.76867, -3.54508
Post Code: F-29360

Finistère, Brittany

www.alanrogers.com/fr29180
contact@camping-les-embruns.com
Tel: 02 98 39 91 07
www.camping-les-embruns.com

Open (Touring Pitches):
5 April - 22 September

Camping les Embruns

This site is unusual in that it is located in the heart of a village, yet is only 250 metres from a sandy cove. The entrance, with its code operated barrier and wonderful floral displays, is the first indication that this is a well tended and well organised site, and the owners have won numerous regional and national awards for its superb presentation. The 176 pitches (100 occupied by mobile homes) are separated by trees, shrubs and bushes, and most have electricity (16A, Europlug), water and drainage. A dedicated area has been created for motorhomes at a special rate. On-site facilities include a heated swimming pool, a circular paddling pool, a water play pool and a wellness centre with sauna and massage facilities.

Two modern sanitary blocks, recently completely renewed and heated in winter, include mainly British style toilets, some washbasins in cubicles, baby baths and good facilities for disabled visitors. Family bathrooms. Laundry facilities. Motorhome services. Shop. Restaurant by entrance, bar and terrace, takeaway . Covered, heated swimming and paddling pools (2/7-26/8). Wellness centre with hairdresser sauna, steam room and fitness equipment. Large games hall. Play area. Football field. Minigolf. Communal barbecue area. Daily activities for children and adults organised in July/Aug. Bicycle and car hire. Internet access and WiFi in reception area (charged).

Key Features

- Pets Accepted
- Disabled Facilities
- Swimming Pool
- Play Area
- Bar/Restaurant

Scan me for more information.

Alan Rogers Code: FR29000
406 accommodations
68 pitches
GPS: 48.65807, -3.92833
Post Code: F-29660

Finistère, Brittany

www.alanrogers.com/fr29000
contact@les-mouettes.com
Tel: 02 98 67 02 46
www.yellohvillage.co.uk/camping/les_mouettes

Open (Touring Pitches):
5 April - 8 September.

Camping Les Mouettes

Yelloh! Village Camping Les Mouettes is a sheltered site on the edge of an attractive bay, with access to the sea at the front of the site. In a wooded setting with many attractive trees and shrubs, the 474 pitches include 68 for touring units, all with electricity, water and drainage. The remainder are taken by tour operators and by 406 mobile homes and chalets to rent. At the centre of the 'village' are shops, a bar, a restaurant, an entertainment stage, sports facilities and an impressive heated pool complex with swimming, paddling and water slide pools, plus a 'Tropical river', jacuzzi and sauna. There is also an excellent indoor swimming pool.

A clean sanitary block with controllable showers and washbasins in cabins. There are showers with washbasins and delightful rooms for children and babies. Facilities for disabled visitors. Laundry. Shop (limited hours outside the main season). Takeaway. Bar with TV. Restaurant/pizzeria/grill. Heated pool complex indoor (all season) and outdoor. Beauty salon. Games rooms (special one for under 5s). Play area. Multisports ground. Minigolf. Bicycle hire. Entertainment all season. Large units should phone first. Free WiFi throughout .

Key Features

- Pets Accepted
- Disabled Facilities
- Swimming Pool
- Play Area
- Bar/Restaurant
- Bike Hire

Scan me for more information.

Alan Rogers Code: FR29400
200 accommodations
256 pitches
GPS: 47.80433, -3.83617
Post Code: F-29910

Finistère, Brittany

www.alanrogers.com/fr29400
contact@camping-bretagne-lapommeraiedelocean.com
Tel: +33(0)2 98 50 02 73
www.camping-bretagne-lapommeraiedelocean.com

Open (Touring Pitches):
1 April - 15 September

La Pommeraie de l'Océan

La Pommeraie is a delightful, rural campsite with all the touring pitches set amongst apple trees. These not only divide the generously sized pitches, but also produce cider which can be purchased on site. The pitches are attractive and well cared for and are separate from the mobile homes. Unfortunately very few of the facilities here, such as the bar, shop or takeaway are open outside July and August, which is when the campsite comes to life. The owners also run a crêperie a short distance away which is open from April to September.

Two toilet blocks include a baby room and facilities for disabled visitors. Laundry with washing machine and dyer. An iron, a hoover and a hairdryer are available at the reception. Shop selling essential items, as well as bread and pastries. Bar and takeaway. Entertainment room and children's room, open July/Aug only. Games room (coin operated) and TV corner is also open throughout the season. Swimming pools (heated July/Aug). In the pool complex, there is a hot tub, massage jets, waterslides, counter-current river and aquabikes. Fitness room. Tennis. Minigolf. Boules. Multisports court. Play area. Trampoline. Bicycle hire. Paddle and kayak hire. WiFi all over site (paid plans, as well as a free hotspot in bar and entertainment area).

Key Features

- Swimming Pool
- Play Area
- Bar/Restaurant
- Bike Hire

Scan me for more information.

Alan Rogers Code: FR22130
50 accommodations
112 pitches
GPS: 48.81311, -3.38598
Post Code: F-22660

Côtes d`Armor, Brittany

www.alanrogers.com/fr22130
reservation@rcn.eu
Tel: +31 85 0400 700
www.rcn.nl/en/rcn-port-l-epine

Open (Touring Pitches):
20 April - 24 September

RCN Port l'Epine

Port l'Epine is a very pretty site in a unique situation on a promontory with direct access to the sea, and with superb views across the bay to Perros Guirec. The site is now part of the Dutch RCN group and is managed by a very enthusiastic young couple who are keen to ensure that all visitors enjoy their stay. There are 112 pitches for touring units, all on closely mown, level grass with electricity (16A). They are well defined and separated by attractive hedging and trees. There are 50 mobile homes for rent. This site is ideal for families with young children, though not necessarily for teenagers looking for lots to do!

The original toilet block is well equipped and a second block has been refurbished in modern style with thermostatically controllable showers and washbasins in cubicles. Baby room. Facilities for disabled visitors. Modern launderette. Shop, bar, restaurant with takeaway, small heated swimming pool and paddling pool (all open all season). Fenced play area near the bar/restaurant. Activity programme. Fishing and boat launching. Free WiFi.

Key Features

- Pets Accepted
- Disabled Facilities
- Beach Access
- Swimming Pool
- Play Area
- Bar/Restaurant
- Fishing

Scan me for more information.

Alan Rogers Code: FR56200
15 accommodations
108 pitches
GPS: 47.50745, -2.76092
Post Code: F-56370

Morbihan, Brittany

www.alanrogers.com/fr56200
contact@camping-lannhoedic.fr
Tel: 02 97 48 01 73
www.camping-lannhoedic.fr

Open (Touring Pitches):
1 April - 1 November

La Ferme de Lann-Hoëdic

Camping la Ferme de Lann-Hoëdic is an attractively landscaped site with many flowering shrubs and trees. The 108 touring pitches, all with 10A electricity, are large and mostly level with mature trees which offer some shade. The 20 pitches with mobile homes are in a separate area. The working farm produces cereal crops and the summer months are an exciting time for children to see the harvest in progress. The owners go out of their way to make this a welcoming and happy place to stay. Located in the countryside on the Rhuys Peninsula, Golfe du Morbihan, it is an ideal base for cycling, walking and water-based activities. Since the site opened in 2002, it has developed into one of the prettiest campsites in the Morbihan region. A visitor remarked that it is like camping in a garden. Ecology is taken very seriously with solar panels for water heating and a composting system that you are encouraged to use for any waste food.

Two quality toilet blocks with facilities for disabled visitors and babies. Washing machines and dryers. Bar. Bread delivery. Ice creams and soft drinks from reception. Takeaway and traditional Breton 'soirées' (high season). Meeting room with TV and library. Sauna and massage. Bicycle hire. Playground with modern, well designed equipment. Pétanque. Internet access. WiFi in some areas (charged).

Key Features

- Pets Accepted
- Disabled Facilities
- Play Area
- Bar/Restaurant
- Bike Hire

Scan me for more information.

Alan Rogers Code: FR56730
101 accommodations
84 pitches
GPS: 47.70669, -3.42193
Post Code: F-56270

Morbihan, Brittany

www.alanrogers.com/fr56730
contact@camping-belleplage.fr
Tel: 02 97 56 77 17
www.camping-belleplage.com/en/

Open (Touring Pitches):
28 March - 27 September

Camping Belle Plage

The Camping Yelloh! Village Belle Plage is situated with direct access to a clean, sheltered, sandy beach on the perennially popular Morbihan peninsula. There are 84 grassy touring pitches (80m^2), some with shade and in pairs. Ten of the pitches (100m^2) have a private water tap. All pitches have 10A electricity connection (EU plug). A short walk around the bay leads to the village of Lomener with shops, restaurants, pharmacy and bank, while it is just a short journey to the attractive old town of Ploemeur. A bus service from outside the gate runs to Ploemeur and Lorient, useful for those with motorhomes.

---

3 well maintained sanitary blocks. One located near to the beach access, open from March to September. One cabin specially designed for people with reduced mobility (toilet, sink and shower). Special cabin for babies. In an adjacent space you may also find washing machines and dryers. 2 other sanitary blocks are open in July and August. On-site station (tap, waste disposal etc) for caravans and campervans. Services available all season: Bread service and small shop. Bar, restaurant and takeaway. Indoor heated pool. Facial and body treatments in massage room. Indoor games room. Playground and Baby Park. Bicycle, Kajak and Stand up Paddle boards for hire. Charcoal barbecues can be rented. Entertainment program and Kids-Club in July/August. Free WiFi at the Bar. Mobile homes for rent.

Key Features

- Pets Accepted
- Disabled Facilities
- Beach Access
- Swimming Pool
- Play Area
- Bar/Restaurant
- Bike Hire
- Fishing

Scan me for more information.

Alan Rogers Code: FR56360
80 accommodations
200 pitches
GPS: 47.49974, -3.12026
Post Code: F-56170

Morbihan, Brittany

www.alanrogers.com/fr56360
camping@domisilami.com
Tel: 02 97 50 22 52
www.domisilami.com

Open (Touring Pitches):
1 April - 30 September

Camping Do Mi Si La Mi

Occupying a five-hectare site on the Quiberon Peninsula, just 100 metres from the sandy beaches, this campsite has plenty to offer and is unusually quiet and laid back in low season. Of the 350 pitches, around 200 are for touring and are set amongst high mature hedges and colourful shrubs giving plenty of shade and privacy; some have sea views. Long leads are required on a few pitches as the 10A electricity points can be shared between three or four pitches. The excellent amenities for children are in a well-fenced area and include climbing frames, bouncy castles and multisports courts. Treasure hunts and other activities are organised daily in high season. The well-managed reception is on the opposite side of the road to the campsite. This site is ideally situated for exploring this fascinating area.

New, high quality sanitary block with hot showers. Facilities for disabled campers and young children. Separate laundry. Shop. Bar, restaurant and takeaway (1/4-15/9). TV room. Bouncy castles. Multisports courts. Bicycle hire. Children's club. WiFi throughout (charged).

Key Features

- Pets Accepted
- Disabled Facilities
- Play Area
- Bar/Restaurant
- Bike Hire

Scan me for more information.

Alan Rogers Code: FR50070
61 accommodations
230 pitches
GPS: 49.66715, -1.48704
Post Code: F-50330

Manche, Normandy

Camping l'Anse du Brick

www.alanrogers.com/fr50070
welcome@anse-du-brick.com
Tel: 02 33 54 33 57
www.anse-du-brick.fr/en

Open (Touring Pitches):
3 April - 13 September

A friendly, family site, Castel Camping Caravaning l'Anse du Brick overlooks a picturesque bay on the northern tip of the Cotentin Peninsula, eight kilometres east of Cherbourg port. This quality site makes a pleasant night halt or an ideal longer stay destination for those not wishing to travel too far. Its pleasing location offers direct access to a small sandy beach and a woodland walk. This is a mature, terraced site with magnificent views from certain pitches. Tarmac roads lead to the 230 touring pitches (all with 10A electricity) which are level, separated and mostly well shaded by many trees, bushes and shrubs. There are also mobile homes for rent.

New sanitary facilities are kept spotlessly clean and are well maintained. Washbasins mainly in cubicles and pushbutton showers. Provision for children, families and disabled visitors. Laundry area. Possibility of private sanitary on the pitch. Motorhome services. Shop (all season), restaurant and bar/ pizzeria. Heated swimming pools (indoor all season, outdoor from 1/6). Tennis. Play area. Pump Track on site. Organised entertainment in season. Miniclub (5-12 yrs). Bicycle, SUP and kayak hire. Free WiFi throughout and faster connection for extra fee.

Key Features

- Pets Accepted
- Disabled Facilities
- Swimming Pool
- Play Area
- Bar/Restaurant
- Bike Hire

Scan me for more information.

Alan Rogers Code: FR50080
35 accommodations
118 pitches
GPS: 48.55836, -1.51429
Post Code: F-50170

Manche, Normandy

Camping Haliotis

www.alanrogers.com/fr50080
camping.haliotis@wanadoo.fr
Tel: 02 33 68 11 59
www.camping-haliotis.com

Open (Touring Pitches):
25 March - 1 November.

The staff at this beautiful campsite offer a warm welcome to visitors. Situated on the edge of the little town of Pontorson, 9 km. from Mont Saint-Michel, the site has 152 pitches, including 118 for touring units. Most have 16A electricity and 24 really large pitches, some of which have water and drainage. Excellent private sanitary facilities are also available on 12 luxury pitches. The comfortable reception area incorporates a pleasant bar where breakfast is served. This opens onto the swimming pool terrace. The site is attractively laid out and includes a Japanese garden. Haliotis (which takes its name from a large shell) is next to the River Couesnon, and it is possible to walk, cycle and canoe along the river to Mont Saint-Michel, though an auberge at half-distance could provide a welcome break!

Well equipped, heated toilet block with controllable showers and washbasins in cubicles. Good facilities for disabled visitors. Baby room. Laundry facilities. Bar serving breakfast. Bread to order. Shop. Outdoor heated swimming pool (1/5-30/9) with jacuzzi and separate paddling pool. Sauna and solarium. Good fenced play areas. Pétanque. Archery. Games room. Tennis. Golf practice range. Multisports court. Outdoor fitness equipment. Bicycle hire. Japanese garden and animal park. Miniclub. Free WiFi over site.

Key Features

- Pets Accepted
- Disabled Facilities
- Swimming Pool
- Play Area
- Bar/Restaurant
- Bike Hire

Scan me for more information.

Alan Rogers Code: FR50050
49 accommodations
102 pitches
GPS: 49.46643, -1.23533
Post Code: F-50480

Manche, Normandy

www.alanrogers.com/fr50050
contact@camping-lecormoran.fr
Tel: 02 33 41 33 94
www.camping-lecormoran.fr

Open (Touring Pitches):
6 April - 29 September

Camping le Cormoran

This welcoming, environmentally friendly, family-run site, close to Cherbourg and Caen, is situated just across the road from a long sandy beach. It is also close to Utah beach and is ideally located for those wishing to visit the many museums, landing beaches and remembrance gardens of WW2. On flat, quite open ground, the site has 102 good sized pitches on level grass, most with 6/10A electricity (Europlug). Eight extra large pitches are available, each with private sanitary facilities. Mature hedges separate the well-kept pitches, and the site is decorated with flowering shrubs.

Four toilet blocks, three heated, are of varying styles and ages but all are maintained to a good standard. Laundry facilities. Shop. Bar and terrace. Snacks and takeaway. Outdoor pool (1/7-31/8, unsupervised). Covered pool, whirlpool, sauna and gym (all season). Play areas. Tennis. Boules. Entertainment, TV and games room. Billiard golf (one of only three in Europe). Playing field with archery (July/Aug). Hairdresser and masseuse. Car, bicycle and shrimp net hire. Riding (July/Aug). Communal barbecues. WiFi (charged).

Key Features

- Pets Accepted
- Disabled Facilities
- Swimming Pool
- Play Area
- Bar/Restaurant
- Bike Hire
- Horse Riding

Scan me for more information.

Alan Rogers Code: FR50240
29 accommodations
71 pitches
GPS: 49.30986, -1.23887
Post Code: F-50500

Manche, Normandy

www.alanrogers.com/fr50240
contact@camping-lehautdick.com
Tel: 02 33 42 16 89
en.camping-lehautdick.com

Open (Touring Pitches):
25 March - 29 September.

Camping le Haut Dick

Le Haut Dick is located at the heart of the south Cotentin peninsula. On the banks of the Haut Dick canal, this is a simple campsite but has a pleasant bar/snack bar and a well maintained sanitary block. It comprises 100 good sized pitches which are flat, grassy and well divided by hedges, 71 for touring, with 10A electricity. The town of Carentan is a ten-minute walk away and features a brand new pool complex. This site is an ideal departure point for visiting the World War Two Landing Beaches and the Marais of the Cotentin Peninsula.

The main sanitary block has showers, baby rooms and facilities for disabled visitors. A second basic block serves the upper pitches in high season. Washing machine. Shop with fresh bread. Bar, snack bar and takeaway (all season). Outdoor swimming pool (15/6-15/9). Minigolf. Play area. Bicycle and go-kart hire. Boules. Accommodation to rent. WiFi (free in bar).

Key Features

- Pets Accepted
- Disabled Facilities
- Swimming Pool
- Play Area
- Bar/Restaurant
- Bike Hire

Scan me for more information.

Alan Rogers Code: FR14210
30 accommodations
102 pitches
GPS: 49.28319, -0.19098
Post Code: F-14810

Calvados, Normandy

www.alanrogers.com/fr14210
contact@camping-lepointdujour.com
Tel: 02 31 24 23 34
camping-lepointdujour.com

Open (Touring Pitches):
1 April - 3 November

Le Point du Jour

Camping le Point du Jour has a very French flavour and is an ideal location for family holidays as it has direct access to a beautiful sandy beach. It is becoming popular with British visitors who will receive a warm welcome from the owner and staff. There are around 40 pitches bordered by shrubs and hedging, including 30 occupied by mobile homes and chalets (ten for hire). There are some seasonal units, but most are removed for high season. All touring pitches have 10A electricity, including those on the sea-dyke, and 12 also have water and drainage. Fishing is possible from the beach, and small boats may be launched. Kite surfing is popular, and sailing and other watersports are possible further along the beach.

Two toilet blocks (one heated, the other uni-sex in low season) provide washbasins in cubicles, pushbutton showers, and facilities for babies and for disabled visitors. Laundry facilities. Motorhome services. All-purpose room with small bar (serving basic drinks and snacks except in very low season; bread delivery), projector for films and football matches, pool table and exercise machines. Indoor swimming pool with section for children.Wellness cabin for hire with sauna, jacuzzi and body care sessions. Play area. Bicycle hire. Children's club. Library. BBQ rental. Entertainment and activity programme in high season. WiFi over site (charged).

Key Features

- Pets Accepted
- Disabled Facilities
- Beach Access
- Swimming Pool
- Play Area
- Bar/Restaurant
- Bike Hire
- Sailing

Scan me for more information.

Alan Rogers Code: FR14010
350 accommodations
132 pitches
GPS: 49.32600, -0.39052
Post Code: F-14750

Calvados, Normandy

La Côte de Nacre

www.alanrogers.com/fr14010
vacances@sandaya.fr
Tel: 04 11 32 90 00
www.sandaya.co.uk/our-campsites/cote-de-nacre

Open (Touring Pitches):
3 April - 20 September

La Côte de Nacre is a large, popular, commercial site with many facilities, all of a high standard. It is an ideal holiday location for families. Two-thirds are given over to mobile homes (approx 350), and there are four tour operators on the site. The 132 touring pitches are reasonable, both in size and condition, all having 10A electricity, water and drainage. There is some hedging and a few trees, and pleasant, well cared for flowerbeds. The state of the art, heated pool complex includes both open and covered (sliding roof) areas, slides, whirlpools and water jets, and on a hot day becomes the focal point of the campsite.

The toilet block provides toilets and showers, washbasins in cubicles, and a large room for toddlers and babies. Facilities for disabled visitors. Dishwashing and laundry room. Motorhome services. Grocery with fresh bread baked on site. Bar, restaurant and takeaway. Pool complex. Hammam, sauna and body treatments (charged). Play area for young children with bouncy castle and climbing frames. Multisports court. Synthetic skating rink. Library. Games room. Bicycle hire. Children's clubs and mini-discos. Entertainment includes bingo, karaoke and discos. WiFi. Mobile homes to rent.

Key Features

- Pets Accepted
- Disabled Facilities
- Swimming Pool
- Play Area
- Bar/Restaurant
- Bike Hire

Scan me for more information.

Alan Rogers Code: FR27010
18 accommodations
51 pitches
GPS: 49.36660, 0.48739
Post Code: F-27500

Eure, Normandy

Risle Seine Les Etangs

www.alanrogers.com/fr27010
infos@camping-risle-seine.com
Tel: 02 32 42 46 65
www.camping-risle-seine.com

Open (Touring Pitches):
1 April - 30 October.

This attractive and well maintained quiet, rural site is well laid out with 51 hedged touring pitches on level grass, 38 with 10A electricity, and 20 with water and wastewater connections also. There is a separate tent field for groups or 'free' camping. Fishing and watersports are possible as the site is positioned next to some large lakes. The River Risle runs close to the site too. In Pont-Audemer you will find shops, restaurants and a good swimming complex. There is plenty to do at and from this site, which is situated in a protected area, having a wide variety of natural habitats including woods, lakes (80 hectares), marsh and river and their associated flora and fauna. All activities are within walking distance of the site. Further afield, the beautiful Normandy villages, countryside and coast are all within easy reach.

Two basic toilet blocks include washbasins in cabins and preset showers. Facilities for disabled visitors. Laundry. Bar area with terrace (soft drinks only as there is no alcohol licence). Bread delivery. Takeaway food. New heated outdoor swimming pool (1/5-30/9). Playing field. TV. Fishing. Some family entertainment (July/Aug). WiFi throughout (free).

Key Features

- Pets Accepted
- Disabled Facilities
- Swimming Pool
- Play Area
- Fishing
- Golf
- Sailing

Scan me for more information.

Alan Rogers Code: FR76010
60 accommodations
224 pitches
GPS: 49.90880, 1.04090
Post Code: F-76550

Seine-Maritime, Normandy

www.alanrogers.com/fr76010
contact@campinglemarqueval.com
Tel: 02 35 82 66 46
www.campinglemarqueval.com

Open (Touring Pitches):
17 March - 15 October.

Camping le Marqueval

Le Marqueval is a well established, lively, family site of 284 pitches (including 60 mobile homes), located close to the seaside town of Hautot-sur-Mer, just west of Dieppe and 1.2 km from the sea. This peaceful site has been developed around three small lakes (one unfenced, suitable for fishing) where you'll find plenty of greenery. It's an ideal starting point for those who wish to discover the Cote d'Albatre, go hiking on the GR21 or explore the rich heritage of the Seine-Maritime area of Normandy. When on-site, you'll find plenty of activities to keep you entertained, including an outdoor water park comprising of two pools and a square metre paddling pool with a mushroom fountain and water spouts. During the season, the site organises karaoke sessions, boule competitions, fishing as well as evening meals and dance evenings.

Two sanitary blocks are equipped with showers. Washing machines and dryers. Motorhome services (charged). Shop (all season). Bar, snack, takeaway (July, August and w/ends). Outdoor, heated swimming pool, hot tub and spa. Fishing. Playground. Basketball court. Entertainment and activity programme. Mobile homes to rent. Wifi throughout (charged).

Key Features

- Pets Accepted
- Swimming Pool
- Play Area
- Bar/Restaurant
- Bike Hire
- Fishing

Scan me for more information.

Alan Rogers Code: FR80020
118 accommodations
79 pitches
GPS: 50.26895, 1.60263
Post Code: F-80120

Somme, Picardy

www.alanrogers.com/fr80020
contact@camping-lechampneuf.com
Tel: 03 22 25 07 94
www.camping-lechampneuf.com

Open (Touring Pitches):
1 April - 31 October

Camping Le Champ Neuf

Le Champ Neuf is located in Saint Quentin-en-Tourmont on the Bay of the Somme. It is a quiet site, 900 m. from the ornithological reserve of Marquenterre, the favourite stop for thousands of migratory birds; birdwatchers will appreciate the dawn chorus and varied species. This eight-hectare site has 197 pitches with 79 for touring, on level grass with 6/10A electricity. The site is only 75 minutes from Calais and 18 km. from the motorway. An excellent covered pool complex has been added, including a flume, jacuzzi and pool for toddlers, and a fitness room and sauna. This area is particularly suitable for cycling with several level, traffic-free routes nearby. The Bay of the Somme, Saint Valéry, watersports and the cathedral city of Amiens are all close.

Four unisex toilet blocks have showers, washbasins in cubicles, family cubicles and facilities for disabled visitors. Laundry facilities. Motorhome services. Bar, snack bar and entertainment area. Play area. TV. Games room. Covered, heated pool complex including slides (from 2/4), jacuzzi and children's pool. Fitness room. Sauna. Multisports court. WiFi over site (free). Gas barbecues not accepted.

Key Features

- Pets Accepted
- Disabled Facilities
- Swimming Pool
- Play Area
- Bar/Restaurant
- Bike Hire

Scan me for more information.

Alan Rogers Code: FR02000
25 accommodations
40 pitches
GPS: 49.78217, 3.21403
Post Code: F-02790

Aisne, Picardy

Vivier aux Carpes

www.alanrogers.com/fr02000
contact@camping-picardie.com
Tel: 03 23 60 50 10
www.camping-picardie.com

Open (Touring Pitches):
20 March - 20 October.

Vivier aux Carpes is a small quiet site close to the A26, two hours from Calais, so is an ideal overnight stop but is also worthy of a more extended stay. The 65 well-spaced pitches are at least 100 sq.m, mainly on flat grass with dividing hedges. The 40 for touring units all have 10A electricity, and there are special pitches on gravel for motorhomes. This is a neat, purpose-designed site imaginatively set out around attractive fishing ponds, which are naturally unfenced, and has a comfortable feel. The enthusiastic owners speak excellent English and are keen to welcome British visitors.

The clean, modern toilet block has spacious shower cubicles (pushbutton controls) and a couple of washbasins in cabins. Toilet facilities may be under a little pressure at busy times. Separate, heated suite for disabled visitors. Laundry facilities. Basic motorhome services. Open-air snack bar and takeaway (July/Aug). Large games room. Large play area with an acrobatic structure and football area. Pétanque. Fishing (about € 6 p/day, € 35 p/week). Gates open 07.00-22.00. Rallies welcome. WiFi over site (charged). Cycling and walking tours from the site.

Key Features

- Pets Accepted
- Disabled Facilities
- Play Area
- Bar/Restaurant
- Fishing

Scan me for more information.

Alan Rogers Code: FR62070
71 accommodations
30 pitches
GPS: 50.87900, 1.70900
Post Code: F-62179

Pas-de-Calais, Hervelinghen

www.alanrogers.com/fr62070
Tel: 03 21 36 73 96
www.alanrogers.com/fr62070

Open (Touring Pitches):
1 April - 31 October.

Camping de la Vallée

De La Vallée is situated in a rural location, in the area known as the Terre des Deux Caps (land of the two headlands). The ground is slightly sloping so levelling blocks may be necessary, but the 101 pitches (30 for touring) are mostly individual and hedged, and all have 6A electricity hook-ups. Most have lovely views of the valley and surrounding countryside. Reception shares space with the attractive bar/café that fronts the campsite and serves a good selection of meals and snacks. A recent change of ownership should see improvements to the site. The surrounding area has several magnificent beaches, 400 hectares of conservation area, and is a crossroads for more than 300 species of migrating birds. The site is also within walking distance of Hervelinghen village centre and within a short drive of both Calais and Boulogne and their shopping opportunities and ferry ports.

A building with up-to-date facilities includes washbasins in cubicles, preset hot showers (on payment - tokens from reception), laundry with washing machine and dryer (key from reception). Excellent unit with three separate rooms for disabled visitors, and dishwashing and laundry sinks set at low level also. A covered area adjacent to this building houses the bar/café.

Key Features

- Pets Accepted
- Swimming Pool
- Play Area
- Bar/Restaurant

Scan me for more information.

Alan Rogers Code: FR62230
141 accommodations
13 pitches
GPS: 50.47373, 1.59168
Post Code: F-62780

Pas-de-Calais, Stella-Plage

La Forêt

Camping La Foret, Stella Plage, is very conveniently situated for Channel hopping visits to north-eastern France, as a first stop once off the ferry at Calais or Dunkirk on the way to other destinations or as a holiday destination in its own right. Thirteen of its 154 pitches are for touring units. Mature trees offer shade and the pitches, which are large and grassy, have electrical hook-ups, but there are no fully serviced pitches. The site has just two taps for motorhome/caravan use, but hoses cannot be attached and so a watering can or similar is required to top up water supply. The site has bread and pastries to order, ice creams, chilled drinks and jars of cooked food to reheat but no restaurant or bar since the resort of Stella plage (one kilometre away) has a shopping area with the opportunity to eat out or buy take-away meals. For those who enjoy a beach holiday, there are miles of sandy beach accessible on foot, by the cycle track or by the bus which stops right outside the campsite.

Games room with table football and table tennis. Toilet block (key required), chemical toilet emptying and facilities for disabled visitors. Washing machines and dryers (charged). Bicycle hire from reception. Wi-Fi (charged).

www.alanrogers.com/fr62230
info@laforetstella.fr
Tel: 03 21 94 75 01
www.laforetstella.fr

Open (Touring Pitches):
1 April - End September.

Key Features

- Pets Accepted
- Disabled Facilities
- Play Area
- Bike Hire

Scan me for more information.

Alan Rogers Code: FR77110
200 accommodations
90 pitches
GPS: 48.91282, 2.67465
Post Code: F-77410

Seine-et-Marne, Paris/Ile de France

Le Parc de Paris

This rural, sloping site (open all year) is conveniently situated as an overnight stop or for a visit to Disneyland or to Paris. The 90 largely level, grassy touring pitches all have access to 6A electricity, though most areas have yet to be fully prepared for use. There are 200 mobile homes to rent. The new owners have ongoing plans for improving the site. A ten-minute drive takes you to a station on a Metro (RER) line to Paris and there is free parking. Disneyland and Parc Astérix are easily reached via the motorways. The Base de Loisirs, with its man-made lakes at nearby Jablines (7 km), provides great opportunities for many types of water-based and other leisure activities and it has the largest beach in the Ile-de-France region. There is a small shop in the nearby village of Villaudé and a bar/restaurant in the next hamlet.

The two toilet blocks have some washbasins in cabins, mainly British-style toilets and pushbutton showers. Facilities for young children and disabled visitors. Laundry. Bar, snack bar and takeaway. Play area. Games area. TV room. Internet access in reception and WiFi over site (charged).

www.alanrogers.com/fr77110
info@campingleparc.fr
Tel: 01 60 26 20 79
www.campingleparc.fr

Open (Touring Pitches):
All year.

Key Features

- Open All Year
- Pets Accepted
- Disabled Facilities
- Play Area
- Bar/Restaurant

Scan me for more information.

Alan Rogers Code: FR78010
65 accommodations
225 pitches
GPS: 48.93990, 2.14589
Post Code: F-78600

Yvelines, Paris/Ile de France

www.alanrogers.com/fr78010
vacances@sandaya.fr
Tel: +33 (0)1 39 12 21 91
www.sandaya.co.uk/our-campsites/paris-maisons-laffitte

Open (Touring Pitches):
3 April - 27 September

Paris Maisons Laffitte

This site on the banks of the Seine, Camping Sandaya Paris Maisons-Laffitte is consistently busy, has multilingual, friendly reception staff and occupies a grassy, tree-covered area bordering the river. There are 336 pitches, 111 occupied by mobile homes and tour operators, plus two areas dedicated to tents. Most pitches are separated by hedges, are of a good size with some overlooking the Seine (unfenced access), and all 225 touring pitches have electricity hook-ups (10A). The roads leading to the site are a little narrow so large vehicles need to take care. There is a frequent train service and occasional noise from aircraft.

Three sanitary blocks, two insulated for winter use and one more open (only used in July/Aug). Facilities are clean with constant supervision necessary due to volume of visitors. Provision for disabled visitors. Motorhome services. Self-service shop. Restaurant/bar. Takeaway food and pizzeria (all open all season). TV in restaurant. Football area. Fishing possible with licence. Internet point and WiFi throughout (charged).

Key Features

- Pets Accepted
- Disabled Facilities
- Play Area
- Bar/Restaurant
- Fishing

Scan me for more information.

Alan Rogers Code: FR77070
21 accommodations
158 pitches
GPS: 48.52502, 2.66940
Post Code: F-77000

Seine-et-Marne, Paris/Ile de France

www.alanrogers.com/fr77070
info@campinglabelleetoile.com
Tel: 01 64 39 48 12
www.campinglabelleetoile.com

Open (Touring Pitches):
1 April - 11 October.

Camping la Belle Etoile

Alongside the River Seine, this site has an overall mature and neat appearance. Although the approach road passes through an industrial area, you will discover that la Belle Etoile enjoys a pleasant position with pitches to the fore of the site within view of the barges passing back and forth. The 158 touring pitches, 125 with 6A electricity connections, are on grass and laid out between the many shrubs and trees. There are 21 chalets for hire. A friendly, family-run site with pleasant and helpful English-speaking owners, it is ideally situated for visiting Fontainebleau and Paris.

The three sanitary blocks are not new but they are kept very clean and the water is very hot. Laundry room. Baby bath. A small block for disabled visitors (shower, washbasin and WC). Motorhome services. Shop, small bar, snacks and takeaway (July/Aug, w/ends in low season). Bread to order. Heated outdoor swimming pool. Play area. Bouncy castle. Trampoline. WiFi over site (charged). Gas and charcoal barbecues only. Tickets for Disney and Vaux le Vicomte are sold by the site.

Key Features

- Pets Accepted
- Disabled Facilities
- Swimming Pool
- Play Area
- Bar/Restaurant

Scan me for more information.

Alan Rogers Code: FR08040
15 accommodations
98 pitches
GPS: 49.42640, 4.94010
Post Code: F-08240

Ardennes, Champagne-Ardenne

www.alanrogers.com/fr08040
contact@camping-lasamaritaine.fr
Tel: 03 24 30 08 88
www.camping-lasamaritaine.fr

Open (Touring Pitches):
15 April - 16 September.

Camping la Samaritaine

This delightful site is situated in the heart of the Ardennes. It is peacefully located just outside the village beside a stream. There may be some high season noise from a nearby lake where you can swim or fish. Flowers decorate the entrance and bushes and saplings separate the pitches. The 98 numbered touring pitches all have electricity (10A) and are on level grass off hard access roads. They vary in size up to 130 sq.m. 55 have water and drainage, and there are small wooden containers for waste. There are also six mobile homes and nine chalets to rent. Just along from the site towards the lake is a playground and a boules pitch, while at the lake is some play equipment (adult supervision only). Lake swimming is supervised only at certain times (2 m. deep, with a paddling area up to 1.2 m).

Sanitary blocks provide private cabins, family room and facilities for disabled visitors. Laundry facilities. Motorhome services. Bread delivered daily. Essential are kept in reception. Snack bar/ takeaway (seasonal). Large recreation room with TV, games and books. Play area. Boules. Accompanied walks and entertainment programme (high season). Bicycle hire. WiFi throughout (free).

Key Features

- Pets Accepted
- Disabled Facilities
- Play Area
- Bike Hire

Scan me for more information.

Alan Rogers Code: FR52030
26 accommodations
180 pitches
GPS: 47.87317, 5.38069
Post Code: F-52200

Haute-Marne, Champagne-Ardenne

www.alanrogers.com/fr52030
contact@camping-liez.fr
Tel: 03 25 90 27 79
www.campingliez.com

Open (Touring Pitches):
11 April - 4 October

Camping de la Liez

This excellent lakeside site is near the city of Langres. Only twenty minutes from the A5/A31 junction, Camping de la Liez provides an ideal spot for an overnight stop en route to the south of France. However, there is also a lot on offer for a longer stay. The site provides 180 fully serviced pitches, 16 with private sanitary units. Attractive terracing on the lower part of the site means that some have views of the 250-hectare lake with its sandy beach and small harbour where boats and pedaloes may be hired. Perfect for watersports, access to the lake is down steps and across quite a fast road.

Two older heated toilet blocks (one closed in low season) have all facilities including washbasins in cabins, controllable showers and facilities for babies and disabled campers. A more recent block has eight en-suite units along with 16 pitches with private sanitary facilities. Laundry facilities. Motorhome services. Shop (from 15/4). Bar and restaurant with takeaway (from 15/4). Indoor pool with spa and sauna. Heated outdoor pool with slide. Games room. Playground. Extensive games area. Tennis (free in low season). Bicycle hire. WiFi throughout (charged). Chalets and Gipsy Wagons for rent.

Key Features

- Pets Accepted
- Disabled Facilities
- Swimming Pool
- Play Area
- Bar/Restaurant
- Skiing
- Bike Hire
- Horse Riding

Scan me for more information.

Alan Rogers Code: FR52140
12 accommodations
42 pitches
GPS: 48.54264, 4.91062
Post Code: F-52130

Haute-Marne, Champagne-Ardenne

www.alanrogers.com/fr52140
lesrelaisdublaiseron@orange.fr
Tel: 06 84 97 93 31
www.camping-lac-du-der.com

Open (Touring Pitches):
1 May - 15 September.

Domaine du Buisson

This independently run campsite is in a rural setting in the grounds of a former château. The camping area occupies only a small part of the nine-hectare site alongside a little stream; the rest is wooded grassland on the slope above the stream. The 42 touring pitches are level, and all have electric connections (6-10A) and individual water taps. Some are grouped in an area around the small pool, play area and toilet block; others are stretched out on one side of the stream (quite a walk from the facilities). There are also a number of pleasant chalets for hire.

Basic sanitary block with some British style and some Turkish style WCs, some washbasins in cabins and old fashioned, preset showers. Unit with WC and washbasin for disabled visitors plus a unit with a bath (possibly to be changed to a shower) and baby changing facilities. Dishwashing and laundry sinks. Washing machine and dryer. Small heated pool (9x4 m). Play area. Fishing. Free WiFi over site.

Key Features

- Pets Accepted
- Disabled Facilities
- Swimming Pool
- Play Area
- Fishing

Scan me for more information.

Alan Rogers Code: FR88120
25 accommodations
64 pitches
GPS: 48.16826, 6.89025
Post Code: F-88430

Vosges, Lorraine

www.alanrogers.com/fr88120
info@camping-closdelachaume.com
Tel: 03 29 50 76 76
www.camping-closdelachaume.co.uk

Open (Touring Pitches):
17 April - 20 September

Au Clos de la Chaume

Sites et Paysages Camping Au Clos de la Chaume is a pleasant site is within walking distance of the town, on level ground with a small stream. The friendly family owners, who are British and French, live on site and do their best to ensure campers have an enjoyable relaxing stay. There are 94 level grassy pitches of varying sizes and with varying amounts of sun and shade. All 64 touring pitches have electricity hook-ups (6/10A) and some are divided by shrubs and trees. The site carries the LPO (League for Bird Protection) label with over 30 species present. There is an attractive, well fenced, new swimming pool and an excellent small adventure-style playground. Wine tasting evenings are held in July and August.

Two modern sanitary blocks provide all the necessary facilities for families and disabled visitors. Childrens sanitary facilities. Laundry with washing machines and dryers. Motorhome services. Reception keeps basic supplies (June-Aug). New covered swimming pool (1/5-20/9). Play area. Games room with pool table, table football and library. Boules. Volleyball. Ping-pong tables. WIFI throughout (charged) and also a FREE WiFi limited zone.

Key Features

- Pets Accepted
- Disabled Facilities
- Swimming Pool
- Play Area

Scan me for more information.

Alan Rogers Code: FR88270
20 accommodations
55 pitches
GPS: 48.18359, 6.95791
Post Code: F-88650

Vosges, Lorraine

www.alanrogers.com/fr88270
contact@acaciascamp.com
Tel: 03 29 57 11 06
www.acaciascamp.com

Open (Touring Pitches):
1 January - 26 September.

Camping Les Acacias

Les Acacias is a small, comfortable site in an area surrounded by stunning lakes, waterfalls and rivers, and is a haven for walkers, mountain bikers and nature enthusiasts. The 75 pitches, 55 for touring units and tents, are mainly level and most have shade. All have 6A electricity. There is a heated pool for the whole family, and all the amenities of the town are close by. There is a choice of accommodation to rent, including chalets, roulottes and bungalows. In summer, forest camping is available with access to all site facilities and to 'Parcours de Sante' trim trail. The region boasts lush, green countryside, and a traditional slow pace of life is felt throughout. To the east is the Route du Vin, a 175 km. tourist route which links some of the region's most picturesque wine-producing villages. Local wines and produce are available from the friendly owners.

The heated sanitary block has showers, washbasins and toilets in cubicles. Family washroom. Facilities for children. Laundry. Drying room. Small shop (baker calls). Gas sales. Snack bar and takeaway. Covered bar/terrace. Heated, open-air pool (seasonal). Games room. Games field and play area for children. Volleyball. Basketball. Trampoline. Barbecues allowed (communal area). WiFi on part of the site.

Key Features

- Pets Accepted
- Disabled Facilities
- Swimming Pool
- Play Area
- Bar/Restaurant
- Skiing

Scan me for more information.

Alan Rogers Code: FR54000
17 accommodations
155 pitches
GPS: 48.66440, 6.14330
Post Code: F-54600

Meurthe-et-Moselle, Lorraine

Campéole Le Brabois

www.alanrogers.com/fr54000
brabois@campeole.com
Tel: +33 (0)3 83 27 18 28
www.campeole.co.uk

Open (Touring Pitches):
30 March - 14 October

This site is within the Nancy city boundary and just 5 km. from the centre. Situated within a forest area, there is shade in most parts and, although the site is on a slight slope, the 155 good sized, numbered and separated pitches are level. Of these, 140 pitches have electricity connections (5A), and ten also have 15A electricity, water and drainage. Being on one of the main routes from Luxembourg to the south of France, le Brabois makes a good night stop. However, Nancy is a delightful city in the heart of Lorraine and well worth a more extended stay. There are many attractions in the area, including the pedestrianised 18th-century Place Stanislas and the 11th-century city centre. The manager has a wide range of tourist literature and is pleased to help plan visits and day trips. Horse racing takes place every two weeks at the Nancy race track next to the campsite, and good wine is produced nearby.

Four sanitary blocks. Facilities for babies and disabled visitors. Laundry facilities. Motorhome services. Shop (incl. eggs and other produce grown on site). Bread to order. Restaurant with bar, takeaway and small shop (seasonal). Library. Two playgrounds. WiFi (free).

Key Features

- Pets Accepted
- Disabled Facilities
- Play Area
- Bar/Restaurant

Scan me for more information.

Alan Rogers Code: FR68280
16 accommodations
117 pitches
GPS: 48.08524, 7.27234
Post Code: F-68230

Haut-Rhin, Alsace

Camping le Médiéval

www.alanrogers.com/fr68280
reception@camping-turckheim.fr
Tel: 03 89 27 02 00
camping-turckheim.fr

Open (Touring Pitches):
Early April - End Oct. & End Nov. - End Dec.

Le Médieval is a friendly site located in the pretty village of Turckheim to the west of Colmar, and bordering the River Fecht. There are about 120 flat pitches here, all are 100 sq. m. and have 16A electricity, including 30 deluxe pitches with water and drainage. There are also fully equipped mobile homes available to rent. On-site facilities include a small shop (including a bread/croissant service), a children's playground and TV room. Shops and restaurants can be accessed on foot (300 m. from the site). This region is well known for its fine wines, and vineyards surround the site. There are many opportunities for wine tasting and vineyard tours (there are occasional tastings on-site in high season). Turckheim is a medieval village and is a delightful base for an exploration of Alsace. Cycling is prevalent, and the site's friendly owners will be pleased to recommend routes (cycle hire is available in the village).

Mobile homes to rent. Small shop. Children's playground. Occasional activities and entertainment (including wine tasting). WiFi throughout (free).

Key Features

- Swimming Pool
- Play Area
- Bar/Restaurant
- Fishing

Scan me for more information.

Alan Rogers Code: FR68030
11 accommodations
110 pitches
GPS: 47.77820, 6.99090
Post Code: F-68290

Haut-Rhin, Alsace

Les Rives de la Doller

www.alanrogers.com/fr68030
info@masevaux-camping.com
Tel: 03 89 39 83 94
www.masevaux-camping.fr

Open (Touring Pitches):
15 March - 31 October.

Masevaux is a pleasant little town in the Haut-Rhin department of Alsace, just north of the A36 Belfort-Mulhouse motorway. The neatly mown 110 pitches for tourers are on level grass, of reasonable size, marked by trees and hedges, and all have electricity (3/6A). Most are well shaded with good views of the surrounding hills. The manager would like to welcome more British visitors to this delightful area. A good choice for one night or a more extended stay to explore this interesting region, and an ideal destination for serious walkers. The site is situated on a quiet edge of town next to the sports complex, which has an excellent indoor pool and other sporting opportunities. A network of walking routes complete with overnight shelter cabins has been set up in the mountains around the area. These overnight cabins are free of charge.

A modern, well designed and well equipped sanitary block has most washbasins in private cabins. Baby room. Laundry. Café/bar serving snacks. Baker calls in high season. Ice creams and soft drinks from reception. TV room, small library. Boules. Play area. Tennis (extra charge). Fishing. WiFi.

Key Features

- Pets Accepted
- Disabled Facilities
- Swimming Pool
- Play Area
- Bar/Restaurant
- Skiing
- Fishing

Scan me for more information.

Alan Rogers Code: FR67050
12 accommodations
85 pitches
GPS: 48.63770, 7.43180
Post Code: F-67310

Bas-Rhin, Alsace

Camping Wasselonne

www.alanrogers.com/fr67050
camping-wasselonne@wanadoo.fr
Tel: 03 88 87 00 08
campingwasselonne.fr

Open (Touring Pitches):
Mid-April - Mid-October.

A good quality municipal site with a resident warden, facilities at Wasselonne include a well-stocked small shop, a crêperie in season and the added bonus of free admission to the superb indoor heated swimming pool adjacent to the site. There are 85 touring pitches and around 20 seasonal units, on grass with a slight slope, all with electricity hook-ups (16A). Six rental chalets are in a separate fenced area, and there are six private chalets. For 2019 3 new lodges were introduced, each able to accommodate five people. A full programme of events is offered in the town by the Tourist Office, including welcome evenings, guided tours, concerts, musical festivals and food tasting evenings.

The single, large and well maintained sanitary unit has unisex facilities with ample sized showers and washbasins in cubicles. Shower, washbasin and WC for disabled visitors. Laundry facilities. Excellent drive-over motorhome service point. Playground. WiFi.

Key Features

- Pets Accepted
- Play Area
- Bar/Restaurant
- Bike Hire

Scan me for more information.

Alan Rogers Code: FR49180
42 accommodations
56 pitches
GPS: 47.35877, -0.22604
Post Code: F-49350

Maine-et-Loire, Pays de la Loire

Voiles d'Anjou

www.alanrogers.com/fr49180
contact@camping-voilesdanjou.com
Tel: 02 41 51 94 33
camping-voilesdanjou.com

Open (Touring Pitches):
5 April - 29 September

The campsite Voiles d'Anjou is a small, attractive site on the outskirts of the village, very close (900 metres) to the River Loire between Saumur and Angers. There are 56 touring pitches, all with 10A electricity, individual water taps and wastewater drainage. In addition, there are 42 pitches used for mobile homes, mostly for hire. Beech hedging provides good privacy. There is a pleasant little bar with a terrace and a new adjacent marquee used for games and entertainment. There are two heated swimming pools, one covered, the other surrounded by sunbathing terraces and with a large (linked) paddling pool. When we visited in late June, everything was tranquil, but in July/August there is a busy programme of activities.

The main toilet block offers all the necessary facilities, including those for babies. Two other blocks are reasonably new, and one of them is adapted to campers with disabilities. Bar with TV serves snacks (fresh bread to order; June-Aug). Covered pool (seasonal). Outdoor pool (seasonal). Spa area. Children's activities, daytime events and outings. Evening entertainment in high season. Play area. Games room. Minigolf. Tennis. WiFi over site.

Key Features

- Pets Accepted
- Disabled Facilities
- Swimming Pool
- Play Area
- Bar/Restaurant

Scan me for more information.

Alan Rogers Code: FR72030
5 accommodations
90 pitches
GPS: 48.10586, 0.34108
Post Code: F-72460

Sarthe, Pays de la Loire

www.alanrogers.com/fr72030
contact@chateaudechanteloup.com
Tel: 02 43 27 51 07
www.chateau-de-chanteloup.com

Open (Touring Pitches):
29 May - 31 August.

Château de Chanteloup

This attractive and peaceful site, close to Le Mans, is situated in the park of a 19th-century château in the heart of the Sarthe countryside. There are 90 very large pitches all with 10A electricity, although long leads may be required in some places. Some pitches adjoin woodland, many are around the edges of the lawns and completely open, and a few overlook a small fishing lake. New premium pitches are also equipped with unlimited WiFi, furniture and parasol, barbecue and fridge. The pitches are unobtrusively marked out and this enhances the feeling of spaciousness around the old château.

All sanitary facilities are in the château outbuildings and are well maintained and kept very clean. Washbasins are in cabins. Baby facilities and good en-suite unit for disabled visitors. Laundry facilities. Small shop (12/6-30/8). Fresh bread daily. Takeaway and restaurant with covered outdoor seating (12/6-31/8). Bar and TV room. Outdoor swimming pool (heated July/Aug). Play area (parental supervision essential). Games room. Volleyball. Organised activities (high season). Rowing boat and fishing rods free to use on site lake. Bicycle hire. WiFi over site (charged).

Key Features

- Pets Accepted
- Disabled Facilities
- Swimming Pool
- Play Area
- Bar/Restaurant
- Bike Hire
- Fishing

Scan me for more information.

Alan Rogers Code: FR44180
275 accommodations
90 pitches
GPS: 47.09805, -2.05176
Post Code: F-44210

Loire-Atlantique, Pays de la Loire

La Boutinardière

www.alanrogers.com/fr44180
info@laboutinardiere.com
Tel: 02 40 82 05 68
www.camping-boutinardiere.com

Open (Touring Pitches):
2 April - 25 September.

La Boutinardière is genuinely a holiday site to suit all the family, whatever their ages, just 200 m. from the beach. It has around 90 individual, good sized pitches, 90-120 sq.m. in size, many bordered by high, well-maintained hedges for shade and privacy. All pitches have electricity available (6/10A). English is spoken by the helpful, accommodating reception staff. There is an excellent site shop and, across the road, a water complex comprising indoor and outdoor pools, a paddling pool and a twin toboggan water slide in addition to sports and entertainment areas.

Toilet facilities are in three heated blocks, one large and centrally situated and two supporting blocks. Washbasins are in cabins. Facilities for families. Laundry facilities. Shop. Bar complex with restaurant and terraces. Three heated swimming pools, one indoor (April-Sept), a paddling pool and water slides (seasonal). Games room. Sports and activity area. Playground. Minigolf. Fitness equipment and wellness suite. Accommodation to rent. WiFi throughout.

Key Features

- Pets Accepted
- Disabled Facilities
- Swimming Pool
- Play Area
- Bar/Restaurant
- Bike Hire

Scan me for more information.

Alan Rogers Code: FR49040
47 accommodations
125 pitches
GPS: 47.36110, -0.43530
Post Code: F-49320

Maine-et-Loire, Pays de la Loire

Camping de l'Etang

www.alanrogers.com/fr49040
info@campingetang.com
Tel: 02 41 91 70 61
www.campingetang.com

Open (Touring Pitches):
23 April - 11 September.

At Camping de l'Etang many of the 125 large, level touring pitches have pleasant views across the countryside. Separated and numbered, some have a little shade and all have electricity (16A) with water and drainage nearby; 24 are fully serviced. A small bridge crosses the River Aubance which runs through the site (well fenced), and there are two lakes where free fishing can be enjoyed. The site has a vineyard and the wine produced can be purchased on the campsite. The adjacent Parc de Loisirs is a paradise for young children with many activities (discounts for campers). A Sites et Paysages campsite.

Three well-maintained toilet blocks provide all the usual facilities. Laundry facilities. Baby room. Disabled visitors are well catered for. Motorhome services. The farmhouse houses reception, a shop (all season) and takeaway snacks (seasonal) when the bar is closed. A bar/restaurant serves crêpes, salads, etc. (evenings July/Aug). Swimming pool (heated and covered) and paddling pool. Fishing. Play area. Bicycle hire. Wide variety of evening entertainment for families in high season. WiFi throughout (charged).

Key Features

- Pets Accepted
- Disabled Facilities
- Swimming Pool
- Play Area
- Bar/Restaurant
- Bike Hire
- Fishing

Scan me for more information.

Alan Rogers Code: FR37120
205 accommodations
394 pitches
GPS: 47.14870, 0.65480
Post Code: F-37800

Indre-et-Loire, Val de Loire

www.alanrogers.com/fr37120
contact@fierbois.com
Tel: 02 47 65 43 35
www.fierbois.com

Open (Touring Pitches):
24 April - 30 August

Camping Parc de Fierbois

Castel Camping Parc de Fierbois has a wide variety of accommodation to rent if you're not bringing your own caravan or tent. There's a range of Mobile homes, Chalets, Gîtes and Tree houses. The campsite provides plenty of opportunity for a restful family holiday, but there are many activities for everyone if you prefer to be more active. As well as a covered heated pool, you'll also find a water-park complex with toboggans, a children's club, adventure park, including archery and a skate park, and a good restaurant and bar. The region also has a rich heritage for you to discover including chateaux Villandry, Azay-le-Rideau and Chenonceau, as well as many famous vineyards.

Two sanitary blocks are equipped with showers, private washing cubicles and facilities for babies. Washing machines and dryers. Well stocked shop. Bar. Restaurant and takeaway. Heated indoor pool. Outdoor pool with waterslides. Activity and entertainment programmes (in July and August). Bicycle hire. Fishing. Adventure park in the trees. Internet access and WiFi (charged).

Key Features

- Pets Accepted
- Disabled Facilities
- Swimming Pool
- Play Area
- Bar/Restaurant
- Bike Hire
- Fishing

Scan me for more information.

Alan Rogers Code: FR37150
18 accommodations
60 pitches
GPS: 47.15786, 1.15986
Post Code: F-37460

Indre-et-Loire, Val de Loire

www.alanrogers.com/fr37150
lescoteauxdulac@wanadoo.fr
Tel: 02 47 92 77 83
www.lescoteauxdulac.com

Open (Touring Pitches):
End March - Early October.

Les Coteaux du Lac

This former municipal site has been refurbished to a high standard and is operated by the owner/manager. There are 60 touring pitches, all with 10A electricity and individual water tap; four have hardstanding for motorhomes. Since our last visit, new trees, bushes and flower beds have been planted, which are now coming into maturity. The site remains smart and very well-tended. The site is in the pleasant countryside above a lake and next to a rapidly developing Base de Loisirs with watersports provision and a bar/restaurant. There is a good, well equipped little swimming pool with a paddling area securely separated from the main pool (open and heated 1/6-30/9). The site is near the town of Loches, which has an attractive château. It is an easy drive from Tours and the many châteaux along the Loire and the Indre, including Chenonceau.

Excellent sanitary block with controllable showers, some washbasins in cabins and en-suite facilities for disabled visitors. Special facilities for children. Laundry facilities. Reception sells a few basic supplies and bread can be ordered. Swimming and paddling pools (14/4-15/9). Playing field. Play equipment for different ages. Fishing. Bicycle hire. WiFi over site (charged). Chalets to rent (15) are grouped at far end of site.

Key Features

- Pets Accepted
- Disabled Facilities
- Swimming Pool
- Play Area
- Bar/Restaurant
- Bike Hire
- Fishing

Scan me for more information.

Alan Rogers Code: FR41100
15 accommodations
164 pitches
GPS: 47.48110, 1.45011
Post Code: F-41700

Loir-et-Cher, Val de Loire

www.alanrogers.com/fr41100
contact@camping-cheverny.com
Tel: 02 54 79 90 01
www.camping-cheverny.com

Open (Touring Pitches):
31 March - 16 September.

Camping les Saules

Set in the heart of the château region, Sites et Paysages Camping les Saules has developed into a popular, friendly campsite run by a local family. The well renovated, traditional reception buildings in their lakeside setting give a very pleasant welcome. There are 164 good size, level pitches with 148 for touring units. All have shade from the many trees on the site, and 10A electricity connections (a few will require leads longer than 25 m), and there are ample water taps. A large, grassy field provides room for youngsters to play safely. There are many designated cycle paths and walking circuits in the area, often linking châteaux through attractive, sleepy countryside.

Two sanitary blocks with toilets, showers, washbasins in cubicles and facilities for disabled visitors. Laundry facilities. Motorhome services. Gas supplies. Shop, snack bar and takeaway (14/5-12/9). Restaurant (July/Aug). Bar. Heated swimming and paddling pools (1/4-17/9). TV/social room with toys, board games, books. Two play areas. Large grass area for ball games. Minigolf (free). Fishing. Bicycle hire. Internet and WiFi.

Key Features

- Disabled Facilities
- Swimming Pool
- Play Area
- Bar/Restaurant
- Bike Hire
- Fishing

Scan me for more information.

Alan Rogers Code: FR45010
80 accommodations
120 pitches
GPS: 47.64152, 2.61528
Post Code: F-45500

Loiret, Val de Loire

www.alanrogers.com/fr45010
contact@bardelet.com
Tel: 02 38 67 47 39
www.bardelet.com

Open (Touring Pitches):
10 April - 13 September

Les Bois du Bardelet

This attractive, high quality site, ideal for families with young children, is in a rural setting and well situated for exploring the less well known eastern part of the Loire Valley. Two lakes (one for boating, one for fishing) and a pool complex have been attractively landscaped in 18 hectares of former farmland, blending old and new with natural wooded areas and more open grassland with rural views. There are 245 large, level grass pitches with 120 for touring units. All have at least 10A electricity, 15 have water, waste water and 16A electricity, and some 30 have hardstanding. Eight have individual en-suite sanitary units beside the pitch.

Two heated toilet blocks (effectively unisex, one open in high season only) have some washbasins in cubicles, controllable showers, an en-suite unit for disabled visitors and a baby room. Washing machines and dryers. Minimart, bar, takeaway and restaurant (13/4-8/9). Heated outdoor pool (1/5-1/9). Heated indoor pool and children's pool (all season). Wellness centre with sauna, hot tub, Shiatsu massage and beauty treatments. Fitness and jacuzzi rooms. Beach on lake. Games area. Canoeing and fishing. Tennis. Minigolf. Volleyball. Pétanque. Play area with trampoline. Kids' club, sports tournaments, excursions and activities, aquagym, archery (July/Aug). Bicycle hire. Chalets/ mobile homes for hire. WiFi (free in bar).

Key Features

- Pets Accepted
- Disabled Facilities
- Swimming Pool
- Play Area
- Bar/Restaurant
- Bike Hire
- Fishing

Scan me for more information.

Alan Rogers Code: FR85380
19 accommodations
35 pitches
GPS: 46.77858, -1.73395
Post Code: F-85220

Apremont, Vendée

www.alanrogers.com/fr85380
campinglescharmes@wanadoo.fr
Tel: 02 51 54 48 08
campinglescharmes.com

Open (Touring Pitches):
1 April - 30 September.

Camping les Charmes

Les Charmes is a peaceful, well laid out campsite, 3 km. from Apremont and 20 minutes from the Vendée's sandy beaches. It is suitable for families with young children and those seeking a quiet, peaceful holiday. There are 55 pitches, including 35 spacious and grassy, level touring pitches with dividing hedges, some under shade from the mature trees around the perimeter. Electrical connections are available for most (10A, long cables required for some pitches), plus communal water points nearby. There is also mobile home and chalet accommodation for rent all year. The campsite has an indoor swimming pool with a smaller area for children within the main pool and a new jacuzzi and sauna. Access may not be suitable for large vehicles.

Two sanitary blocks have washbasins and showers in cubicles. Facilities for children & disabled visitors. Washing machine and dryer. Small shop. Bread to order (July/Aug). Swimming pool with paddling pool (seasonal). Sauna and jacuzzi. Small play area. Pétanque. Barbecue area with picnic tables. TV room. Football pitch. WiFi over site (charged). Torches useful.

Key Features

- Pets Accepted
- Disabled Facilities
- Swimming Pool
- Play Area
- Bar/Restaurant

Scan me for more information.

Alan Rogers Code: FR85645
180 accommodations
270 pitches
GPS: 46.72283, -1.97922
Post Code: F-85270

Saint Hilaire-de-Riez, Vendée

www.alanrogers.com/fr85645
riez85@free.fr
Tel: 02 51 54 36 59
campingplagederiez.com

Open (Touring Pitches):
1 April - 30 October.

La Plage de Riez

Plage de Riez is a family campsite in the heart of a 600-hectare National Forest, with direct access to a glorious sandy beach. It is a modern site and is very busy during July and August. The heated pool area is ideal for everyone, whether you want a refreshing dip, a drink on the adjacent terrace or just a chance to relax in the endless sunshine. The site has 465 pitches of which 270 are for tourers, including seven for motorhomes. Mobile homes and bungalow tents occupy some 180 pitches, some for hire. Each pitch has electricity (6A), is of average size and marked by low hedges. The port of Saint Giles Croix-de-Vie is well worth exploring and has some excellent quayside restaurants. For the more energetic, the many accessible cycle routes are a must. There are also many excellent day trips to choose from, with lively resorts such as St. Hilaire and St. Jean-de-Monts both just a few kilometres away.

Five sanitary blocks (two in low season) have washbasins and showers in cubicles. Facilities for disabled visitors. Laundry. Motorhome services. Bread to order. Shop, bar, snack bar and takeaway (all July/Aug). Outdoor swimming pool (mid-May to mid-Sept). TV rooms. Aquagym. Multisports pitch. Boules. Children's and adult's entertainment. Bicycle hire. WiFi (charged). Electric barbecues only on pitches.

Key Features

- Pets Accepted
- Disabled Facilities
- Beach Access
- Swimming Pool
- Play Area
- Bar/Restaurant
- Bike Hire
- Fishing

Scan me for more information.

Alan Rogers Code: FR85680
212 accommodations
224 pitches
GPS: 46.66622, -1.75528
Post Code: F-85220

La Chapelle-Hermier, Vendée

www.alanrogers.com/fr85680
contact@campingpinparasol.fr
Tel: 02 51 34 64 72
www.campingpinparasol.fr/en

Open (Touring Pitches):
15 May - 13 September

Camping Le Pin Parasol

Tucked away in the Vendée countryside, just 15 minutes' drive from the beach, this campsite enjoys a rural setting above the Lac du Jaunay, well away from the bustle of the coast. There are 224 good sized touring pitches, all with 10A electricity (Europlug) and 25 with water tap, drainage and 16A power. Some have shade, and others are in the open with mature hedges and trees. The enthusiastic family owners are very hands-on, and the facilities are of a high standard, most notably the entrance and reception building, and the pool area with its excellent indoor and outdoor pools, slides, flumes, jacuzzi, steam room and fitness suite. Fishing is well-catered for with direct access to the lake. You can buy your fishing licence, store equipment in a secure room, keep your bait in a fridge at the site.

Six excellent toilet blocks (three heated) include hot showers, washbasins in cabins and facilities for babies and disabled visitors. Washing machines and dryers. Shop whith fresh breads and pastries. Bar with terrace. Takeaway and restaurant. Two heated pool complexes (indoor and outdoor pools), paddling pool, slides with rubber rings, swim lane, balneotherapy. Wellness centre (massages, steam room, sauna, jacuzzi) and fitness equipment. Play areas with zip-line. Football and volleyball fields. Games room. Pedal go-karts. Skatepark. Minigolf. Games room. Boules. Bicycle, canoe and pedalo hire. Entertainment in low and high season. Children's club. Fishing. Tennis. WiFi over site.

Key Features

- Pets Accepted
- Disabled Facilities
- Swimming Pool
- Play Area
- Bar/Restaurant
- Bike Hire
- Golf
- Horse Riding

Scan me for more information.

Alan Rogers Code: FR85250
224 accommodations
90 pitches
GPS: 46.45163, -1.70202
Post Code: F-85440

Talmont-Saint-Hilaire, Vendée

www.alanrogers.com/fr85250
info@campinglelittoral.com
Tel: 02 51 22 04 64
www.sandaya.co.uk/our-campsites/le-littoral

Open (Touring Pitches):
3 April - 20 September

Camping Le Littoral

One hundred metres from the sea, five minutes from Les Sables-d'Olonne, le Littoral is situated on the south Vendée coast. It has been thoroughly modernised over recent years by the managers. The site's 460 pitches are mainly used for mobile homes and chalets, but there are 90 touring pitches, hedged, of a good size and all with water, electricity (10A) and drainage. The site has a heated pool complex with outdoor and indoor pools. The mini-market, bar and restaurant are open all season with frequent themed evenings and lots of entertainment and activities in high season.

Two sanitary blocks have both British and Turkish style WCs, showers and washbasins in cubicles. Baby rooms. Facilities for disabled visitors. Laundry facilities. Fridge hire. Shop, bar, restaurant and takeaway, pizzeria and crêperie, outdoor pool complex with slides, indoor pool (all open all season). Bicycle hire. Multisports court. Excellent play areas. Games room with TV. Club for younger children (all season), teens club (July/Aug). Activities, entertainment and excursions, July/Aug and holiday weekends. Bicycle hire. WiFi (free at bar). Free shuttle bus to beach and town (July/Aug). Mobile homes and chalets for hire.

Key Features

- Pets Accepted
- Disabled Facilities
- Swimming Pool
- Play Area
- Bar/Restaurant
- Bike Hire

Scan me for more information.

Alan Rogers Code: FR85970
132 accommodations
291 pitches
GPS: 46.78008, -2.05588
Post Code: F-85164

Saint Jean-de-Monts, Vendée

www.alanrogers.com/fr85970
sirenes@campeole.com
Tel: +33 (0)2 51 58 01 31
www.campeole.co.uk

Open (Touring Pitches):
30 March - 30 September

Campéole Les Sirènes

Les Sirènes is a large campsite located in the forest behind the popular resort of Saint Jean-de-Monts. The nearest beach, just 700 m. away, is long and sandy, shelving very gradually into the sea. The 291 touring pitches vary considerably in size and level; some, ideal for tents, are among the tall pine trees, whilst others are on flat ground but still have shade provided by a variety of younger trees (192 have 6-10A electrical connections - long leads required on some - and water taps nearby). A number of equipped tents and mobile homes (including specially adapted models for disabled visitors) are available to rent.

Several small sanitary blocks serve the different parts of the site, though in low season only the main block is open. Some modern preset showers and mainly open-style washbasins (a few are in cabins). Washing machines and dryers. Shop, bar and takeaway (July/Aug). Heated outdoor swimming pools with paddling pool (seasonal, supervised July/Aug). Multisports pitch. Bicycle hire. Bouncy castle. Archery. Play area. Children's and teenagers' club and activities programme (July/Aug). WiFi around reception (charged). Gas and electric barbecues only.

Key Features

- Pets Accepted
- Disabled Facilities
- Swimming Pool
- Play Area
- Bar/Restaurant
- Bike Hire

Scan me for more information.

Alan Rogers Code: FR85490
183 accommodations
127 pitches
GPS: 46.67094, -1.90387
Post Code: F-85800

Saint Gilles-Croix-de-Vie,
Vendée

Le Domaine de Beaulieu

www.alanrogers.com/fr85490
info@chadotel.com
Tel: 02 51 55 59 46
www.chadotel.com

Open (Touring Pitches):
5 April - 20 September.

Domaine de Beaulieu has an open, airy feel in a semi-rural setting on the edge of the village of Givrand, a short drive from an excellent sandy beach and the fishing port and resort of Saint Gilles. The 127 touring pitches all with electricity (10A, Europlug) and water nearby, are pleasantly laid out and separated by hedges or bushes; most have shade from mature trees, others are more open. A little stream in an unfenced cutting runs through the site. There are around 180 mobile homes, most to rent, and tour operators occupy 90 pitches. Early and late in the season, the campsite is quiet, whereas in July and August there is a lively and wide-ranging entertainment programme for all ages, including teenagers.

Three well-maintained toilet blocks include preset showers, washbasins in cubicles and baby room. Unit for disabled visitors. Washing machines and dryers. Shop, restaurant and takeaway (seasonal). Bar (seasonal). Heated outdoor and indoor swimming pools, water slides, toboggan, paddling pool and jacuzzi (seasonal). Play area. Multisports area. Games room. Boules. Minigolf. Tennis. Bicycle hire. WiFi (charged). Gas barbecues only.

Key Features

- Pets Accepted
- Disabled Facilities
- Swimming Pool
- Play Area
- Bar/Restaurant
- Bike Hire

Scan me for more information.

Alan Rogers Code: FR85710
150 accommodations
46 pitches
GPS: 46.47207, -1.72646
Post Code: F-85180

Les Sables d'Olonne, Vendée

Camping le Bel Air

www.alanrogers.com/fr85710
lebelair@cybelevacances.com
Tel: 02 51 22 09 67
www.campingdubelair.com

Open (Touring Pitches):
6 April - 3 November.

Le Bel Air is a well established site close to the Vendée's largest resort, Les Sables-d'Olonne. It is now very much dedicated to mobile homes and chalets, and for 2019 they have introduced mobile homes with private Jacuzzi's. Of its 286 pitches, just 46 are for touring – 40 on grass mostly with electricity (16A), water and drainage and a further six on concrete for motorhomes. This is a very well equipped site with the focal point being a new and impressive pool complex including a large covered pool and separate outdoor pool.

Five well equipped small sanitary blocks with facilities for babies and disabled visitors. Laundry with washing machines and dryers. Motorhome services. Bar, snack bar, takeaway and shop. Heated outdoor pool with children's pool and waterslides (April-Sept). Heated indoor pool with sauna, spa and gym (all season). TV room. Games room. Multisports court. Playground. Bicycle hire. Skate park for teenagers. Charging stations for electric vehicles (new for 2019). Activities in high season. Mobile homes and chalets for rent. Charcoal barbecues not permitted. WiFi throughout (charged).

Key Features

- Pets Accepted
- Disabled Facilities
- Swimming Pool
- Play Area
- Bar/Restaurant
- Bike Hire

Scan me for more information.

Alan Rogers Code: FR85040
58 accommodations
154 pitches
GPS: 46.66365, -1.71340
Post Code: F-85150

Saint Julien-des-Landes, Vendée

www.alanrogers.com/fr85040
info@garangeoire.com
Tel: 02 51 46 65 39
www.camping-la-garangeoire.com

Open (Touring Pitches):
3 May - 21 September

Camping La Garangeoire

Castel Camping La Garangeoire is a stunning campsite, situated some 15 km inland, near the village of Saint Julien-des-Landes. Set in 200 hectares of parkland surrounding the small château of la Garangeoire, of which there is an outstanding view as you approach through the gates. With a spacious, relaxed atmosphere, the main camping areas are on either side of the old road which is edged with mature trees. The 357 pitches (154 for touring), all named rather than numbered, are individually hedged, some with shade. They are well spaced and are especially large (most 150-200 sq.m), 87 have electricity (16A, Europlug), 45 have water and drainage also, and 4 have private WC/shower facilities.

Ample, first class sanitary toilet facilities. All have washbasins in cabins and showers. Facilities for babies & disabled visitors. Laundry facilities. Motorhome services. Chemical toilet point. Shop, full restaurant and takeaway with bars & terrace. Outdoor swimming lagoon and beach. Pool complex with heated, covered pool, water slides, fountains and a children's pool. Spa & well-being centre. Safe hire. Vending machine for still and sparkling water. Play field with play equipment. Football pitch. Games room. Dog shower. Tennis courts (charged July/Aug). Multisports court. Bicycle hire. Minigolf. Seasonal Archery and Riding. Fishing and Boating. Bouncy castle. Trampolines. Children's club. Only gas barbecues allowed. Shuttle bus to beach. WiFi on part of site (free). Car hire. Evening entertainment H/S.

Key Features

- Pets Accepted
- Disabled Facilities
- Swimming Pool
- Play Area
- Bar/Restaurant
- Bike Hire
- Fishing
- Horse Riding

Scan me for more information.

Alan Rogers Code: FR17856
84 accommodations
114 pitches
GPS: 46.16568, -1.33470
Post Code: F-17740

Charente-Maritime, Poitou-Charentes

www.alanrogers.com/fr17856
iledere@huttopia.com
Tel: 05 46 30 23 75
europe.huttopia.com/en/site/ile-de-re

Open (Touring Pitches):
19 May - 16 October.

Huttopia Chardons Bleu

Chardons Bleus is a recently redeveloped 4.8-hectare site situated in a pine forest on the Ile de Ré, only 1,500 m. from the sea. It is often a bustling site in the high season, so booking is advised. Since taking ownership of the site, Huttopia has embarked on a program of redevelopment works, which include a new reception building, restaurant, playgrounds and swimming pools. The site is divided into two areas on either side of the quiet entrance road. Hedges separate some of the 114 level, but natural touring pitches and mature trees give plenty of shade from the hot sun; all have electricity (6A Europlug). A further 77 pitches are dedicated to glamping in safari-style tents, roulottes or cabins. In high season a snack bar provides takeaway food.

New sanitary blocks for 2019 provide showers and washbasins in cubicles. Facilities for disabled visitors. Washing machines and dryer. Motorhome services. Snack bar/takeaway (seasonal). Swimming pool redeveloped in 2019. Playground. TV/games room. Basketball. Table tennis. Tennis. Volleyball. Boules. Picnic areas. Bicycle hire. WiFi over part of the site (free). Communal barbecues only.

Key Features

- Pets Accepted
- Disabled Facilities
- Play Area
- Bar/Restaurant
- Bike Hire

Scan me for more information.

Alan Rogers Code: FR17140
400 accommodations
240 pitches
GPS: 45.81095, -1.06109
Post Code: F-17320

Charente-Maritime, Poitou-Charentes

www.alanrogers.com/fr17140
info@sequoiaparc.com
Tel: 0033 (0)5 46 85 55 55
www.sequoiaparc.com

Open (Touring Pitches):
16 May - 6 September

Camping Séquoia Parc

The overall winner of the Alan Rogers Campsite of the Year Awards in 2018, Séquoia Parc is just 7 km from the beach (Marennes-Plage). This is a high-quality family campsite in the heart of the Charente-Maritime region, set in the grounds of La Josephtrie, a castle with beautifully restored outbuildings and courtyard area with a bar and restaurant. The pitches are between 120 and 140m^2 with 6/10A electricity connections, separated by shrubs providing plenty of privacy. The site has mobile homes, chalets and fully equipped tents for up to 7 people. This is a popular site and reservations are necessary for high season. This site is a member of Leading Campings group.

Three spotless toilet blocks include units with washbasins and showers. Facilities for disabled visitors & children. Large laundry. Motorhome services. Supermarket with fresh bread. Restaurant/bar. Take-away with wood oven pizzas. 2000 m^2 swimming pool complex with water slides, lazy river and large paddling pool. Wellness & Fitness centre with indoor swimming pool, sauna, hammam and Jacuzzi. Massage rooms, spa treatments & fitness area with cardio & weight training equipment. Playgrounds. Multisports pitch. Tennis. Games & TV rooms. Bicycle & pedal-go-kart hire. Entertainment/excursions in high season. Free children's club for children from 4-12 years. Animal farm. Equestrian centre (seasonal). New playgrounds with zipline. WiFi zones (charged).

Key Features

- Pets Accepted
- Disabled Facilities
- Swimming Pool
- Play Area
- Bar/Restaurant
- Bike Hire
- Horse Riding

Scan me for more information.

Séquoia Parc
Camping Village
5-star holiday fun for the entire family on the Atlantic coast!
Séquoia Parc
Camping Village
LeadingCampings
TOP 2019
QUALITÉ TOURISME
Online bookings:
www.sequoiaparc.com
Tel.: 0033 5 46 85 55 55
17320 Saint-Just-Luzac
France
TOP RESORT!
Wellness with indoor pool, kids clubs & playgrounds
Open in 2020: 16/05 - 06/09

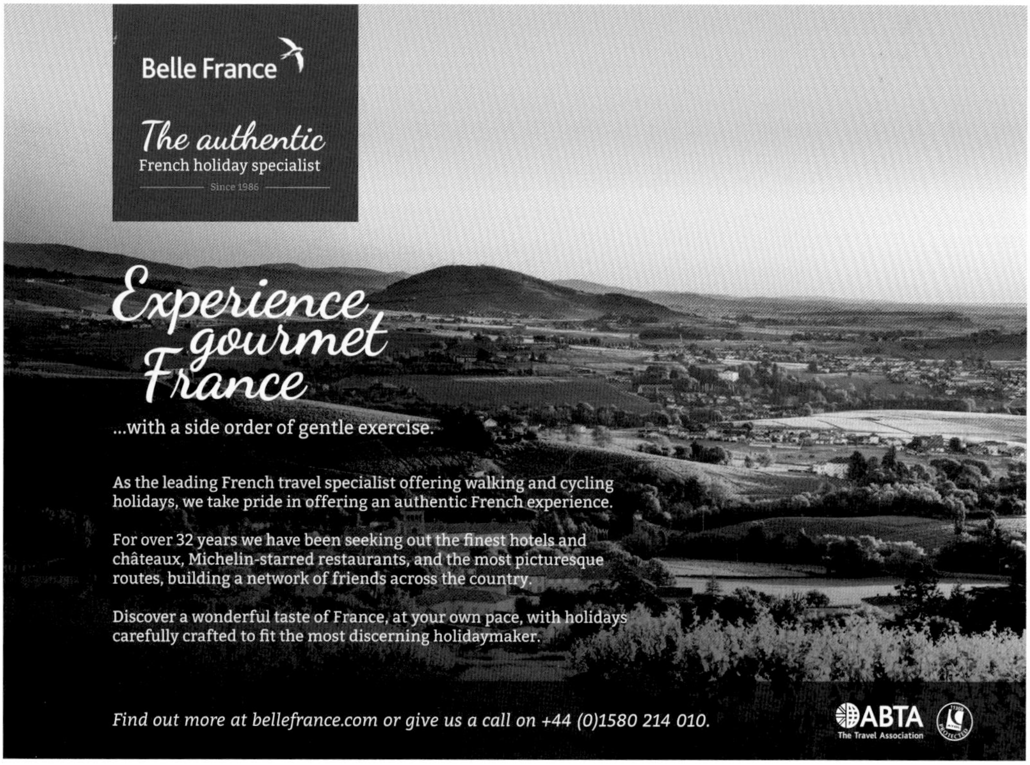

Belle France
The authentic
French holiday specialist
Since 1986
Experience gourmet France
...with a side order of gentle exercise.
As the leading French travel specialist offering walking and cycling holidays, we take pride in offering an authentic French experience.
For over 32 years we have been seeking out the finest hotels and châteaux, Michelin-starred restaurants, and the most picturesque routes, building a network of friends across the country.
Discover a wonderful taste of France, at your own pace, with holidays carefully crafted to fit the most discerning holidaymaker.
Find out more at bellefrance.com or give us a call on +44 (0)1580 214 010.
ABTA
The Travel Association

Alan Rogers Code: FR17010
120 accommodations
251 pitches
GPS: 45.58358, -0.98653
Post Code: F-17110

Charente-Maritime, Poitou-Charentes

www.alanrogers.com/fr17010
info@bois-soleil.com
Tel: 05 46 05 05 94
www.bois-soleil.com

Open (Touring Pitches):
12 April - 29 September

Camping Bois Soleil

Close to the sea, Bois Soleil is a large site in three parts, with serviced pitches for touring units and a few for tents. All the touring pitches are hedged and have electricity (10A), with water and drainage between two. The main part, Les Pins, is attractive with trees and shrubs providing shade. Opposite is La Mer with direct access to the beach, some areas with less shade and an area for tents. The third part, La Forêt, is for caravan holiday homes. It is best to book your preferred area as it can be full mid June to late August. Excellent private sanitary facilities are available to rent, either on your pitch or at a block (subject to availability).

Each area has one large and one small sanitary block. Heated block near reception. Cleaned twice daily, they include facilities for disabled visitors and babies. Launderette. Supermarket, bakery, beach shop (all 12/4-15/9). Restaurant, bar and takeaway (all 15/4-15/9). Swimming pool (heated 15/5-15/9). Steam room. Fitness room. Tennis. Play area. TV room and library. Internet terminal (free). WiFi throughout (charged). Charcoal and electric barbecues are not permitted. Dogs are not accepted 30/6-25/8.

Key Features

- Pets Accepted
- Disabled Facilities
- Beach Access
- Swimming Pool
- Play Area
- Bar/Restaurant
- Bike Hire
- Sailing

Scan me for more information.

Alan Rogers Code: FR17470
100 accommodations
60 pitches
GPS: 45.96747, -1.31926
Post Code: F-17190

Charente-Maritime, Poitou-Charentes

Le Domaine d'Oléron

www.alanrogers.com/fr17470
info@chadotel.com
Tel: 05 46 76 54 97
www.chadotel.com

Open (Touring Pitches):
6 April - 21 September.

Camping le Domaine d'Oléron is a neat, well presented and well managed site where you will receive a warm and friendly welcome from Anneke and Freddy who speak excellent English. The site is set in a peaceful rural location between Saint Pierre and Saint Georges and is part of the Chadotel group. At present there are 172 pitches of which 60 are for touring units. The pitches are generously sized (100-150 sq.m) and are mostly sunny, level and easily accessible, all with 10A electricity. The site is just 3 km. from the beach and the Forest of Saumonards. The local port, shops and restaurants are also nearby.

Two modern sanitary blocks include facilities for disabled visitors and babies. Laundry facilities. Motorhome services. Snack bar and takeaway, bar with TV (all 15/5-10/9). Bread delivered daily. Swimming pool with slides (1/5-14/9). Adventure style play area. Six pétanque lanes. Bicycle hire. Organised entertainment two or three times a week in July/Aug. Gas barbecues only on pitches, communal areas for charcoal. WiFi over site (charged). Max. 1 dog per pitch.

Key Features

- Pets Accepted
- Disabled Facilities
- Swimming Pool
- Play Area
- Bar/Restaurant
- Bike Hire

Scan me for more information.

Alan Rogers Code: FR86110
23 accommodations
96 pitches
GPS: 46.88636, -0.02181
Post Code: F-86330

Vienne, Poitou-Charentes

Active Camping Moncontour

www.alanrogers.com/fr86110
info@map86.fr
Tel: 05 49 22 38 50
moncontour-active-park.com

Open (Touring Pitches):
1 April - 29 September.

On the edge of a ten-hectare lake, this site is ideal for watersports enthusiasts. It includes activities for the whole family - wakeboarding, swimming, kayaking, sailing, pedalos, beach volleyball and much more. This site offers around 100 marked grass pitches (120 sq.m., all with 16A electricity) for touring, small hedges and some shade from mature trees. The site is popular with youth groups, but the touring area is separate and seemed quite tranquil when we visited in July. The site claims to have the only water ski tow in Western France suitable for both expert and novice. Bring your cycle as you will want to explore the route around the lake — chalets and gîtes to rent (all year). Futuroscope is easily accessible from this location.

Two modern sanitary blocks with WCs, showers and washbasins in cabins. Facilities for disabled visitors. Bar and restaurant (seasonal). Small shop with bread to order. Motorhome services. Tennis. Minigolf. Football pitch. Fishing. Pedalos. Canoes. Direct access to lake. No barbecues. Mobile homes and chalets to rent. WiFi.

Key Features

- Disabled Facilities
- Bar/Restaurant
- Fishing

Scan me for more information.

Alan Rogers Code: FR86040
16 accommodations
123 pitches
GPS: 46.66447, 0.39456
Post Code: F-86130

Vienne, Poitou-Charentes

www.alanrogers.com/fr86040
camping-le-futuriste@wanadoo.fr
Tel: 05 49 52 47 52
www.camping-le-futuriste.fr

Open (Touring Pitches):
All year.

Camping le Futuriste

Le Futuriste is a neat, modern site, open all year and very close to Futuroscope. Its location is also very convenient for the A10 and N10 motorway network. There is a total of 123 individual, level, grassy pitches of a generous size, divided by flowering hedges, 74 with 6A electricity and 55 of those also have water. There are also six chalets and 10 Mobil Homes to rent. The large pitches mostly have the benefit of shade from trees. All are accessed via tarmac roads. There are lovely panoramic views from this site, and the popular attraction of Futuroscope can be clearly seen across the valley. Large units are accepted by prior arrangement.

Excellent, clean, sanitary facilities in two heated blocks. Good facilities for disabled visitors and babies. Laundry facilities. Shop (Seasonal, bread to order). Bar/restaurant snack bar and takeaway (July/Aug). Heated pool with slide and paddling pool (July/Aug). Covered pool (Seasonal). Games room. Boules. Multisports area. Lake fishing. Daily activities in season. Youth groups not accepted. Only gas and electric barbecues allowed. WiFi throughout (charged).

Key Features

- OPEN 365 Open All Year
- Pets Accepted
- Disabled Facilities
- Play Area
- Bar/Restaurant
- Fishing

Scan me for more information.

Alan Rogers Code: FR89170
55 accommodations
29 pitches
GPS: 47.75819, 3.09963
Post Code: F-89350

Yonne, Burgundy

www.alanrogers.com/fr89170
camping@bois-guillaume.com
Tel: 03 86 45 45 41
bois-guillaume.com

Open (Touring Pitches):
All year.

Camping le Bois Guillaume

This traditional rural campsite, located in oak woodland in Burgundy, is surrounded by agricultural land and is within striking distance of the towns of Auxerre, Gien, Joigny and Montargis. There are 29 good-sized touring pitches, with electrical connections (10A) available, and a further seven tent pitches; the remaining 55 are occupied by seasonal units and rental accommodation, including two wooden chalets. The nearby village of Champignelles has a few shops and cafés and a couple of restaurants, while Auxerre is a lively city, a Ville d'Art et d'Histoire and a major centre for wine and gastronomy, with the vineyards of Chablis just a few kilometres east.

Heated sanitary facilities include provision for disabled visitors. Bar and restaurant (with a menu of local produce). Bread and pastries, wines, souvenirs and gas available. Heated swimming pool and paddling pool (seasonal). Tennis, bowling, volleyball and basketball. Orientation course. Games for children. Bicycle hire. Wifi (charged). Entertainment programme in high season.

Key Features

- Open All Year
- Pets Accepted
- Disabled Facilities
- Swimming Pool
- Play Area
- Bar/Restaurant
- Bike Hire

Scan me for more information.

Alan Rogers Code: FR71090
12 accommodations
39 pitches
GPS: 46.33646, 4.61183
Post Code: F-71520

Saône-et-Loire, Burgundy

www.alanrogers.com/fr71090
contact@campingsaintpoint.com
Tel: 03 85 50 52 31
campingsaintpoint.com

Open (Touring Pitches):
1 April - 31 October.

Lac de Saint-Point

This attractive, rural site is situated just below a small reservoir on the side of a valley and forms part of an amenity complex for a group of communes. The lake offers swimming, fishing and pedaloes. Situated 25 km. from the A6, this could be a useful stopover site. The area is renowned for its wine and cheese as well as Roman churches, abbeys and châteaux. There are 39 level touring pitches with electricity (4/8/13A), mostly separated by low hedges, and 46 tent pitches on a sloping and partly terraced field behind. Twelve mobile homes are set on high terraces overlooking the lake, with views across the valley. There are lifeguards at the lake in July and August, and the communes organise many events during the year. During a recent visit, there was a competition for model speed boats. If you enjoy the quiet life and outdoor activities, this is an ideal location.

Two sanitary blocks, provide all the usual facilities and a washing machine. Shower and toilet/washbasin in separate cabins for campers with disabilities. Bar and snacks (high sesaon). Play area. Games room. Boules. Mountain bike hire.

Key Features

- Pets Accepted
- Disabled Facilities
- Play Area
- Bar/Restaurant
- Bike Hire
- Fishing

Scan me for more information.

Alan Rogers Code: FR71070
45 accommodations
120 pitches
GPS: 46.65485, 4.94463
Post Code: F-71240

Saône-et-Loire, Burgundy

Château de l'Eperviére

www.alanrogers.com/fr71070
info@domaine-eperviere.com
Tel: 03 85 94 16 90
www.domaine-eperviere.com

Open (Touring Pitches):
1 April - 30 September.

Castel Camping Château de l'Epervière is a popular high quality site, peacefully situated in the wooded grounds of a 16th-century château, close to the A6 and near the village of Gigny-sur-Saône. It is within walking distance of the river where you can watch the cruise boats on their way to and from Châlon-sur-Saône. There are 160 pitches arranged over two areas separated by a small fishing lake, 120 are used for touring. All have 10A electricity, some are on hardstanding and 30 are fully serviced. Close to the château and fishing lake, the pitches are hedged and have shade from mature trees; whilst the area behind the lake has a more open aspect.

Two well equipped, very clean toilet blocks with all necessary facilities including those for babies and disabled campers. Washing machine/dryer. Motorhome services. Basic shop, takeaway and restaurant with good menu (all 26/4-30/9). Cellar with wine tasting. Converted barn with bar, large TV. Heated outdoor swimming pool and new heated paddling pool with slides (26/4-30/9) partly enclosed by old stone walls. Smaller indoor heated pool (all season). Play areas and open field. Fishing. Bicycle hire. Free WiFi in bar area.

Key Features

- Pets Accepted
- Disabled Facilities
- Swimming Pool
- Play Area
- Bar/Restaurant
- Bike Hire
- Fishing

Scan me for more information.

Alan Rogers Code: FR21160
7 accommodations
30 pitches
GPS: 47.26543, 4.54864
Post Code: F-21320

Côte d`Or, Burgundy

www.alanrogers.com/fr21160
contact@camping-vert-auxois.fr
Tel: 03 80 90 71 89
camping-vert-auxois.fr

Open (Touring Pitches):
26 March - 1 October.

Camping Vert Auxois

Camping Vert-Auxois is a small, lush green site surrounded by mature trees on the outskirts of Pouilly-en-Auxois. The setting is between fields and the Burgundy Canal, which passes through a 3 km. tunnel under the town. This well cared for campsite has about 30 pitches for touring units, all with 16A electrical connections (long leads may be needed). The pitches are on level grass with many bordered by high hedges. A further 40 tent pitches are also available. The campsite also offers mobile homes for rent and Eco-lodge tents, fully equipped for two people. This site is popular with cyclists, hikers and those looking for a peaceful countryside break. On the outskirts of the town and close to the site is a fully equipped port and tourist centre. The area is a haven for walking, boat trips and bike rides through countryside rich in woods and lakes. On the wine trail, you'll discover cellars of the Côte de Beaune and Côtes de Nuits and many inns and Michelin starred restaurants along the way.

New, heated sanitary block which includes washbasins in cubicles. Laundry. Small shop selling essentials. Breakfast and bread to order. Snack bar and takeaway. WiFi throughout (free).

Key Features

- Pets Accepted
- Bar/Restaurant

Scan me for more information.

Alan Rogers Code: FR39100
38 accommodations
142 pitches
GPS: 46.46844, 5.68847
Post Code: F-39260

Jura, Franche-Comté

www.alanrogers.com/fr39100
info@trelachaume.fr
Tel: 03 84 42 03 26
www.trelachaume.fr

Open (Touring Pitches):
27 April - 8 September

Camping Trélachaume

This spacious campsite is situated in an attractive part of the Jura. The site has 180 stony and occasionally uneven pitches of varying sizes, many quite large. There are 142 for touring units, 140 have electricity (6/10A, long leads may be needed). Rock pegs are essential. Mature trees and high hedges provide pleasant shade and privacy. From just outside the entrance, a path leads steeply down to a sandy beach on the edge of a large leisure lake, the Lac de Vouglans, Alternatively, the journey can be made by car (2 km). There is no restaurant on the site, but a bar with snacks and a takeaway operates 20 m from the site entrance (seasonal). In high season events and activities are organised, many of them in the municipal 'salle des fêtes' on the edge of the site.

Three modern toilet blocks (a long walk from some pitches) contain British style WCs, washbasins and preset showers. En-suite facilities for disabled visitors. Baby room. Washing machine, spin dryer and ironing board. Shop for basics (seasonal). Gas supplies. Bar and takeaway (seasonal). Large heated swimming pool, with a nice view of Lake Vouglans. Paddling pool for children. Playground. TV room. Boules. Family entertainment (July/Aug). WiFi over part of the site (charged).

Key Features

- Pets Accepted
- Disabled Facilities
- Play Area
- Bar/Restaurant

Scan me for more information.

Alan Rogers Code: FR39090
144 accommodations
140 pitches
GPS: 47.01660, 5.48160
Post Code: F-39100

Jura, Franche-Comté

www.alanrogers.com/fr39090
contact@jura-camping.com
Tel: 03 84 71 03 82
www.jura-camping.fr

Open (Touring Pitches):
1 April - 11 October.

Camping les Bords de Loue

This spacious campsite, beside the river Loue, enables canoeing, boating and fishing to be enjoyed directly from the site. It is also at the western end of the Val d'Amour, where the attractive countryside and villages make for pleasant walking and cycling. The site has 284 grass pitches, 140 are for touring. Many are undulating or slightly sloping, and few have shade. All have electricity (6A), but long leads are advised. Some pitches at the western end of the site are some distance from the nearest facilities. Events and activities, including pony rides, are organised in July/August.

Three modern toilet blocks with all the necessary facilities, including for disabled visitors. Motorhome services. Washing machines and dryers. Gas supplies. Bar (all season). Snack bar and takeaway (July/Aug). Satellite TV. Swimming pool and paddling pool (seasonal). Playground. Tennis (free outside July/Aug). Archery. Boules.

Key Features

- Disabled Facilities
- Swimming Pool
- Play Area
- Bar/Restaurant
- Fishing

Scan me for more information.

Alan Rogers Code: FR25160
9 accommodations
99 pitches
GPS: 47.26588, 6.07151
Post Code: F-25220

Doubs, Franche-Comté

www.alanrogers.com/fr25160
contact@campingdebesancon.com
Tel: 03 81 88 04 26
www.campingdebesancon.com/

Open (Touring Pitches):
15 March - 31 October

Camping de Besançon

You'll find no noisy entertainment at Camping de Besançon La Plage, so the site is perfect for those looking for peace. That said, children will enjoy the sprawling lawns, sports field, the large swimming pool and playground, and the adults will love the location on the River Doubs. The pitches are of a good size, and all have electricity (16A), water and drainage. Choose from shaded, partially shaded or no shade pitches, on hard ground or grass. There also bungalows and tents for rental. Within a short walk from the site is a large supermarket, and nearby is a tram stop from where you can get to the town centre. Cycling, walking and fishing are prevalent in the area, and travelling eastward for approximately an hour will have you at the Swiss border.

Clean sanitary facilities with unisex private sinks and showers. Baby room. Washing machines. Dryers. Washing up sinks. Snack bar. Fresh bread daily. Large swimming pool with diving boards. Playground. Crazy golf. Multi-sports field. Table tennis. Boules. WiFi.

Key Features

- Pets Accepted
- Swimming Pool
- Play Area
- Bar/Restaurant

Scan me for more information.

Alan Rogers Code: FR19170
40 accommodations
30 pitches
GPS: 45.36489, 1.87101
Post Code: F-19800

Corrèze, Limousin

www.alanrogers.com/fr19170
auboisdecalais@orange.fr
Tel: 05 55 26 26 27
auboisdecalais.com

Open (Touring Pitches):
1 April - 31 October.

Camping Au Bois de Calais

The name of this site may be misleading – it is nowhere near Calais! Au Bois de Calais is located within the Parc Naturel Régional de Millevaches in the Limousin. This is a holiday centre comprising a campsite, chalets, gîtes and mobile homes. The 30 touring pitches are huge (minimum 100 sq.m), and all have water and electricity. On-site amenities include a bar and restaurant (with terrace), and a shop specialising in local produce. Sports amenities include a swimming pool and volleyball. There is also a small fishing pond, with the River Corrèze running along one side of the site.

Sanitary facilities include hot showers. Laundry facilities. Motorhome services. Bar. Restaurant. Shop. Heated swimming pool. Fishing pond. Multisports field. Minigolf. Basketball. Play area. Activities and entertainment programme. WiFi over part of the site (charged). Chalets, mobile homes and gîtes to rent.

Key Features

- Pets Accepted
- Swimming Pool
- Play Area
- Bar/Restaurant
- Fishing

Scan me for more information.

Alan Rogers Code: FR23010
31 accommodations
113 pitches
GPS: 46.37243, 2.20268
Post Code: F-23600

Creuse, Limousin

Le Château de Poinsouze

www.alanrogers.com/fr23010
campingpoinsouze@gmail.com
Tel: 05 55 65 02 21
camping-de-poinsouze.com

Open (Touring Pitches):
07 May - 08 September.

Le Château de Poinsouze is a well established site arranged on an open, gently sloping, grassy park with views over a small lake and château. It is an attractive, well maintained, high quality site situated in the unspoilt Limousin region. The 113 very large (120m^2-300m^2), grassy touring pitches, some with lake frontage, all have electricity (6-20A Europlug), water and drainage and 57 have sewerage connections. The site has a friendly, family atmosphere with many organised activities in main season including a children's club. There are marked walks around the park and woods. All facilities are open all season.

High quality sanitary unit includes suites for disabled visitors located central on site. Facilities for babies. Washing machines and dryers. Motorhome services. Shop for basics. Takeaway. Bar and restaurant. Swimming pool, slide, children's pool and new water play area with fountains. Fenced playground. Pétanque. Bicycle hire. Free fishing in the lake, boats and lifejackets can be hired. Sports facilities. Accommodation to rent (pets not accepted) . WiFi over site (charged). No dogs in high season (accepted from 07/05-10/07 and 21/08-08/09).

Key Features

- Pets Accepted
- Disabled Facilities
- Swimming Pool
- Play Area
- Bar/Restaurant
- Bike Hire
- Fishing
- Sailing

Scan me for more information.

Alan Rogers Code: FR87150
13 accommodations
47 pitches
GPS: 45.61159, 1.50135
Post Code: F-87380

Haute-Vienne, Limousin

Camping de Montréal

www.alanrogers.com/fr87150
contact@campingdemontreal.com
Tel: 05 55 71 86 20
campingdemontreal.mobi

Open (Touring Pitches):
All year.

Camping de Montreal is an all-year campsite, located just a few minutes from J42 on the A20. You can be sure of a warm welcome from Hans and Leonie, the Dutch owners of Camping de Montréal, in the heart of the Limousin countryside. The site provides 60 terraced pitches; 13 are occupied by chalets, mobile homes or bungalows, while 47 pitches are reserved for touring units. The pitches are mainly level, and most have excellent views over the eight-hectare leisure lake. All have electricity (10A), some have shade, and tall cypress hedges separate many. There are a few pitches near the sanitary block which have hardstandings and are used in the winter or after heavy rain. The single toilet block has recently been refurbished to a high standard. The small restaurant, open much of the year, is popular with campers and users of the lake.

One refurbished toilet block on the lower level has preset showers, baby changing and good facilities for disabled visitors. A second small sanitary block on the upper level provides WCs, showers and washing up sinks. Laundry. Bar/restaurant with takeaway. Swimming pool. Play area. Small library. Lake for fishing and swimming. WiFi (charged).

Key Features

- Open All Year
- Pets Accepted
- Disabled Facilities
- Swimming Pool
- Play Area
- Bar/Restaurant
- Fishing

Scan me for more information.

Alan Rogers Code: FR63250
24 accommodations
127 pitches
GPS: 45.56979, 2.90185
Post Code: F-63790

Puy-de-Dôme, Auvergne

Camping les Bombes

www.alanrogers.com/fr63250
lesbombes@orange.fr
Tel: 04 73 88 64 03
www.camping-les-bombes.com

Open (Touring Pitches):
23 April - 17 September.

Les Bombes is a beautifully situated and well maintained site within easy walking distance of Lac Chambon and the nearby amenities. On-site there is a heated swimming pool and sunbathing area, a snack bar and 24 chalets to rent (single night bookings accepted in low season). The site extends over five hectares and has 127 touring pitches. These are large (minimum 100 sq.m), flat, grassy and with 16A electricity (Europlug). The site is well located for walking and mountain biking, with a number of tracks leading directly from the site. The site owners will be delighted to recommend possible routes.

Three well maintained toilet blocks have washbasins in cabins and preset showers. Baby room. Facilities for disabled visitors. Motorhome services (at entrance). Laundry facilities. Bread to order (July/Aug). Bar/snack bar/takeaway (1/5-17/9). Swimming pool (1/6-15/9, no Bermuda shorts). Paddling pool. Games room. Play area. Giant chess. Fitness equipment for adults. TV and games room. Bicycle hire. Weekly entertainment (high season). Free WiFi over part of site. Chalets to rent.

Key Features

- Pets Accepted
- Disabled Facilities
- Swimming Pool
- Play Area
- Bar/Restaurant
- Bike Hire
- Fishing

Scan me for more information.

Alan Rogers Code: FR63040
44 accommodations
119 pitches
GPS: 45.50875, 3.28488
Post Code: F-63500

Puy-de-Dôme, Auvergne

Château la Grange Fort

www.alanrogers.com/fr63040
chateau@lagrangefort.com
Tel: 04 73 71 02 43
www.lagrangefort.eu

Open (Touring Pitches):
10 April - 15 October.

This tranquil campsite of seven hectares is within the 25-hectare estate of the picturesque 15th-century Château of Grange Fort. There are 163 pitches (119 for touring units) some with panoramic views over the River Allier, others with views of the historic château. There is a mix of well-drained grass and hardstanding pitches with varying degrees of shade. A short, steep path leads down to the river. Guided tours of the château are available and high-quality evening meals are provided in its vaulted restaurant. The campsite is just ten minutes from the A75.

Three good sanitary blocks have facilities for disabled visitors and a hydra-shower. Laundry room. Bread to order. Restaurant and takeaway (seasonal). Bar (seasonal). Indoor pool, sauna and massage table (seasonal). Large outdoor swimming pool with jacuzzi (seasonal). Play area. Games room. WiFi (charged). Tennis. Football. Boules. Organised activities in season. Torches useful.

Key Features

- Pets Accepted
- Disabled Facilities
- Swimming Pool
- Play Area
- Bar/Restaurant
- Skiing
- Bike Hire
- Fishing

Scan me for more information.

Alan Rogers Code: FR43020
72 pitches
GPS: 45.05042, 3.88094
Post Code: F-43000

Haute-Loire, Auvergne

www.alanrogers.com/fr43020
camping.puyenvelay@aquadis-loisirs.com
Tel: 04 71 09 55 09
aquadis-loisirs.com

Open (Touring Pitches):
1 April - 27 October

Camping de Bouthezard

This city site is located at the foot of a towering needle of volcanic rock with a church on top which is spectacularly lit at night. This is one of three major attractions in Le Puy-en-Velay, a World Heritage site. The excellent location, in a wooded area within walking distance of the medieval city, is protected by a good security barrier and the manager, who speaks good English, lives on site. Tarmac roads lead to 72 marked, grassy pitches with 6A electricity and a designated area for tents. Access is good and as the site may be popular in high season, early arrival is advised. This very popular urban site is within ten minutes walk of the medieval town with its very interesting old centre and is well worth the trip. It is close to the river and screened from the city noise by a good covering of mature trees. The Office de Tourisme is in Place du Clauzel, next to the Mairie.

Main unisex toilet block with facilities for disabled visitors. Second unisex block at rear of site. The facilities may be stretched in high season. Motorhome services. Bread to order. Volleyball and badminton. TV room. WiFi (free near reception).

Key Features

- Pets Accepted
- Disabled Facilities

Scan me for more information.

Alan Rogers Code: FR69020
29 accommodations
60 pitches
GPS: 46.18790, 4.69916
Post Code: F-69820

Rhône, Rhône Alpes

www.alanrogers.com/fr69020
info@beaujolais-camping.com
Tel: 04 74 69 80 07
www.beaujolais-camping.com

Open (Touring Pitches):
13 April - 5 October

La Grappe Fleurie

With easy access from both the A6 autoroute and the N6, this attractive and welcoming site is situated in the heart of Beaujolais. It is perfect for overnight stops and equally inviting for longer stays to explore the vineyards and historic attractions of the region. Virtually surrounded by vineyards, but within walking distance (within 1 km) of the pretty village of Fleurie, this popular site has 60 generous, grassy and fairly level touring pitches with individual access to water, drainage and electricity connections (10A). Wine tasting on site is arranged twice weekly in high season. Restaurant and shopping facilities are available in the village.

Two modern sanitary blocks provide more than ample facilities. Facilities for disabled visitors. Washing machine and dryer. Fridge. Bread to order. Snack bar with homemade pizza (May-Sept). Covered and heated swimming pool (15x7 m). Playground. Tennis court. Large TV/games room. Pétanque. Free Wine tasting (Tue. & Fri). Only gas barbecues are allowed. Accommodation to rent. Free WiFi.

Key Features

- Pets Accepted
- Disabled Facilities
- Swimming Pool
- Play Area

Scan me for more information.

Alan Rogers Code: FR07120
24 accommodations
220 pitches
GPS: 44.39804, 4.39878
Post Code: F-07150

Ardèche, Rhône Alpes

www.alanrogers.com/fr07120
info@ardechois-camping.com
Tel: 04 75 88 06 63
www.ardechois-camping.com

Open (Touring Pitches):
4 April - 10 October

Nature Parc l'Ardéchois

Camping Nature Parc l'Ardéchois is a very high quality, family run site within walking distance of Vallon-Pont-d'Arc. It borders the River Ardèche and canoe trips are run, professionally, direct from the site. This campsite is ideal for families with younger children seeking an active holiday. The facilities are comprehensive and the central toilet unit is of an extremely high standard. Of the 250 pitches, there are 225 for touring units, separated by trees and individual shrubs. All have electrical connections (6/10A) and with an additional charge, 125 larger pitches have full services (22 include a fridge, patio furniture, hammock and free WiFi). Forming a focal point are the bar and restaurant (excellent menus) with an attractive terrace and a takeaway service. A member of Leading Campings group.

Two very well equipped toilet blocks, one superb with everything working automatically. Facilities are of the highest standard, very clean and include good facilities for babies, children and disabled visitors. Laundry facilities. Four private bathrooms to hire. Well stocked shop. Excellent restaurant, bar and takeaway. Heated swimming pool and paddling pool (no Bermuda shorts). Wellness area with sauna, hammam, jacuzzi and 4 seasons-shower. Different types of massage and treatments. Yoga. Gym. Tennis. Very good play area. Organised activities, canoe trips. Bicycle hire. Only gas barbecues are permitted. Communal barbecue area. WiFi throughout (charged).

Key Features

- Pets Accepted
- Disabled Facilities
- Swimming Pool
- Play Area
- Bar/Restaurant
- Bike Hire
- Fishing

Scan me for more information.

Alan Rogers Code: FR07630
420 pitches
GPS: 44.44470, 4.36630
Post Code: F-07120

Ardèche, Rhône Alpes

www.alanrogers.com/fr07630
contact@alunavacances.fr
Tel: 04 75 93 93 15
www.alunavacances.fr

Open (Touring Pitches):
3 April - 28 September

Aluna Vacances

Nestled on the doorstep of the Ardèche Gorges, surrounded by nature and outdoor pursuits of all varieties; energetic ones such as rafting, cycling and swimming, and relaxing ones like walking, picnicking and exploring nature, camping at Sunêlia Aluna Vacances has something for all the family. This leafy site prides itself on its large 'closer to nature' pitches set on grass, some with hardstanding, measuring 100 to 120 sq.m. Electricity (10A) is available and there are four sanitary blocks throughout the site. There is rental accommodation on site as well as a new water park, both indoor and outdoor pools with many slides, a large restaurant with a terrace and bar, kid's club, a grocery store and a spa. Many sports are available during high season; football, tennis, volleyball, badminton, basketball, table tennis, jeu-de-boules, aquagym and dance, plus an outdoor fitness area.

Four sanitary blocks are equipped with showers, private washing cubicles and facilities for babies and disabled guests. Washing machines and dryers. Well stocked shop. Bar with TV. Restaurant and takeaway. Waterpark with heated outdoor pools, indoor pool and slides. Sports and kid's club (seasonal). Tennis & Volleyball court. Table tennis. Boules. Multisports field. Playground. Entertainment programmes. Some off site activities bookable on site (cycling, horse riding, canoeing). WiFi (extra charge).

Key Features

- Pets Accepted
- Disabled Facilities
- Swimming Pool
- Play Area
- Bar/Restaurant

Scan me for more information.

Alan Rogers Code: FR07410
30 accommodations
134 pitches
GPS: 44.43119, 4.32959
Post Code: F-07120

Ardèche, Rhône Alpes

www.alanrogers.com/fr07410
camping@chapouliere.com
Tel: 04 75 39 64 98
www.lachapouliere.com

Open (Touring Pitches):
24 March - 4 November

Camping la Chapoulière

Camping la Chapoulière is a medium sized site, alongside the Ardèche river, some two kilometres south of Ruoms. Grassy banks allow easy access to the river with a deeper area for bathing. The site is in two areas: the upper level, above the pool, has chalets and touring pitches; the older, more established area is for touring pitches nearer the river, with some chalets/mobile homes close to the restaurant. Trees provide dappled shade. There are 134 fairly level touring pitches (no hedges) on sand and grass, all with 6/8A electricity. This site is a good choice for those who prefer to make their own entertainment, and many visitors return year after year, creating a lively community and a sociable atmosphere.

Modern and adequate sanitary blocks. Facilities for babies and disabled visitors in main block. Preset hot showers and some washbasins in cabins. Washing machine. Shop (June/Aug), bread to order all season. Bar (April-Sept). Restaurant (July/Aug and w/ends). Pizza takeaway. Heated swimming pool. Spa and fitness centre with Hammam and massage. Play area. Games room with large TV screen. Organised activities (July/Aug). Riding trips. River bathing. Fishing. Canoe trips. WiFi on most of site (free).

Key Features

- Pets Accepted
- Disabled Facilities
- Swimming Pool
- Play Area
- Bar/Restaurant
- Fishing

Scan me for more information.

Alan Rogers Code: FR07050
307 accommodations
50 pitches
GPS: 44.41410, 4.27290
Post Code: F-07120

Ardèche, Rhône Alpes

www.alanrogers.com/fr07050
contact@rancdavaine.fr
Tel: 04 75 39 60 55
www.camping-ranc-davaine.fr

Open (Touring Pitches):
12 April - 23 September

Sunêlia Le Ranc Davaine

Sunêlia Le Ranc Davaine is a large, busy, family oriented site with direct access to the River Chassezac. There are approximately 500 pitches with 50 for touring, all with electricity (10/16A) for which very long leads are required (some may cross roads). Most pitches are scattered between static caravan and tour operator pitches on fairly flat, stony ground under a variety of trees, some of which are quite low giving much needed shade. The site can get very busy for much of the season. A lively entertainment programme is aimed at young children and teenagers with an enclosed disco three nights a week until 03.00.

Three fully equipped sanitary blocks, very clean and modern include facilities for people with reduced mobility. Washing machines and dryers. Large shop. Internet access. Bar/restaurant, pizzeria, takeaway. Indoor swimming pool (heated), pools for relaxation and swimming, water slide and water park (all facilities all season, no shorts allowed). Large playground. Tennis. Fishing nearby. Extensive entertainment programme (Jul/Aug). Discos. Fitness area. Free WiFi on part of the site.

Key Features

- Pets Accepted
- Disabled Facilities
- Swimming Pool
- Play Area
- Bar/Restaurant

Scan me for more information.

Alan Rogers Code: FR07540
73 accommodations
127 pitches
GPS: 44.42900, 4.33208
Post Code: F-07120

Ardèche, Rhône Alpes

Camping la Grand Terre

www.alanrogers.com/fr07540
contact@campinglagrandterre.com
Tel: 04 75 39 64 94
www.campinglagrandterre.com

Open (Touring Pitches):
4 April - 13 September

La Grand Terre is a large campsite offering a comprehensive range of facilities for its visitors. It has 296 pitches (127 for tourers) which are set out in back-to-back rows with plenty of shade. One camping area is particularly shaded. A large modern building housing reception, and the bar/restaurant area is located at the front of the site with an attractive aquatic complex immediately to the rear. The large parking area at the entrance makes check-in and departure easy. Large outfits may find access to some of the pitches difficult (some narrow roads and overhanging branches) so arrive early in high season.

Four sanitary blocks offer reasonable facilities, but perhaps a long walk from a few locations. Water points are limited. Laundry. Ironing service. Shop (from 06 Apr). Bar (from 06 Apr). Restaurant and fast food service (from 6 Apr). Aquatic complex with 2 heated outdoor pools, paddling pool, 2 waterslides, Jacuzzi and aqua games (06/04 - 09/09). Playground. Tennis. Petanque. TV and games room. Outdoor cinema. Internet access. Gas. Bike rental. Fishing. Charcoal barbecues are not allowed. Useful torches in some areas.

Key Features

- Disabled Facilities
- Swimming Pool
- Bar/Restaurant
- Bike Hire
- Fishing

Scan me for more information.

Alan Rogers Code: FR07660
56 accommodations
GPS: 44.43415, 4.41099
Post Code: F-07150

Ardèche, Rhône Alpes

www.alanrogers.com/fr07660
contact@domaine-sevenier.fr
Tel: 04 75 88 29 44
www.domaine-sevenier.fr

Open (Touring Pitches):
3 April - 31 October

Domaine de Sévenier

Le Domaine de Sévenier is a modern, high quality chalet complex enjoying a hilltop location with fine panoramic views over the surrounding garrigue, a unique mix of oak trees, juniper, rosemary and thyme. There are no touring pitches at this site. Located 4 km. from Vallon-Pont-d'Arc and 800 m. from the pretty village of Lagorce, the domaine is an old winery which has been sensitively converted and offers accommodation in well appointed wooden chalets serving the needs of families, both large and small. Rest and relaxation is the theme here and the restaurant has a good reputation. On-site amenities include a swimming pool and a separate children's pool. The site has links to Nature Parc Camping de l'Ardèche and guests are welcome to enjoy the camping site's evening entertainment.

The sanitary block includes hot showers and provision has been made for disabled visitors. Washing machine. Shop. Bar. Restaurant. Outdoor heated swimming pool. Paddling pool. Activity programme. Play area. Minigolf. Bicycle hire. Fully equipped chalets to rent.

Key Features

- Pets Accepted
- Disabled Facilities
- Swimming Pool
- Play Area
- Bar/Restaurant
- Bike Hire

Scan me for more information.

Alan Rogers Code: FR38140
35 accommodations
120 pitches
GPS: 45.05260, 6.03550
Post Code: F-38520

Isère, Rhône Alpes

Camping le Colporteur

www.alanrogers.com/fr38140
info@camping-colporteur.com
Tel: 04 76 79 11 44
www.camping-colporteur.com

Open (Touring Pitches):
1 April - 30 September.

Le Colporteur is within a few minutes level walk of an attractive market town and ski resort, making this an ideal spot for motorhome owners. There are 150 level grassy pitches, 120 for touring. All pitches have 16A electricity and rock pegs are advised. They are mostly separated by hedging and a variety of mature trees that offer some shade. There is no pool on site but campers have free entry to the adjacent municipal pool. In July and August the attractive bar/restaurant is the focal point for evening activities.

Two large, clean toilet blocks are well equipped, modern and airy with all the necessary facilities including washbasins in cabins, baby room and en-suite room for disabled campers. Shop with fresh bread to order (July/Aug). Restaurant, bar and takeaway (1/6-31/8). Games room. Boules. Small play area. Organised family activities (July/Aug). Fishing. WiFi over site (charged).

Key Features

- Pets Accepted
- Disabled Facilities
- Swimming Pool
- Bar/Restaurant
- Fishing

Scan me for more information.

Alan Rogers Code: FR33110
252 accommodations
618 pitches
GPS: 45.22372, -1.16318
Post Code: F-33990

Gironde, Aquitaine

La Côte d'Argent

www.alanrogers.com/fr33110
info@cca33.com
Tel: 05 56 09 10 25
www.cca33.com

Open (Touring Pitches):
6 May - 14 September

Camping de la Côte d'Argent is a large, well equipped site for leisurely family holidays. It makes an ideal base for walkers and cyclists with over 100 km. of cycle lanes in the area. Hourtin-Plage is a pleasant invigorating resort on the Atlantic coast and a popular location for watersports enthusiasts. The site's top attraction is its pool complex, where wooden bridges connect the pools and islands and there are sunbathing and play areas plus an indoor heated pool. The site has 618 touring pitches (all with 10A electricity), not always clearly defined, arranged under trees with some on sand. High quality entertainment takes place at the impressive bar/restaurant near the entrance.

Very clean sanitary blocks include provision for disabled visitors. Washing machines. Motorhome services. Grocery store, restaurant, takeaway, pizzeria and bar. Four outdoor pools with slides and flumes (1/6-13/9). Indoor pool (all season). Fitness room. Massage (Institut de Beauté). Tennis. Multisport area. Beach volleyball. Pétanque. Play areas. Miniclub, fitness and organised entertainment in high season. Bicycle hire (adults only). WiFi partial site (charged). Charcoal barbecues are not permitted (gaz barbecue rental on site). Hotel (12 rooms).

Key Features

- Pets Accepted
- Disabled Facilities
- Swimming Pool
- Play Area
- Bar/Restaurant
- Bike Hire

Scan me for more information.

Camping Caravaning
La Côte d'Argent
★★★★★
HOURTIN PLAGE
• Situated 300 m from the beach and 4 km from the largest natural lake in France.
• 5000m² of water park, fully heated.
• Over 100km of bike paths from the campsite.
33990 HOURTIN-PLAGE - Tél : +33 (0)5 56 09 10 25 - info@cca33.com
www.camping-cote-dargent.com
Airotel

CARAVAN AND MOTORHOME CLUB
SINCE 1907
Worldwide Caravan and Motorhome Holidays
Wherever you're dreaming of discovering this year, we have a range of destinations that are guaranteed to inspire. Whether you're looking for a once in a lifetime holiday or are seeking your next big adventure, let us take you there.
Brought to you by Alan Rogers Travel, a wholly owned subsidiary of the Caravan and Motorhome Club.
Visit our website camc.com/worldwide
Call us on 01324 779349
maui
alan rogers
ABTA
The Travel Association
11309
ATOL
PROTECTED

Alan Rogers Code: FR33460
533 accommodations
95 pitches
GPS: 44.73439, -1.19598
Post Code: F-33950

Gironde, Aquitaine

Siblu Les Viviers

www.alanrogers.com/fr33460
lesviviers@siblu.fr
Tel: 0208 610 0186
siblu.com/camping-les-viviers

Open (Touring Pitches):
4 April - 12 September

Les Viviers is a large family site on the Lège-Cap-Ferret peninsula. There pitches are dispersed around a 33-hectare wood, 400 of which are occupied by mobile homes and chalets. The site borders the Bassin d'Arcachon and is 5 km. from the nearest Atlantic beach. Pitches are well shaded and of a good size. Most have electrical connections. A large range of amenities are on offer, including a well stocked supermarket, restaurant, pizzeria and a twice weekly street market. A lively activity and entertainment programme is on offer in peak season.

Toilet blocks have free preset showers and facilities for children and disabled visitors. Laundry rooms. Private lake and its private beach. Direct access to the Bassin d'Arcachon by the beach. Supermarket (open all the season). Bar/snack bar, restaurant/pizzeria and takeaway. Pool complex 620m2 with heated and covered pool. Bike hire. Minigolf, ping-pong and tennis court. Gym. Games room. Play area. Entertainment and activity programme. Mobile homes and chalets to rent. WiFi (charged). Gas and charcoal barbecues are not permitted.

Key Features

- Disabled Facilities
- Beach Access
- Swimming Pool
- Play Area
- Bar/Restaurant
- Bike Hire
- Fishing
- Golf

Scan me for more information.

Alan Rogers Code: FR33400
100 accommodations
114 pitches
GPS: 45.48355, -1.11952
Post Code: F-33780

Gironde, Aquitaine

www.alanrogers.com/fr33400
info@camping-les-lacs.com
Tel: 05 56 09 76 63
www.camping-les-lacs.com

Open (Touring Pitches):
2 April - 2 November.

Camping Club les Lacs

Given its proximity to the Gironde ferry terminal at Le Verdon, many campers head south through Soulac. It is, however, a smart resort with a fine sandy beach. Camping Club les Lacs is one of the best sites here and has 228 pitches on offer, of which 114 are available to touring units. All pitches have electrical connections (10A). Site amenities are impressive with a large, modern complex at the entrance housing a large bar, restaurant, shop and stage for evening entertainment (high season). There is a large outdoor pool and covered pool adjacent (open for the full season). The site has recently been extended and 40 new pitches, although large are currently lacking shade. The nearest beach is 3 km. away and Soulac has many attractive shops and restaurants. The northern Médoc vineyards are also within easy access.

Good quality, modern toilet blocks. with showers and washbasins in cubicles. Facilities for disabled visitors and children. Washing machines and dryers. Shop. Bar, restaurant and takeaway (seasonal). Swimming and paddling pools (seasonal). Indoor pool all season. Water slide. Minigolf. Games room. Playground. Entertainment and children's club in peak season. WiFi. Communal barbecues only.

Key Features

- Pets Accepted
- Disabled Facilities
- Swimming Pool
- Play Area
- Bar/Restaurant

Scan me for more information.

Alan Rogers Code: FR24865
80 accommodations
110 pitches
GPS: 44.77125, 0.41182
Post Code: F-24240

Dordogne, Aquitaine

Camping Pomport Beach

www.alanrogers.com/fr24865
info@pomport-beach.com
Tel: 05 24 10 61 13
www.pomport-beach.com

Open (Touring Pitches):
22 May - 12 September.

In the heart of the Bergerac wine-growing region of the Dordogne, Pomport Beach boasts 190 pitches, 110 of which are for touring. Pitches offer a good balance of shade and sun, and all are grassy, level and of a generous size with 10A electrical hook-ups and free WiFi (for one device per pitch). Visitors can enjoy the heated, covered pool, the outdoor fun-pool with a slide or bathe or fish in the lake which forms part of the site. The beach is sandy and is overlooked by the restaurant (extended in 2018). The family-run, friendly site successfully combines its natural environment of mature oaks and sycamores with a lively holiday atmosphere when, in the high season, children's play area and entertainment, tennis courts, mini-golf and multisports courts come into their own. New in 2019 is a one-night stopping place outside the site for motorhomers.

Two recently refurbished sanitary blocks. Separate unit for disabled visitors. Washing machine, dryer and ironing board. Motorhome services. Bar. Restaurant. Swimming pool. Play area. Multisports area. Playing field. Tennis courts. Minigolf. Fishing. Bicycle hire. Watersports. WiFi throughout (free).

Key Features

- Pets Accepted
- Swimming Pool
- Play Area
- Bar/Restaurant
- Bike Hire
- Fishing

Scan me for more information.

Alan Rogers Code: FR24740
12 accommodations
40 pitches
GPS: 44.91806, 1.27778
Post Code: F-24200

Dordogne, Aquitaine

www.alanrogers.com/fr24740
info@mathevies.com
Tel: 05 53 59 20 86
www.mathevies.com

Open (Touring Pitches):
End April - end September.

Domaine des Mathevies

This gem of a small, family-run site is situated in the rural heart of the Périgord, and the delightful owners will give you a warm and friendly welcome. There are only 50 slightly sloping, grass pitches, 40 for touring and all have 10A electricity. They are separated by hedging, and flowering shrubs and trees give varying amounts of shade. A shaded terrace is next to the beautiful, original Perigordine building and the barn has been lovingly converted into a bar/restaurant, a superb children's playroom and the toilet facilities. The play area makes this a paradise for toddlers.

Excellent, very clean toilet block with all necessary facilities including a good room for young children and disabled campers. Washing machine and dryer. Bar. Snacks. Swimming and paddling pools. Tennis court. Library. Selection of games. Satellite TV. Playground. Indoor playroom. Pétanque. Crèche (under 5 yrs). Basketball. Bicycle hire. WiFi over part of the site (free). Special interest groups catered for.

Key Features

- Pets Accepted
- Disabled Facilities
- Swimming Pool
- Play Area
- Bar/Restaurant
- Bike Hire

Scan me for more information.

Alan Rogers Code: FR40690
87 accommodations
446 pitches
GPS: 43.75387, -1.35230
Post Code: F-40140

Landes, Aquitaine

Camping l'Airial

Opposite the popular lake at Soustons, in the shade of mature pine trees, Camping l'Airial combines a natural setting with a lively, friendly holiday atmosphere. Of its 446 touring pitches, 154 have 10A electricity. On-site are two swimming pools, both heated, one covered, and tennis, multisport and pétanque facilities where qualified staff provide supervised activities throughout the season. Bicycles can be hired on-site; a cycle track leads directly from the campsite to the centre of Soustons and to the Atlantic coast where bathing and surfing are popular. Alternatively, a shuttle bus runs four times daily, and free of charge, to take holidaymakers to and from neighbouring villages and the beach. L'Airial campsite is the starting point for a range of outdoor pursuits in the immediate vicinity: sailing, canoeing, paddleboard, surfing, cycling and walking. Less than an hour's drive from Bayonne, Biarritz.

A large, well equipped sanitary block plus washing machines, dryers, TV and computer rooms with free wifi, recycling facilities, restaurants, take-away meals, evening entertainment (free). There is a range of glamping accommodation, chalets and mobile homes for four to seven people.

www.alanrogers.com/fr40690
contact@campinglairial.fr
Tel: 05 58 41 12 48
www.camping-airial.com

Open (Touring Pitches):
1st April - 30th September

Key Features

- Pets Accepted
- Swimming Pool
- Play Area
- Bar/Restaurant
- Bike Hire

Scan me for more information.

Alan Rogers Code: FR40060
129 accommodations
356 pitches
GPS: 43.95166, -1.35212
Post Code: F-40560

Landes, Aquitaine

Camping Club Eurosol

www.alanrogers.com/fr40060
contact@camping-eurosol.com
Tel: 05 58 47 90 14
www.camping-eurosol.com

Open (Touring Pitches):
13 May - 13 September

Privately owned, Camping Club International Eurosol is an attractive, friendly and well maintained site extending over 15 hectares of undulating ground, amongst mature pine trees giving good shade. Of the 356 touring pitches, 231 have electricity (10A) with 120 fully serviced. A wide range of mobile homes and chalets, which are being updated, are available for rent. This is very much a family site with multi-lingual entertainers. Many games and tournaments are organised and a beach volleyball competition is held regularly in front of the bar. The adjacent boules terrain is floodlit. An excellent sandy beach 700 metres from the site has supervised bathing in high season and is ideal for surfing.

Four main toilet blocks and two smaller blocks are comfortable and clean with facilities for babies and disabled visitors. Motorhome services. Fridge rental. Well stocked shop and bar (all season). Restaurant, takeaway (1/6-7/9). Stage for live shows arranged in July/Aug. Outdoor swimming pool, paddling pool (all season) and heated, covered pool (May-July). Tennis. Multisports court. Bicycle hire. WiFi (charged). Charcoal barbecues are not permitted.

Key Features

- Pets Accepted
- Disabled Facilities
- Swimming Pool
- Play Area
- Bar/Restaurant
- Bike Hire

Scan me for more information.

Alan Rogers Code: FR40100
260 accommodations
190 pitches
GPS: 44.46052, -1.13065
Post Code: F-40600

Landes, Aquitaine

www.alanrogers.com/fr40100
info@larive.fr
Tel: 05 58 78 12 33
www.larive.fr

Open (Touring Pitches):
6 April - 1 September

Camping & Spa La Rive

Surrounded by pine woods, La Rive has a superb beach-side location on Lac de Sanguinet. With approximately 500 pitches (including mobile home accommodation), it provides 190 mostly level, numbered and clearly defined touring pitches of 80-100 sq.m. all with electricity connections (10A), 100 also with water and waste water. The swimming pool complex is wonderful with pools linked by water channels and bridges. There is also a jacuzzi, paddling pool and two large swimming pools all surrounded by sunbathing areas and decorated with palm trees. An indoor pool is heated and open all season. This is a friendly site with a good mix of nationalities.

Three good clean toilet blocks have washbasins in cabins and mainly British style toilets. Facilities for disabled visitors. Baby baths. Motorhome services. Shop with gas. New bar/restaurant complex with entertainment. Swimming pool complex (supervised July/Aug) with aquapark for children. Games room. Play area. Tennis. Bicycle hire. Boules. Fishing. Water-skiing. Watersports equipment hire. Tournaments (June-Aug). Skateboard park. Trampolines. Miniclub. No charcoal barbecues on pitches. Communal barbecue areas. WiFi throughout (charged).

Key Features

- Pets Accepted
- Disabled Facilities
- Swimming Pool
- Play Area
- Bar/Restaurant
- Bike Hire
- Fishing
- Sailing

Scan me for more information.

LA RIVE
RESORT & SPA
At the heart of the forest of Landes and with direct access to the Biscarrosse lake, the Domaine de La Rive will have the pleasure of welcoming you in its new modern and bright reception.
You will also discover an aquatic park of more than 6500 m² including 3370 m² covered and heated with a wave pool, a hot tub, a Jacuzzi and outside a new swim lane of 30m long in addition to the 200 m of slides and the wild river, our great success.
In 2020, new sanitaires worthy of the largest Resorts, are being build, to reflect even more the spirit of a 5 stars! Always in an eco-responsible spirit, these new facilities reflect our desire to integrate our facilities into the environment around us: new functional spaces in an innovative setting!

Alan Rogers Code: FR65260
138 accommodations
92 pitches
GPS: 43.10171, -0.12944
Post Code: F-65270

Hautes-Pyrénées, Midi-Pyrénées

www.alanrogers.com/fr65260
contact@ombredestilleuls.com
Tel: 05 62 41 81 54
www.ombredestilleuls.com

Open (Touring Pitches):
Early April - Late October.

A l'Ombre des Tilleuls

Camping à l'Ombre des Tilleuls is a quiet, spacious, wooded site which sits alongside the river Gave de Pau (not accessible from the site directly). There are 92 grassy pitches suitable for vans or tents, all with 6-10A electric hook-ups. The site also offers a range of bungalow, gite and mobile home accommodation. On-site facilities include an outdoor pool complex, children's play area, bar, restaurant serving eat-in or takeaway meals, TV area and shop selling basic necessities and local produce. This campsite is an ideal base for exploring Lourdes and the Pyrenees. The site provides a good choice of sports activities and creative workshops for children in the morning in high season and themed evenings such as night swimming, boules, dancing and karaoke.

WiFi available on all pitches (charged) but free next to reception. Showers/toilets housed in modern block. Access to facilities and sanitary provision for disabled campers but pool not adapted to give access to disabled visitors. Bread available to order. Bus route. River Gave de Pau and beach 2 km from site (fast flowing) fishing, walking. Riding 4km, golf 6 km. Dogs welcome (not dangerous breeds).

Key Features

- Pets Accepted
- Disabled Facilities
- Swimming Pool
- Play Area
- Bar/Restaurant

Scan me for more information.

Alan Rogers Code: FR12140
34 accommodations
151 pitches
GPS: 44.21512, 2.77788
Post Code: F-12290

Aveyron, Midi-Pyrénées

Camping Soleil Levant

www.alanrogers.com/fr12140
contact@camping-soleil-levant.com
Tel: 05 65 46 03 65
www.camping-soleil-levant.com

Open (Touring Pitches):
1 May - 30 September

Soleil Levant has a superb lakeside beach as part of the campsite with shady grassy banks for picnics. Very reasonably priced, this is a site for lovers of nature, peace and quiet. There are competitions and games for all ages in July and August, but at other times there is just the sound of the birds. The 205 level pitches (151 for touring) all have electricity (6/10A) and water nearby. Most have shade from the maturing trees. Many activities are possible on the lake and there is a ramp for launching boats. This is a good area for walking and biking with several marked routes.

Three toilet blocks provide British and Turkish style WCs, preset showers and most washbasins in the main blocks are in cubicles. Superb facilities for disabled visitors. Baby rooms with bath, shower and child's WC. Washing machines. Fridge hire. No shop, but bread and gas are available at the bar. Snack bar/pizzeria (27/6-10/9). Bar with TV and video games. Pedalo, zodiac and canoe hire. Free WiFi in bar.

Key Features

- Pets Accepted
- Disabled Facilities
- Play Area
- Bar/Restaurant
- Skiing
- Fishing

Scan me for more information.

Alan Rogers Code: FR46370
19 accommodations
91 pitches
GPS: 44.86171, 1.55937
Post Code: F-46200

Lot, Midi-Pyrénées

www.alanrogers.com/fr46370
contact@campinglariviere.com
Tel: 05 65 37 02 04
www.campinglariviere.com

Open (Touring Pitches):
29 April - 17 September.

Camping la Rivière

Camping la Rivière is situated on the banks of the Dordogne with direct access to the river and a sand and pebble beach. It is a natural rural site and in a pleasant location. The A20 motorway and the town of Souillac are just 15 km away. The welcome from the owners is warm and friendly and they place much importance on customer service and a pleasant family atmosphere. There are 110 pitches of which 19 are for mobile homes (all for rent). The remaining 91 pitches are for touring units, and all have electricity (10A). Of a good size, all are level and on grass and divided by trees and shrubs which provide a good amount of shade.

Three toilet blocks include hot showers, facilities for disabled visitors and a heated nursery for babies. Laundry with 2 x washing machines and 1 x dryer. Shop. Restaurant/bar (June-Aug). Snack bar and takeaway (July/Aug). Two swimming pools including a paddling pool. Two games areas. Minigolf. Barbecue and picnic areas. Organised excursions. Disco and karaoke evenings. Free WiFi in bar/reception. Fishing.

Key Features

- Pets Accepted
- Disabled Facilities
- Swimming Pool
- Play Area
- Bar/Restaurant
- Fishing

Scan me for more information.

Alan Rogers Code: FR65440
36 accommodations
89 pitches
GPS: 42.87242, -0.01512
Post Code: F-65120

Hautes-Pyrénées, Midi-Pyrénées

Camping le Hounta

www.alanrogers.com/fr65440
le-hounta@wanadoo.fr
Tel: 05 62 92 95 90
www.campinglehounta.com

Open (Touring Pitches):
1 February - 15 October.

This friendly, family run site is set in spectacular mountain scenery close to the head of la Vallée de Lumière in the Pyrenees, making it an ideal base from which to explore the Parc National des Pyrénées and to visit the Col du Tourmalet and the Cirque de Gavarnie. Winter sports enthusiasts have a choice of three ski stations with cross-country skiing, snow-boarding and snow-biking among the options. There are 125 level, grassy pitches, of which 89 are available for touring units and electrical connections (2-10A, Europlug) are charged accordingly. The nearby mountain resort of Luz-Saint-Sauveur has shops, bars and restaurants and is the starting point for many activities.

Two sanitary blocks with mainly British style toilets, hot showers and washbasins in cabins. Facilities for disabled visitors. Baby bath. Washing machine, dryer and iron. Drying room. Motorhome services. Small shop selling basics. Bread delivery (July/Aug). Fast food to order (19.00-20.00, July/Aug). TV room. Pétanque. Playground. Charcoal barbecues only. WiFi on part of site (charged).

Key Features

- Pets Accepted
- Disabled Facilities
- Play Area
- Skiing

Scan me for more information.

Alan Rogers Code: FR65450
30 accommodations
68 pitches
GPS: 43.09566, -0.07468
Post Code: F-65100

Hautes-Pyrénées, Midi-Pyrénées

La Forêt

www.alanrogers.com/fr65450
info@campingdelaforet.fr
Tel: 05 62 94 04 38
www.sites-et-paysages.co.uk

Open (Touring Pitches):
26 March - 31 October.

As its name suggests, camping La Foret can be found in a peaceful, wooded valley just one kilometre from Lourdes. This 4.5-hectare site has a relaxed atmosphere and a popular restaurant serving traditional specialities. The 98 grass pitches are level and shaded; 68 are for touring and have 3 – 10A electricity (French plugs) and easy access. The remainder are occupied by tastefully arranged chalets and mobile homes for rent and the owner has created a 'tents only' area where car-owners leave their cars on a designated car park close by, making it a very safe place for campers with young children. The newly-created farm animal area with its geese, hens and a pig, all of whom are allowed out of their compound in the evening to get to know campers, is very popular with animals and humans alike. The heated swimming pool with jacuzzi and paddling pool area has splendid views of 'Le Grand Couvent' at the sanctuary of Lourdes

---

Sanitary block has hot showers and wash basins in cubicles. Facilities for babies, children and disabled campers. Washing machine and dryer. Motorhome services. Bread to order. Bar with TV. Restaurant (evenings only in low season). Snack bar. Heated swimming pool, paddling pool and jacuzzi (1/6 – 30/9). Play area. Trampoline, volleyball, boules, basketball, junior football. WiFi throughout (charged) No charcoal barbecues as there are five fixed barbecues. Daily bus service to Lourdes.

Key Features

- Pets Accepted
- Swimming Pool
- Play Area
- Bar/Restaurant

Scan me for more information.

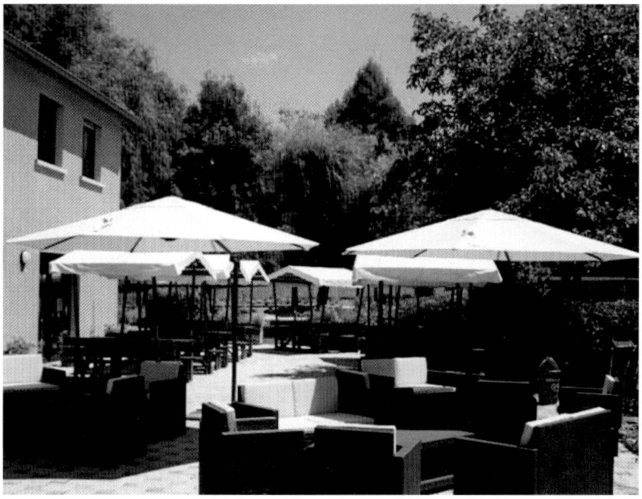

Alan Rogers Code: FR09160
13 accommodations
83 pitches
GPS: 42.87119, 1.21986
Post Code: F-09140

Ariège, Midi-Pyrénées

www.alanrogers.com/fr09160
camping.ariege@gmail.com
Tel: 05 61 96 55 55
camping4saisons.com

Open (Touring Pitches):
1 March - 5 November.

Les Quatre Saisons

Pleasant and well maintained, this riverside campsite has pitches of average size with 83 used for touring units. They are reasonably level with hedges and some shade. For those people who are interested in WW2 exploits, they can follow the walk that Nancy Ward and other members of the French Resistance made when smuggling allied aircrew over the Pyrenees. She was known to the Germans as the White Mouse and was the most decorated lady in WW2. Oust is a typically sleepy French village, while Seix, around 3 km. away, is livelier. The area is ideal for walking in summer and skiing in the winter months. The ski station at Guzet-Niege is just 20 minutes away.

Two fully equipped sanitary blocks are both heated. Washbasins in cubicles. Full facilities for disabled visitors. Baby room. Laundry room with washing machine and dryer. Bar, takeaway, restaurant (July/Aug). Outdoor swimming pool (July/Aug). Play area. Pétanque. Fishing in river beside site. Organised entertainment in high season.

Key Features

- Disabled Facilities
- Swimming Pool
- Play Area
- Bar/Restaurant
- Fishing

Scan me for more information.

Alan Rogers Code: FR12010
69 accommodations
128 pitches
GPS: 44.04467, 3.30228
Post Code: F-12230

Aveyron, Midi-Pyrénées

RCN Val de Cantobre

www.alanrogers.com/fr12010
reservation@rcn.eu
Tel: +31 85 0400 700
www.rcn.nl

Open (Touring Pitches):
20 April - 30 September

Imaginatively and tastefully developed by the Dupond family over 30 years, this delightful terraced site is now owned by the RCN group. Most of the pitches have 10A electricity (and most with water) are peaceful, generous in size and blessed with views of the valley. The terrace design provides some peace and privacy, especially on the upper levels. Rock pegs are advised. An activity programme is supervised by qualified instructors in July and August, and a new pleasure pool has been added. The magnificent carved features in the bar create a delightful ambience, complemented by a recently built terrace. Passive recreationists appreciate the scenery, especially Cantobre, a medieval village that clings to a cliff in view of the site. Nature lovers will be delighted to see black vultures wheeling over the gorges alongside more humble rural residents.

The fully equipped toilet blocks are well appointed and include facilities for disabled visitors and children. Fridge hire. Well stocked shop including many regional specialities, attractive bar, restaurant with large screen TV, pizzeria and takeaway (all season). There is some fairly steep up-and-down walking from furthest pitches to some facilities. Heated outdoor swimming pools with lazy river (all season). Minigolf. Play area. Activity programme. Bicycle hire. All-weather multisports pitch. Torch useful. WiFi over site (free). Motor home service point. Chemical toilet point. Boules pitch. Defibrillator.

Key Features

- Pets Accepted
- Disabled Facilities
- Swimming Pool
- Play Area
- Bar/Restaurant
- Bike Hire

Scan me for more information.

Alan Rogers Code: FR30290
45 accommodations
75 pitches
GPS: 43.76579, 4.09743
Post Code: F-30250

Gard, Languedoc-Roussillon

www.alanrogers.com/fr30290
camping@massereau.com
Tel: 04 66 53 11 20
www.massereau.com

Open (Touring Pitches):
4 April - 31 October

Domaine de Massereau

Two brothers, one a wine producer and one an hotelier, opened Domaine de Massereau in August 2006. It is set within a 50-hectare vineyard dating back to 1804, and the idea was to promote their wine, so tours are arranged and they now produce their own olive oil as well. There are 149 pitches, with 75 available for touring units, all with electricity (45 with 16A electricity, water and drainage). Pitch sizes range from 150-250 sq.m. but the positioning of trees on some of the pitches could limit the usable space. The area is lightly wooded and most pitches are now hedged with flowering shrubs. The other pitches are used for chalets and mobile homes to rent. The site is a member of the Castels Group and good English is spoken.

The modern toilet block incorporates excellent facilities for children and disabled visitors. Laundry area. Motorhome services. Well stocked shop and newspapers. Restaurant, bar, pizzeria and outdoor grill, takeaway, (all season). Heated swimming pool with slide (all season). Paddling pool. Sauna, steam bath, jacuzzi and massage. New Balnéotherapie heated pool. Play area. Trampoline. Minigolf. Bicycle hire. Multisports area. Fitness trail. Pétanque. Short tennis. TV room. Barbecue hire. Fridge hire. Tent hire (2 person). Gas. WiFi (charged). Charcoal barbecues are not allowed.

Key Features

- Pets Accepted
- Disabled Facilities
- Swimming Pool
- Play Area
- Bar/Restaurant
- Bike Hire
- Horse Riding

Scan me for more information.

Alan Rogers Code: FR48040
15 accommodations
39 pitches
GPS: 44.19498, 3.45559
Post Code: F-48150

Lozère, Languedoc-Roussillon

www.alanrogers.com/fr48040
contact@camping-la-cascade.com
Tel: 04 66 45 45 45
camping-la-cascade.com

Open (Touring Pitches):
9 April - 2 October.

Camping la Cascade

A delightful small site run by a friendly family, la Cascade is located in the Lozère, where there is some truly spectacular, rugged scenery, beautiful flora and fauna and old towns and villages. This site has 54 good sized, grassy pitches, separated by trees giving varying amounts of shade. There are 39 for touring, all with 10A electricity. The small river just outside the campsite is lovely, with a low waterfall, shallow water running over stones and deeper pools. The access road is narrow at the entrance but is passable with care by most units. This is an ideal site for unwinding and exploring this beautiful region on foot, on a bike or by car. There is a 'wilder' camping area with ecological dry toilets. The site is calm and tranquil, especially in low season. Some recently introduced bearded vultures can be seen from the site as they fly over the mountainside. Occasional entertainment is provided; when we were there, the park rangers presented an evening show on the vultures, with brioche, coffee and plenty of fun.

Two small heated toilet blocks with good facilities, including a baby bath. Washing machine. Bread to order, cold drinks and local specialities. Takeaway (July/Aug). Family room. Play area. Trout fishing. Communal barbecue. Bicycle hire. Guided walks. Fitness equipment. Boules. Free WiFi.

Key Features

- Pets Accepted
- Disabled Facilities
- Play Area
- Bar/Restaurant
- Bike Hire
- Fishing

Scan me for more information.

Alan Rogers Code: FR34350
177 accommodations
466 pitches
GPS: 43.23467, 3.26867
Post Code: F-34350

Hérault, Languedoc-Roussillon

www.alanrogers.com/fr34350
contact@camping-plageetmer.com
Tel: 04 67 37 34 38
www.camping-plageetmer.com

Open (Touring Pitches):
1 June - 8 September.

La Plage & du Bord de Mer

A very impressive entrance leads you to this large site beside the beach, yet close to all the amenities of Valras-Plage with its own 'centre commercial.' There about 450 level pitches on rough sandy grass with very little shade, all with electricity (6A/10A) and a further 60 with water and drain. There are just 20 privately owned mobile homes which makes a pleasant change in this day and age. This is very much a seaside site, busy in high season, with three gates to the beach. It also has a good seafood restaurant that is popular with the public. There is an impressive, well kept swimming pool complex.

Six fully equipped toilet blocks with facilities for disabled visitors and babies. Laundry. Motorhome services. Range of shops, bar and restaurant. Takeaway (1/7-8/9). Tennis. Minigolf. Play area. Entertainment (July/Aug). No dogs or barbecues allowed.

Key Features

- Disabled Facilities
- Beach Access
- Play Area
- Bar/Restaurant
- Bike Hire

Scan me for more information.

Alan Rogers Code: FR34070
637 accommodations
493 pitches
GPS: 43.26308, 3.31976
Post Code: F-34410

Hérault, Languedoc-Roussillon

www.alanrogers.com/fr34070
info@leserignanplage.com
Tel: 04 67 32 35 33
www.leserignanplage.com

Open (Touring Pitches):
24 April - 28 September

Camping le Sérignan-Plage

Yelloh! Village le Sérignan-Plage is a lively and vibrant site with direct access onto a superb 600 m. sandy beach (including a naturist section), plus two swimming pool complexes and an indoor pool - this is a must for a Mediterranean holiday. It is a busy, friendly, family orientated site with a very comprehensive range of amenities and activities for children. There are now over 1,400 pitches with 493 for touring units. They are fairly level, on sandy soil and all have 10A electricity. The collection of spa pools (balnéo) built in Romanesque style with colourful terracing and columns is overlooked by a very smart restaurant, Le Villa, available to use in the afternoons (used by the adjacent naturist site in the mornings).

Seven modern individually designed sanitary blocks with good amenities including showers with WC and washbasins. Facilities for people with reduced mobility. Baby bathroom. Automatic laundromat. Motorhome services. Supermarket, bakery and newsagent. Other shops (2/6-14/9). ATM. Restaurants, bars and takeaway. Hairdresser. Balnéo spa (afternoons). Gym. Indoor heated pool. Outdoor pools, water playground and waterslides (all season). Tennis court. Multisport courts. Playgrounds. Trampolines. Children's clubs. Evening entertainment. Sporting activities. Bike rental. Bus to Sérignan village (Jul/Aug). Beach (lifeguards 15/6-15/9). WiFi on site (charged). gas barbecues only.

Key Features

- Pets Accepted
- Disabled Facilities
- Beach Access
- Swimming Pool
- Play Area
- Bar/Restaurant
- Bike Hire

Scan me for more information.

Alan Rogers Code: FR11240
140 accommodations
130 pitches
GPS: 43.13270, 3.13890
Post Code: F-11430

Aude, Languedoc-Roussillon

www.alanrogers.com/fr11240
infos@loisirs-vacances-languedoc.com
Tel: 04 68 49 81 59
www.camping-soleil-mer.com

Open (Touring Pitches):
20 March - 10 November

Camping Les Ayguades

Sites with direct access to the sea are popular, particularly those with a long season. Camping LVL Les Ayguades is situated between Gruissan Plage and Narbonne Plage and is overlooked by the Montagne de la Clape. The site is owned by the LVL group who have recently updated the facilities and are committed to running the site with an eco-friendly mindset. There are sandy pitches of various sizes, all with 10A electricity. The pitches are hedged and there is some shade. The site also has chalets and mobile homes to rent, plus a number of privately owned accommodation. An upstairs restaurant has panoramic views of the sea.

Two fully equipped toilet blocks have been renovated and include facilities for disabled visitors. Launderette. Motorhome services. Shop, bar and takeaway (286-31/8). Restaurant (15/4-10/11). Play area and skate park. Fitness room. Children's club. Evening entertainment in high season. Direct access to the Beach. Heated swimming pool with Jaccuzi . Free WiFi.

Key Features

- Pets Accepted
- Disabled Facilities
- Beach Access
- Swimming Pool
- Play Area
- Bar/Restaurant

Scan me for more information.

Alan Rogers Code: FR11070
124 accommodations
130 pitches
GPS: 43.13662, 3.02562
Post Code: F-11100

Aude, Languedoc-Roussillon

Camping les Mimosas

www.alanrogers.com/fr11070
info@lesmimosas.com
Tel: 04 68 49 03 72
www.camping-les-mimosas.fr

Open (Touring Pitches):
4 April - 15 October

Six kilometres inland from the beaches of Narbonne and Gruissan, Yelloh! Village les Mimosas is a family owned site which benefits from a less hectic situation than others by the sea. Set amongst the vineyards, it is welcoming, peaceful in low season, but lively in July and August with plenty to amuse and entertain the younger generation, including a separate paddling pool for toddlers, but still offering facilities for the whole family. A free club card is available in July/August for use at the children's club, gym, sauna, tennis, minigolf, billiards etc. There are 266 pitches, 130 for touring, hedged and on level grass, and of a very good size, most with 6/10A electricity. There are a few 'grand confort' pitches with reasonable shade, mostly from two metre high hedges.

Sanitary buildings refurbished to a high standard include a baby room. Washing machines. Shop and restaurant (all season, incl. breakfast). Takeaway. Bar (low season only at w/ends). Small lounge, amusements (July/Aug). Landscaped heated pool with slides and islands (12/4-mid Oct), plus the original large pool and excellent new paddling pool and play room. Play area. Minigolf. Mountain bike hire. Tennis. Wellness area with massage, beauty treatments and sauna. Gym. Children's activities, sports, entertainment (high season). Bicycle hire. Multisports court. WiFi throughout (charged).

Key Features

- Pets Accepted
- Disabled Facilities
- Swimming Pool
- Play Area
- Bar/Restaurant
- Bike Hire

Scan me for more information.

Alan Rogers Code: FR66070
289 accommodations
705 pitches
GPS: 42.70830, 3.03552
Post Code: F-66141

Pyrénées-Orientales,
Languedoc-Roussillon

Yelloh Village Le Brasilia

www.alanrogers.com/fr66070
info@lebrasilia.fr
Tel: 468802382
www.brasilia.fr

Open (Touring Pitches):
13 April - 5 October

Situated across the yacht harbour from the resort of Canet-Plage, le Brasilia is an impressive, well managed family site directly beside the beach. The state-of-the-art reception incorporates an information centre. Although large, it is pretty, neat and well kept with an amazingly wide range of facilities – indeed, it is camping at its best. The touring pitches are neatly hedged, all with electricity (6-10A) and 304 with water and drainage. They vary in size from 80 to 120 sq.m. and some of the longer pitches are suitable for two families together. There is a variety of shade from pines and flowering shrubs, with less on pitches near the beach. A member of Yelloh! Village and Leading Campings group.

Nine modern sanitary blocks are very well equipped and maintained, with British style WCs and washbasins in cabins. Good facilities for children and for disabled campers. Laundry room. Motorhome services. Range of shops. Gas supplies. Bars and restaurant. Renovated pool complex (heated). New wellness centre including jacuzzi, massage and beauty rooms. Play areas. Sports field. Tennis. Sporting activities. Library, games and video room. Hairdresser. Internet café and WiFi. Daily entertainment programme. Bicycle hire. Fishing. Post office. Weather forecasts. No charcoal barbecues. Free WiFi in bar.

Key Features

- Pets Accepted
- Disabled Facilities
- Beach Access
- Swimming Pool
- Play Area
- Bar/Restaurant
- Bike Hire

Scan me for more information.

Alan Rogers Code: FR66150
42 accommodations
204 pitches
GPS: 42.53372, 3.06792
Post Code: F-66701

Pyrénées-Orientales,
Languedoc-Roussillon

www.alanrogers.com/fr66150
contactcdp@lescriques.com
Tel: 04 68 81 12 73
www.lescriques.fr

Open (Touring Pitches):
28 March - 24 October.

Les Criques de Porteils

Les Criques de Porteils is a fantastic site situated on the cliff top with views across the sea to Argelès, set against a backdrop of mountains and close to Collioure, the artists' paradise. A lot of work has been carried out to improve the facilities here, and pitches have been redeveloped for easier access. There are around 200 of varying sizes and shapes due to the nature of the terrain, level in places, up and down in others. All have 10A electricity available and either a sea view or views towards the mountains. There are eight small coves accessed by steep steps (gated). There is a bar and restaurant and some unusual artistic workshops for children. Classical music sessions and guided walks are also available.

Two renovated toilet blocks (one can be heated) are colourful, fully equipped with super children's room, and all small equipment. Laundry room with Internet point. Motorhome services. Shop. New bar and terraced restaurant with takeaway. Swimming pool. TV/games room. Play area. Golf practice. Tennis. Volleyball. Boules. Fishing. Yoga classes. Guided hikes. Duck pond and small animal area. No charcoal barbecues. WiFi over site (charged).

Key Features

- Pets Accepted
- Disabled Facilities
- Beach Access
- Swimming Pool
- Play Area
- Bar/Restaurant
- Fishing
- Golf

Scan me for more information.

Alan Rogers Code: FR04100
152 accommodations
122 pitches
GPS: 43.85866, 6.49803
Post Code: F-04120

Alpes-de-Haute-Provence,
Provence

www.alanrogers.com/fr04100
terraverdon@cielavillage.com
Tel: 04 92 83 66 67
www.terraverdon.cielavillage.fr

Open (Touring Pitches):
19 April - 23 September

Camping Terra Verdon

Now part of the Ciela Village Group, Camping Terra Verdon has amiable, English-speaking owners and is a reasonably priced, less commercialised site situated in some of the most dramatic scenery in France. The 274 pitches, 122 good sized ones for touring, are clearly marked, separated by trees and small hedges, some are on a slight slope, and all have electricity and water. Access is suitable for larger units. The bar/restaurant overlooks the swimming pool with its sunbathing area set in a sunny location with fantastic views. In high season, English-speaking young people entertain children (3-8 years) and teenagers. There are guided walks into the surrounding hills in the nearby Gorges du Verdon – a very popular excursion, particularly in high season. The weather in the hills here is enjoyable without the excessive heat of the coast.

Three modern toilet blocks are distributed around the site with modern facilities, including those for disabled visitors. Washing machines and dryer. Motorhome services. Fridge and barbecue hire. Shop, bar, restaurant/takeaway (seasonal). Heated swimming pool (seasonal). Children's entertainment, occasional evening entertainment (July/Aug). Play area. Sports area with beach volley. Boules. WiFi throughout (charged).

Key Features

- Pets Accepted
- Disabled Facilities
- Swimming Pool
- Play Area
- Bar/Restaurant
- Bike Hire

Scan me for more information.

Alan Rogers Code: FR04540
161 accommodations
101 pitches
GPS: 43.73396, 6.07585
Post Code: F-04500

Alpes-de-Haute-Provence,
Provence

www.alanrogers.com/fr04540
lafarigoulette@cielavillage.com
Tel: 0422547355
www.lafarigoulette.cielavillage.fr

Open (Touring Pitches):
10 April - 5 October

Camping la Farigoulette

On the edge of Lake Saint-Laurent-du-Verdon in the Provence region, this 5-star campsite is perfect for a family holiday in the Gorges du Verdon which has direct access to the lake and its nautical base. Here you can enjoy kayaking, canoeing, paddle boating and electric boating. Discover the new sports area: two padel courts, a badminton court, a beach volleyball court, a tennis court and a shooting area. The accommodations are modern and functional, in the heart of a shady pine forest. The site offers many daily activities, a large secure playground and entertainment in the heated outdoor pool. Many sports activities are organised, as well as football, badminton and table-tennis tournaments.

Outdoor heated swimming pool. Children's pool. Laundry facilities. Children's playground, bouncy castle & games room. Snack bar, pizzeria & restaurant. Shop. eBikes and bikes available to hire. Table tennis, tennis court, crazy golf, boules available. Pedal boats, canoes and kayaks for hire. Some entertainment (not daily - seasonal)Max 2 dogs allowed. Free Wifi available. Electric & gas BBQs permitted.

Key Features

- Pets Accepted
- Play Area
- Bar/Restaurant

Scan me for more information.

Alan Rogers Code: FR13150
16 accommodations
110 pitches
GPS: 43.78855, 4.84144
Post Code: F-13210

Bouches du Rhône, Provence

www.alanrogers.com/fr13150
contact@campingpegomas.com
Tel: 04 90 92 01 21
campingpegomas.fr

Open (Touring Pitches):
16 March - 26 October.

Camping Pegomas

Camping Pégomas is a well-organised, family-run site and is open for a long season. It is located on the edge of the beautiful Provençal town of Saint Rémy-de-Provence, probably best known for its Roman remains and its links with Van Gogh. There are 110 flat and well-shaded pitches here, mostly with 6A electricity. Several mobile homes are available to rent. Onsite amenities include a swimming pool, a bar and a small shop. There is a good range of shops in Saint Rémy, which is just five minutes away on foot. Gas and electric barbecues are allowed on site, and there is also a stone fireplace available for use by all.

Good, modern sanitary facilities are in three blocks. Motorhome services. Shop for drinks and bread. Bar (May-Sept). Takeaway. Swimming pool (from April). Play area. Boules. Fitness equipment. WiFi throughout (free). Gas barbecues are permitted. Mobile homes to rent.

Key Features

- Pets Accepted
- Disabled Facilities
- Swimming Pool
- Play Area
- Bar/Restaurant

Scan me for more information.

Alan Rogers Code: FR13030
17 accommodations
66 pitches
GPS: 43.67772, 5.06476
Post Code: F-13300

Bouches du Rhône, Provence

www.alanrogers.com/fr13030
camping.nostradamus@gmail.com
Tel: 04 90 56 08 36
www.camping-nostradamus.com

Open (Touring Pitches):
1 March - 31 October.

Camping le Nostradamus

Only some 5 km. from Salon-de-Provence, near the village of Eyguières, this is a charming campsite with shaded grassy pitches thanks to the many trees which have been preserved here as a result of the imaginative irrigation scheme developed by the owners in the 18th century. The campsite, edging the canal, was first opened about 50 years ago as a farm site but has been developed to offer 83 hedged pitches including 17 used for mobile homes. There are 20 with full services, the rest having 6A electricity connections. This is a good site for families but, having said that the fast-running canal at the entrance is unfenced.

One large sanitary block with showers and toilets upstairs, and one small block (both recently renovated) provide all modern facilities including en-suites unit for babies and children. Very good facilities for disabled visitors (key). Washing machine. Motorhome services. Shop (fresh bread and basics) and bar. Restaurant with takeaway (from 15/5). Swimming and paddling pools (15/5-30/9). Play area outside entrance. Pétanque. Fishing. WiFi in some areas (charged). Gas and charcoal barbecues are permitted.

Key Features

- Pets Accepted
- Disabled Facilities
- Swimming Pool
- Play Area
- Bar/Restaurant
- Fishing

Scan me for more information.

Alan Rogers Code: FR05140
90 accommodations
160 pitches
GPS: 44.82483, 6.52566
Post Code: F-05120

Hautes-Alpes, Provence

Campéole Le Courounba

www.alanrogers.com/fr05140
courounba@campeole.com
Tel: +33 (0)4 92 23 02 09
www.campeole.co.uk/camping/post/le-courounba-les-vigneaux

Open (Touring Pitches):
19 May - 16 September

Le Courounba is a member of the Campéole group, located at the entrance to the magnificent Parc National des Ecrins. Pitches are shady and spacious, dispersed around 12 hectares of woodland. Many of the 160 touring pitches have superb views of the surrounding mountain scenery. Ninety mobile homes for rent (including specially adapted units for disabled campers). There is also a new ecological swimming pool with water slides and watergames and other on-site amenities include two tennis courts and a volleyball pitch. Most facilities are free of charge (including tennis). Adjacent to the site is a friendly bar/restaurant and a small, basic shop during high season only.

Four modern sanitary blocks include washbasins and showers. Facilities for children and disabled visitors. Motorhome services. Washing machine. Heated swimming pool (14/6-20/9, closed Sat. in July/Aug). Sauna and jacuzzi. Volleyball. Tennis. Multisports court. Bouncy castle. Play area. BMX track. Activity and entertainment programme in high season. Mobile homes for rent. WiFi (charged). Electric barbecues and camp fires not permitted.

Key Features

- Pets Accepted
- Disabled Facilities
- Swimming Pool
- Play Area
- Bar/Restaurant

Scan me for more information.

Alan Rogers Code: FR05000
35 accommodations
68 pitches
GPS: 44.31121, 5.69677
Post Code: F-05700

Hautes-Alpes, Provence

Princes d'Orange

www.alanrogers.com/fr05000
campingorpierre@wanadoo.fr
Tel: 04 92 66 22 53
www.campingorpierre.com

Open (Touring Pitches):
1 April - 31 October.

This attractive, terraced site, set on a hillside above the village has been thoughtfully developed. The owner, speaks excellent English and the genuine, friendly welcome means many families return year upon year, bringing, in turn, new generations. Divided into five terraces, each with a dedicated toilet block, some of its 100 generously sized pitches (68 for touring) enjoy the pleasant shade from trees and have electricity connections (10A). In high season, one terrace is reserved as a one-star camping area for young people. Orpierre has an enchanting maze of medieval streets and houses, almost like a trip back through the centuries. Whether you choose to drive, climb, walk or cycle, there is plenty of wonderful scenery to discover in the immediate vicinity, whilst not far away, some exhilarating hang-gliding and parascending can be enjoyed. It is renowned as a world-class rock climbing venue, with over 600 climbing routes in the surrounding mountains.

Six well equipped toilet blocks. Excellent bathrooms for children and babies. Laundry facilities. Bread. Bar (15/6-15/9). Heated swimming pool, paddling pool (15/6-15/9). Play area with inflatable climbing tower. Boules. Games room. Fridge hire. Only gas and electric barbecues are permitted. WiFi throughout (charged).

Key Features

- Pets Accepted
- Swimming Pool
- Play Area
- Bar/Restaurant
- Bike Hire

Scan me for more information.

Alan Rogers Code: FR84090
35 accommodations
265 pitches
GPS: 43.95661, 4.80215
Post Code: F-84000

Vaucluse, Provence

www.alanrogers.com/fr84090
camping.avignon@aquadis-loisirs.com
Tel: 04 90 80 63 50
www.aquadis-loisirs.com

Open (Touring Pitches):
1 March - 17 November

Camping du Pont d'Avignon

Pont d'Avignon is on the Ile de la Barthelasse in the centre of the river, within walking distance of the town centre, via the bridge, or on the free ferry. Separated by trees and flowering shrubs, there are 265 level touring pitches, some on grass and some with gravel; 200 have 10A electricity. All are shaded and neatly laid out with good access. A good play area, tennis courts and volleyball pitch are in the centre of the site separating the two halves. The restaurant, bar and terrace overlook the attractive pool. During the season there are musical and themed evenings in the restaurant.

Five adequate sanitary blocks (two open in low season) have good facilities for disabled visitors. Washing machines, dryer. Motorhome services. Well stocked shop. Bar/restaurant and takeaway. Swimming pool, paddling pool and jacuzzi (15/5-15/9). TV/games room. Boules. Play area with climbing frame. Tennis (free). Bicycle hire (and electric). Internet access. WiFi throughout (charged). Bungalow, tents and mobile homes for hire.

Key Features

- Pets Accepted
- Disabled Facilities
- Swimming Pool
- Play Area
- Bar/Restaurant
- Bike Hire
- Fishing

Scan me for more information.

Alan Rogers Code: FR83400
190 accommodations
40 pitches
GPS: 43.26978, 6.57311
Post Code: F-83310

Var, Côte d'Azur

Holiday Marina Resort

www.alanrogers.com/fr83400
info@holiday-marina.com
Tel: 04 94 56 08 43
www.holiday-marina.com

Open (Touring Pitches):
1 March - 31 October.

Owned and operated by an English family, this site is an established favourite with British families. It is located in the busy holiday area of the Gulf of Saint Tropez. The site has a large and well-kept pool area and its own adjacent moorings for boats up to 10 meters. Smaller than many campsites in this area, there are 230 good sized pitches of which 40 are for touring units comprising of 20 Prestige and 20 Majestic pitches. Each of these has its own spacious bathroom with a good shower, washbasin, WC and outdoor kitchen with sink and fridge. All have a hard standing area for a caravan or motorhome plus a synthetic grassed area ensuring green grass throughout the year!

Individual private bathrooms include washbasin, shower and WC, heated towel rail, hairdryer, outside kitchen sink, outside fridge, exterior power source, plus outside dishwasher (on Majestic pitches only). Facilities for disabled visitors include one fully adapted mobile home. Laundry. Shop. The main building houses a bar, restaurant, games and TV room. The restaurant has a varied and full menu, snacks and takeaway. Heated swimming and paddling pools and jacuzzi (1/4-30/9). New salon and spa. Miniclub and evening entertainment in the main season. Adventure playground. Sports field with football, volleyball and basketball pitches. Fishing in the adjacent river. Holiday homes and Lodges for hire. Airport shuttle. WiFi. Boat mooring and school. Vehicle wash station.

Key Features

- Pets Accepted
- Disabled Facilities
- Swimming Pool
- Play Area
- Bar/Restaurant
- Bike Hire
- Fishing

Scan me for more information.

Alan Rogers Code: FR83120
200 accommodations
1173 pitches
GPS: 43.11779, 6.35176
Post Code: F-83230

Var, Côte d'Azur

www.alanrogers.com/fr83120
mail@campdudomaine.com
Tel: 04 94 71 03 12
www.campdudomaine.com

Open (Touring Pitches):
6 April - 31 October.

Camp du Domaine

Camp du Domaine, 3 km. south of Le Lavandou, is a large, attractive, beachside site with 1,173 touring pitches set in 45 hectares of pinewood, yet surprisingly it does not give the impression of being so big. The pitches are large and most are reasonably level; 957 have 10/16A electricity. The most popular pitches are beside the beach, but those furthest away are generally larger and have more shade. Amongst the trees, many pitches are more suitable for tents. There are also 200 mobile homes/bungalows to rent, located on the hillside with super sea views. The beach is the attraction and everyone tries to get close. American motorhomes are accepted.

Ten modern, well used but clean toilet blocks. Facilities for disabled visitors. Baby room with showers, WC and changing facilities. Washing machines. Fridge hire. Well stocked supermarket, bars, pizzeria (all open all season). No swimming pool, but direct beach access. Several excellent play areas for all ages. Activities and entertainment for children and teenagers (July/Aug). 6 tennis courts. Kayaks and paddle boards for hire. Wide range of watersports. Water games. New gym. Multisports courts (one indoor for wet or hot weather) for football, basketball. Only gas and electric barbecues are allowed. Direct beach access. Dogs not accepted 21/7-18/8. Free WiFi at tennis bar.

Key Features

- Pets Accepted
- Disabled Facilities
- Beach Access
- Play Area
- Bar/Restaurant
- Skiing
- Fishing
- Sailing

Scan me for more information.

Alan Rogers Code: FR06070
60 accommodations
60 pitches
GPS: 43.95763, 6.86088
Post Code: F-06260

Alpes-Maritimes, Côte d'Azur

www.alanrogers.com/fr06070
origan@orange.fr
Tel: 04 93 05 06 00
www.origan-village.com

Open (Touring Pitches):
16 April - 16 October.

Origan Village Naturiste

Origan is a naturist site set in the mountains behind Nice at a height of 500 m. The access road is single track and winding with passing places. The site's terrain is fairly wild and some roads are stony, so it is unsuitable for caravans longer than six metres due to the steep slopes. The 60 touring pitches across the site, are irregular shapes and sizes and have good views. Electricity connection (6A) is possible on most pitches (by long cable). The bar area, backing onto an impressive rock face (lit at night), overlooks a very attractive pool complex. Reservation is necessary in high season. The scenery is impressive and footpaths in and around the site offer good, if fairly strenuous, walks up to a height of 1,000 m. A wide range of activities are arranged including guided walking tours in the mountains, days out to the Mediterranean coast for boat trips and the occasional musical evening in the bar/restaurant.

Sanitary facilities are clean and of a standard and type associated with most good naturist sites – mostly open plan hot showers. Laundry facilities. Well stocked shop (1/6-30/8). Bar/restaurant/takeaway (all season). Heated swimming pools with toboggan and Jacuzzi (1/6-30/8). Wellness centre (June-Sept). Sauna. Gym. Play area. Archery. Tennis. Fishing. Organised activities for all (high season). Naturist hikes. Only gas or electric barbecues are permitted (communal provided). Torches advised. WiFi (charged.

Key Features

- Naturist Site
- Pets Accepted
- Disabled Facilities
- Swimming Pool
- Play Area
- Bar/Restaurant
- Fishing

Scan me for more information.

Alan Rogers Code: FR20290
126 accommodations
69 pitches
GPS: 41.53430, 8.86330
Post Code: F-20100

Corse-du-Sud, Corsica

www.alanrogers.com/fr20290
avena@campeole.com
Tel: +33 (0)4 95 77 02 18
www.campeole.co.uk

Open (Touring Pitches):
18 May - 16 September

Campéole L'Avena

Part of the Campéole group, l'Avena is primarily a beach site which sits in an attractive valley. The beach is within ten minutes walk away along a sandy track. There are 194 flat pitches with 69 for tourers, all with 16A electricity. Some are closely placed, and there are differing levels of shade from young trees. There are also chalets and bungalows for rent. The small snack bar, bar and shop provide an adequate service but remember the closest village is 15 km. away for extra supplies. A little play area is supplemented with a bouncy castle. Visitors are left to their own devices here. There are many Bangali-style tents here, but the touring area is kept separate and is closest to the track for beach access. Other than the beach, there is little to do here for young families, although a limited amount of entertainment is provided in high season. Nevertheless, the peaceful nature of the site will suit some campers, especially those seeking keen prices.

The single unisex sanitary block is a little under pressure during peak periods. Hot showers. Provision for disabled visitors. Washing machines. Shop/bar/snack bar (seasonal). Motorhome services. WiFi (charged). Communal barbecue.

Key Features

- Pets Accepted
- Disabled Facilities
- Play Area
- Bar/Restaurant

Scan me for more information.

Alan Rogers Code: FR20040
90 accommodations
199 pitches
GPS: 42.16151, 9.55269
Post Code: F-20270

Haute-Corse, Corsica

www.alanrogers.com/fr20040
rivabella.corsica@gmail.com
Tel: 04 95 38 81 10
www.naturisme-rivabella.com

Open (Touring Pitches):
All Year (naturist 16 May - 30 September).

Riva Bella Resort & Spa

This is a relaxed, informal, spacious site alongside an extraordinarily long and beautiful beach. Riva Bella is open all year and is exclusively naturist from 1st April to 5th November only. The site is divided into several areas with 199 pitches (with 6A electricity), some of which are alongside the sandy beach with little shade. Others are in a shady, wooded glade on the hillside. The vast fish-laden lakes are an excellent feature of this site, and a superb balnéotherapy centre offers the very latest beauty and relaxation treatments (men and women) based on marine techniques. An excellent, beachside restaurant offers a sophisticated menu and has superb sea views.

High standard toilet facilities. Provision for disabled visitors, children and babies. Laundry. Large shop (15/5-15/10). Fridge hire. Lovely restaurant with sea views and menu for children. Ice creams. Excellent beach restaurant/bar. Watersports, sailing school, pedaloes, fishing. Balnéotherapy centre. Sauna. Aerobics. Giant chess. Petanque. Archery. Fishing. Mountain bike hire. Half-court tennis. Walking with llamas. Professional evening entertainment programme. Baby sitting service. Internet. Very good WiFi over most of site (charged).

Key Features

- Naturist Site
- Open All Year
- Pets Accepted
- Disabled Facilities
- Beach Access
- Swimming Pool
- Play Area
- Bar/Restaurant

Scan me for more information.

Neuschwanstein Castle, Bavaria >

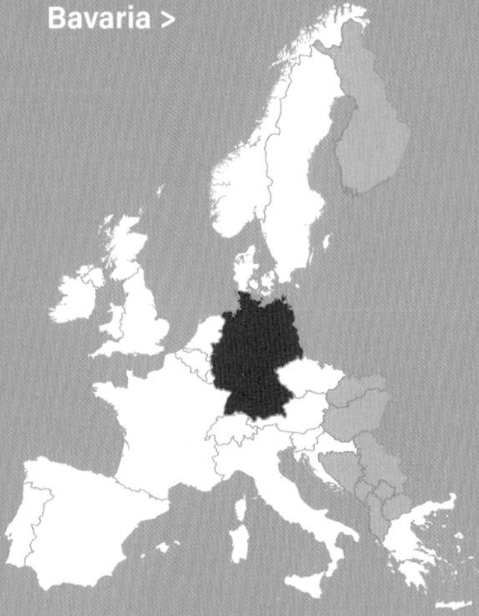

Capital Berlin
Currency Euro (€)
Language German
Time Zone CET (GMT+1)
Telephone Code 00 49

Tourist Website
germany.travel

Climate Temperate climate. In general, winters are a little colder and summers a little warmer than in the UK.

Shops Opening hours vary throughout the year. In high-season 9.30am to 8pm Monday to Saturday.

Banks 9am to 4pm weekdays, extended hours on Tuesdays and Thursdays, and some open Saturday.

Accessible Travel Access and assistance for wheelchair users and those who are less able is widespread.

Travelling with Children Very children-friendly with a variety of attractions. Public transport is usually half price for children. Most attractions will let under 18s in for free. Many restaurants offer a kids menu, but children are also expected to behave.

See campsite map page

479

Public Holidays New Year's Day, Good Friday, Easter Monday, Labour Day, Ascension, Whit Monday, Day of German Unity (3 Oct), Christmas Day, Boxing Day. Epiphany, Corpus Christi, Assumption, Reformation Day, All Saints and Repentance Day are regional public holidays.

Motoring Germany's network of toll-free motorways (autobahns) is among the best in the world. It's roads are well maintained and traffic flows freely. While many parts of the Autobahn have no speed limit, towing a caravan or trailer requires you to display a 100 km/h sticker at all times.

Environmental Policies Low Emission Zones are enforced in all major cities and some large towns and apply to all motor vehicles. It is a legal requirement for vehicles to feature an emissions sticker, these cost six euros and are available online. Glass, plastics, aluminium and paper and cardboard are widely recycled. A deposit scheme, often referred to as pfand (deposit), is in place.

View all campsites in Germany
alanrogers.com/germany

Germany

With its wealth of scenic, historical and cultural interests, Germany is a land of contrasts. From the flat lands of the north to the wooded mountains in the south, with forests in the east and west, regional characteristics are a strong feature of German life, and present a rich variety of folklore and customs.

Each region in Germany has its own unique identity. Home of lederhosen, beer and sausages is Bavaria in the south, with small towns, medieval castles and Baroque churches. It is also home to the fairytale 19th-century Romanesque Revival castle of Neuschwanstein. In the south-west, Baden Württemberg is famous for its ancient Black Forest and its spas, and boasts the most hours of sunshine. Further west is the stunningly beautiful Rhine Valley, where the river winds through steep hills dotted with castles, ruins and vineyards.

Eastern Germany is studded with lakes and rivers, and undulating lowlands that give way to mountains. The north has busy cities such as Bremen and Hamburg as well as traditional North Sea family resorts. The capital city of Berlin, situated in the north-east of the country, and once divided by the Berlin Wall, is an increasingly popular tourist destination, with its blend of old and modern architecture, zoos and aquariums, museums, art galleries, green spaces and lively nightlife.

Alan Rogers Code: DE26000
300 accommodations
60 pitches
GPS: 53.92001, 10.23439
Post Code: D-23829

Wittenborn, Schleswig-Holstein

Weisser Brunnen

www.alanrogers.com/de26000
camping@weisser-brunnen.de
Tel: 04554 1413
www.weisser-brunnen.de

Open (Touring Pitches):
22 March - 20 October.

Weisser Brunnen is a family campsite bordering Lake Mözener, close to the village of Wittenborn. It lies in the heart of the Schleswig-Holstein region, close to the Baltic Sea, in the triangle formed by Hamburg, Lübeck and Kiel. The site is popular with long-stay campers from the Hamburg area, as well as with other types of tourists, from cyclists to those with large motorhomes or caravans. There are around 400 level, grassy pitches (60 for touring), all with electricity and water. There is some shade from a variety of mature trees, and a few pitches benefit from views over the lake. Bicycles are available for hire so that you can enjoy the surrounding countryside. You can relax on the lakeside beach or take advantage of the sporting facilities available. The nearby village of Bad Segeberg has one of Europe's largest bat centres, and the Karl May 1870s Wild West extravaganza takes place every year in July and August in a huge, natural arena. New owners in 2019 promise many new developments and have already introduced a number of glamping options.

Large modern toilet block with all necessary facilities, including those for children and disabled campers. Laundry. Motorhome services. Bar, restaurant and takeaway with home-made ice cream. Children's club (July/Aug). Lake with beach, swimming, kayaking, surfing and fishing. Football. Volleyball. Bicycle hire.

Key Features

- Pets Accepted
- Disabled Facilities
- Play Area
- Bar/Restaurant
- Bike Hire
- Fishing

Scan me for more information.

Alan Rogers Code: DE25490
220 accommodations
139 pitches
GPS: 54.71590, 9.99051
Post Code: D-24376

Hasselberg, Schleswig-Holstein

Ostseecamp Gut Oehe

www.alanrogers.com/de25490
camping@gut-oehe.de
Tel: 04642 6124
www.camping-oehe.de

Open (Touring Pitches):
28 March - 30 September.

This campsite is in the grounds of the Gut Oehe estate, right behind the dykes on the East Sea. Campers can enjoy the vast stretches of sandy beach here, or visit the ancient fishermen's town of Kappeln. The 359 marked and numbered pitches (139 for tourers, all with 6A Europlug) are on large, grassy fields off hardcore access roads. Pitches are average in size, but as there is no separation, large units will fit just fine. To the front of the site are 20 motorhome pitches with hardstanding. An area with bar, a restaurant/takeaway and sanitary facilities is centrally situated. This is an excellent base for cyclists, as a public cycle route runs over the dyke in front of the site.

Heated toilet blocks have controllable hot showers, some washbasins in cabins, baby room and facilities for disabled visitors. Motorhome services. Excellent shop. Bar, restaurant and takeaway. Watersports. Fishing. Diving school. Beach volleyball. Entertainment programme (July/Aug). WiFi (charged).

Key Features

- Pets Accepted
- Disabled Facilities
- Play Area
- Bar/Restaurant
- Fishing

Scan me for more information.

Alan Rogers Code: DE30040
70 pitches
GPS: 53.86000, 10.63000
Post Code: D-23556

Lübeck-Schönböcken,
Schleswig-Holstein

www.alanrogers.com/de30040
info@camping-luebeck.de
Tel: 045 189 3090
www.camping-luebeck.de

Open (Touring Pitches):
Easter - 31 October.

Camp Lübeck Schönböcken

Handily located on the outskirts of Lübeck, this site is only 3 km. from the autobahn exit and only a few minutes from the city centre. Camping Lübeck-Schönböcken is ideally located for an overnight stop and as a base for visiting the city and the surrounding region or travelling to Scandinavia. the site is located less than 10 miles away from the Travemünde ferry port with connections to (Trelleborg & Malmo) Sweden, (Helsinki) Finland and Latvia (Liepāja.) The site has 70 touring pitches in large open grass areas, on reasonably level ground. All pitches have electrical hook-ups (6A). The site owner, Herr Wulf, will happily give advice on visiting the medieval city, which is one of north Germany's most visited tourist towns, famous for its many medieval buildings and for its marzipan. There is a separate field for caravans (max 15metres) and motorhomes (max 8.5metres).

The heated sanitary block houses modern facilities. Showers are token operated. Laundry areas. Facilities for motorhomes. Essential items sold in reception. Play area. WiFi (charged).

Key Features

- Pets Accepted
- Play Area

Scan me for more information.

Alan Rogers Code: DE30050
115 pitches
GPS: 53.65015, 9.92927
Post Code: D-22457

Hamburg, Hamburg

www.alanrogers.com/de30050
hamburg@knauscamp.de
Tel: 04055 94225
www.knauscamp.de

Open (Touring Pitches):
All year.

Knaus Camping Hamburg

Situated some 15 km. from the centre of Hamburg on the northern edge of the town, this is a suitable base either for visiting this famous German city, or as a night stop before catching the Harwich ferry or travelling to Denmark. There is some traffic noise because the autobahn runs alongside (despite efforts to screen it out) and also some aircraft noise. However, the proximity of the A7 (E45) does make it easy to find. The 115 pitches for short-term touring are of about 100 sq.m, on grass with access from gravel roads. All have 6A electricity and are marked out with small trees and hedges. Only basic food supplies are stocked in reception as the site is about ten minutes' walk from the restaurants and shops in town. Apart from some road traffic 'hum', as previously mentioned, this is a quiet, well laid out site. A large number of trees and shrubs offer shade and privacy. Ten gravel roads are reserved for large motorhomes.

A deposit is required for the key to the single sanitary block, a well constructed modern building with high quality facilities and heated in cool weather. Good facilities for disabled visitors, with special pitches close to the block. Washing machines and dryers. Motorhome services. Shop with essentials. Playground. Dogs are not accepted. WiFi (charged).

Key Features

- Open All Year
- Disabled Facilities
- Play Area

Scan me for more information.

Alan Rogers Code: DE38180
50 accommodations
100 pitches
GPS: 53.28411, 12.94844
Post Code: D-17255

Wesenberg, Mecklenburg-West Pomerania

Camping Am Weissen See

www.alanrogers.com/de38180
info@haveltourist.de
Tel: 03981 24790
www.haveltourist.de

Open (Touring Pitches):
End March - Mid September.

This site lies just 300 metres from, and overlooks, the Weissen See which is open to the public and used for swimming and boating. Of the 150 pitches, 100 are for touring units, all with 16A electricity and in an open-plan arrangement. Although the site is somewhat undulating in places, the pitches are reasonably level with a grass/sand base and shaded by mature, tall pine trees. There are also overnight parking places outside of the barrier. A local train service (more a bus on rails) passes the site, allowing easy access to the towns of Mirow and Neustrelitz. Am Weissen See is well suited to visitors who like a quiet site set in a natural forested location, where the swimming facilities are within easy reach but far enough away from the campsite to enable a peaceful atmosphere to be maintained. In the restaurant that adjoins the site, local food and beers can be enjoyed on the terrace overlooking the lake without disturbing the tranquillity of the campsite.

Key Features

- Pets Accepted
- Disabled Facilities
- Play Area
- Bar/Restaurant

Two traditional, well maintained sanitary blocks have open style washbasins and controllable showers (payment by token). Facilities for disabled campers. Washing machines and dryers. Motorhome services. Hot plates for hire. Small shop. Fresh bread to order. Play area. Children's entertainment (high season). WiFi (charged).

Scan me for more information.

Alan Rogers Code: DE38210
70 pitches
GPS: 53.34740, 12.82659
Post Code: D-17252

Schillersdorf, Mecklenburg-West Pomerania

www.alanrogers.com/de38210
info@haveltourist.de
Tel: 03982 92500
www.haveltourist.de

Open (Touring Pitches):
1 April - 31 October.

Camping Am Leppinsee

Bordering and with direct access to the Leppinsee via a meadow, a beach and a small jetty, Am Leppinsee offers 70 well-shaded, grassy pitches, all with 10A electricity, arranged amongst the trees. This is a very quiet site and borders Germany's largest national park where cranes, red deer, the white-tailed eagle, osprey and much more can be found. Close to the site is an eight-acre 'dendrologischer' garden (the study of wooded plants); founded in 1906, it contains many rare examples of trees as well as 600-year-old oak and beech. The Leppinsee is connected to many other lakes and waterways, all favoured by those travelling by canoe, and a trip along the Seerosenstrasse (Water Lilly route) to the Schoss in Mirow is popular. Boats can be rented on site. For those that prefer to travel to Mirow with less effort, a small passenger ship service operates between the site and the town.

The modern bright sanitary building is heated and well maintained. Entry and use of showers requires chip key. Washing machines and dryers. Kitchen and dishwashing facilities. Motorhome services. Bread to order from reception. Play area. Volleyball pitch. Boat jetty. Limited entertainment. Bicycle hire. WiFi over part of site (charged).

Key Features

- Pets Accepted
- Play Area
- Bike Hire
- Fishing
- Sailing

Scan me for more information.

Alan Rogers Code: DE38160
86 accommodations
65 pitches
GPS: 53.20879, 13.07326
Post Code: D-17255

Priepert, Mecklenburg-West Pomerania

Campingplatz Am Ziernsee

www.alanrogers.com/de38160
info@haveltourist.de
Tel: 03981 24790
www.haveltourist.de

Open (Touring Pitches):
8 April - 31 October.

Accessed along a two-kilometre long, narrow forest road, this is a very quiet and remote lakeside site that slopes gently down to the water's edge. Most of the touring area is fairly open, with a little shade, however, views of the lake are restricted by tall trees and high reed beds. Of the 150 grass pitches, around 60 are for tourers, numbered and in an open plan arrangement, all with 16A electricity. Most of the jetties leading into the lake are reserved for boat owners, but the jetty at the far end of the site allows lake access and is used by the canoeists. The Ziernsee lies to the very south of the Mecklenburger area of lakes, and the lakes region of Brandenburg can be reached and from there, Berlin. There is no doubt that although this region has a great deal to offer holidaymakers in general, touring by canoe is understandably a most popular and healthy way of getting around, with campsites offering special rates and facilities for canoe tourers. A beginners' course in canoeing and canoe and equipment hire are available at this site's main office in Havelberge

Modern well maintained sanitary facilities with controllable showers (on payment card). Washing machines and dryers. Motorhome services. Small shop in reception. Fresh bread. Playground. Volleyball. Fishing. Special area for canoe touring units with a campfire and covered table. Bicycle hire. WiFi over site (charged).

Key Features

- Pets Accepted
- Play Area
- Bar/Restaurant
- Fishing
- Sailing

Scan me for more information.

Alan Rogers Code: DE38110
70 accommodations
150 pitches
GPS: 53.26250, 13.05130
Post Code: D-17255

Ahrensberg, Mecklenburg-West Pomerania

www.alanrogers.com/de38110
info@haveltourist.de
Tel: 039 832 2950
www.haveltourist.de

Open (Touring Pitches):
19 March - 31 October.

Campingplatz Am Drewensee

The Drewensee (2000 sq.m), popular with anglers, is connected to many waterways so this is a useful site for tourers who enjoy canoeing and motorboating. Nevertheless, boating regulations ensure that it is quiet. The site has around 150 level, grassy touring pitches. Most are well shaded beneath mature trees and all have 16A electricity. Two jetties are provided, one for boat users, the other for swimmers, and a grassed area bordering the lake is a popular relaxation area. Like most of the campsites in this region, formally part of East Germany, the site is surrounded by mature forests and large areas of open water connected by numerous waterways. Touring by canoe is very popular over the entire region and canoe hire is found on most campsites. In addition, special areas on sites and generous discounts are available for those travelling by canoe.

Modern, heated and well maintained sanitary building with some washbasins in cubicles and controllable showers (payment by chip key). Family rooms. Washing machine and dryer. Motorhome services. Small shop. Beach snack bar. Play area. Children's entertainment (high season). Boat launching. Boat rental. Bicycle hire. Fishing. WiFi over part of site (charged).

Key Features

- Pets Accepted
- Disabled Facilities
- Play Area
- Bike Hire
- Fishing

Scan me for more information.

Alan Rogers Code: DE38150
22 accommodations
65 pitches
GPS: 53.31883, 12.94506
Post Code: D-17237

Zwenzow, Mecklenburg-West Pomerania

Camping Zwenzower Ufer

www.alanrogers.com/de38150
info@haveltourist.de
Tel: 03981 24790
www.haveltourist.de

Open (Touring Pitches):
1 April - 2 November.

On the edge of Zwenzower village, this is a small, attractive, well-kept campsite with 65 touring pitches. It slopes gently down to the banks of Grosser Labussee which is suitable for swimming, is connected to other lakes and where motorboats are permitted. The site has direct access to the lake and a separate lakeside area is reserved for FKK guests. The pitches (60-100 sq.m) are level and all have 16A electricity and are on grass; many have views over the lake and there is good tree shade over parts of the site. Access to the lake is between two reed beds where there is a small jetty and a slide leading into the water. From here, small boats can be launched into the lake. Adjacent is a playground and a generous grassy area for sunbathing, lazing around and enjoying the view over the lake. With its waterway connection to other lakes in the region, it is a popular stopover site for canoeists, in addition, boats can be hired from the site.

The traditional sanitary facilities are heated and well maintained with controllable showers (payment by key). Facilities for disabled visitors. Washing machine and dryer. Motorhome services. Small shop/snack bar in reception. Playground. Limited entertainment. Fishing. Bicycle hire. Boat launching. WiFi over most of site (charged).

Key Features

- Pets Accepted
- Disabled Facilities
- Play Area
- Bike Hire
- Fishing

Scan me for more information.

Alan Rogers Code: DE38420
15 accommodations
150 pitches
GPS: 51.86929, 13.98039
Post Code: D-03222

Lübbenau, Brandenburg

www.alanrogers.com/de38420
info@spreewaldcamping.de
Tel: 03542 3533
spreewaldcamping-schloss.de

Open (Touring Pitches):
All year.

Camping am Schlosspark

With a delightful waterside and woodland setting, Spreewald-Natur-Camping "Am Schlosspark" is about ten minutes walk from the centre of the much-visited old town of Lübbenau, on the banks of the Hauptspree. There are 150 units (they may be rather close together at very busy times), all with 16A electricity connections, and six now have water and waste water. They are mainly on flat grass but with a central hardstanding area for motorhomes and a long area for tents at the end. At public holidays and during the high season, the site can be very busy and facilities may be stretched. You can paddle your own boat, go for a trip in a gondola, explore the Spreewald Biosphere Nature Reserve or just look round the interesting old town from this pleasant site. A public path passes between the site and the river; insect repellent is advisable.

The refurbished, heated sanitary facilities are quite good with free hot water for the washbasins (some private cabins), but the showers require tokens from reception. Facilities for disabled visitors. Motorhome services. Kitchen. Laundry. Small shop for basics at reception (all year). Fresh bread and breakfast available. Small play area. Boat and bicycle hire. Fishing.

Key Features

- Open All Year
- Play Area
- Bike Hire
- Fishing

Scan me for more information.

Alan Rogers Code: DE39120
110 accommodations
140 pitches
GPS: 51.68848, 11.11076
Post Code: D-06485

Quedlinburg OT Gernrode,
Saxony-Anhalt

www.alanrogers.com/de39120
harz-camp-bremer-teich@web.de
Tel: 03948 560810
harz-camp-gernrode.de

Open (Touring Pitches):
All year.

Harz Camp Bremer Teich

Adjacent to the four-hectare Bremer Teich lake in Saxony-Anhalt, and with views of the Harz mountains, this idyllic site has been extensively upgraded in recent years. There are 140 level touring pitches (80 sq.m), the majority with 16A electricity, and 20 fully serviced. The main attraction is the lake, whose shallow banks make it suitable for paddling, and a lifeguard is present in high season. It is an ideal base for visiting the local area, in particular, the medieval town of Quedlinburg, a UNESCO World Heritage town with half-timbered houses, castle and cathedral. Accommodation on site includes cottages and a hostel, making it a popular destination for groups and school trips.

Renovated sanitary blocks can be heated and have hot showers, private cabins, family shower room and facilities for children and disabled visitors. Washing machines. Motorhome services. Shop (1/5-31/10). Restaurant (15/4-31/10). Lake swimming. Playground. Fishing.

Key Features

- Open All Year
- Pets Accepted
- Disabled Facilities
- Swimming Pool
- Play Area
- Bar/Restaurant
- Skiing
- Fishing

Scan me for more information.

Alan Rogers Code: DE37150
100 accommodations
183 pitches
GPS: 49.08285, 12.85224
Post Code: D-94234

Viechtach, Bavaria (N)

Kanus Viechtach

www.alanrogers.com/de37150
viechtach@knauscamp.de
Tel: 09942 1095
www.knauscamp.de

Open (Touring Pitches):
All year.

Camping-Park Viechtach, although reached via a small industrial area, is a relaxing place at which to stay, well laid out in a woodland setting on the edge of the village. The various trees and shrubs give a garden effect and there is good shade in most parts. A tarmac road winds its way between the grass pitches (most terraced) which are separated by rocks and trees and marked by plaques. There are 263 pitches (183 for touring units), all with 6A electricity, and size varies from small for some motorhomes to quite large for bigger units (100 sq.m). Whether for a night stop or for a longer stay to visit the Bavarian Forest, this site is well worth considering.

Two heated sanitary blocks, one central to the touring pitches, the other at the top end of the site on the ground floor of a larger building, with a drying room. Facilities are similar with washbasins (some private cabins), sinks and showers. Washing machines, dryers and irons. Gas supplies. Bread to order. Attractive bar/restaurant. Small shop. Heated indoor pool with sauna and solarium. Playgrounds for all ages. Bicycle hire. Two small games rooms. Large screen TV. WiFi (charged).

Key Features

- Open All Year
- Pets Accepted
- Disabled Facilities
- Swimming Pool
- Play Area
- Bar/Restaurant
- Bike Hire

Scan me for more information.

Alan Rogers Code: DE37050
100 accommodations
222 pitches
GPS: 48.74886, 13.81723
Post Code: D-94089

Neureichenau, Bavaria (S)

www.alanrogers.com/de37050
lackenhaeuser@knauscamp.de
Tel: 08583 311
www.knauscamp.de

Open (Touring Pitches):
All year.

Kanus Lackenhäuser

This extensive site is some 40 km. from Passau, right at the southeast tip of Germany - the border with Austria runs through one side of the site and the Czech Republic is very close too. It is a very popular site and reservations may be advisable from mid-June to September and it is very busy in winter with skiing and other winter activities. Mainly on sloping ground with good views from some parts, it has 400 pitches with terracing in some areas, nearly all for touring units, and 100 seasonal pitches. Electricity connections (16A) are available and water points are fed from pure springs. An area provides 50 pitches for motorhomes, all with electricity and some fully serviced. The site is open all year and has much winter sports trade, with its own ski lift. It is a most pleasant site in a beautiful setting with 7 km. of walks available within the campsite perimeters and an attractive fishing lake.

Three sanitary buildings are of good quality with some washbasins in cabins and underfloor heating for cool weather. Baby room. Laundry. Gas supplies. Motorhome services. Cooking facilities. Supermarket (1/12-31/10). Restaurant/bar (1/12-31/10). Hairdressing salon. General room for young. Caravan shop. Heated indoor pool (free) with child's pool, sauna and fitness room, and an outdoor spring water pool. Sauna, fitness room and massage. Small lake (ice sports in winter). Fishing. Bowling. Church. Organised activities (July/Aug. and Xmas). Ski hire. Dog free area.

Key Features

- Open All Year
- Pets Accepted
- Disabled Facilities
- Swimming Pool
- Play Area
- Bar/Restaurant
- Skiing
- Bike Hire

Scan me for more information.

Alan Rogers Code: DE37200
7 accommodations
100 pitches
GPS: 49.06959, 11.96204
Post Code: D-93188

Pielenhofen, Bavaria (S)

www.alanrogers.com/de37200
camping.pielenhofen@t-online.de
Tel: 094 093 73
www.camping-pielenhofen.de

Open (Touring Pitches):
All year.

Campingplatz Naabtal

International Camping Naabtal is an attractive riverside site in a beautiful tree-covered valley and makes an excellent base for exploring the ancient city of Regensburg on the Danube and other areas of this interesting part of Germany. It is also a good overnight site for those wishing to visit or pass through Austria or the Czech Republic. The best 100 of the 270 pitches, all with electricity, are reserved for touring units. They are mainly located on the banks of the river on flat or gently sloping ground under willow and other trees. This is good walking and biking country with many marked trails. Small boats can be launched on the placid river (where you may also swim at your own risk) and there are two good-sized tennis courts. Reception will advise on local excursions, walks, cycle routes, canoeing and other sports.

---

2 good sanitary blocks are part of larger buildings and there is a newer block for the tent area. Some washbasins are in cabins, showers are on payment. First-class unit for disabled campers. Washing machines and dryers. Gas supplies. Motorhome services. Sauna and solarium. Bar/restaurant (1/4-31/10 plus Xmas/New Year). Small shop (Easter-end Sept). Playground with imaginative apparatus. Large meeting room. Tennis. Bicycle hire. Fishing (permit required). Small boats on the river. Electric barbecues are not permitted. WiFi (free).

Key Features

- Open All Year
- Pets Accepted
- Disabled Facilities
- Play Area
- Bar/Restaurant
- Bike Hire
- Fishing

Scan me for more information.

Alan Rogers Code: DE34650
100 accommodations
280 pitches
GPS: 47.71459, 9.40924
Post Code: D-88677

Markdorf, Baden-Württemberg

Camping Wirthshof

www.alanrogers.com/de34650
info@wirthshof.de
Tel: 07544 96270
www.wirthshof.de

Open (Touring Pitches):
15 January - 15 December.

Lying 7 km. back from the Bodensee, 12 km. from Friedrichshafen, this friendly site with excellent facilities will be of interest to families with young children as well as those seeking a tranquil holiday in a delightful region. The 280 individual touring pitches have electrical connections (6-12A) and are of about 80 sq.m. on well-tended flat grass, adjoining access roads. There are 78 larger (120 sq.m) pitches with water, wastewater and electricity and 30 hardstandings for motorhomes. Dogs are only accepted by prior arrangement, on pitches in a reserved area. Many activities are organised and a multi-crafts room offers creative activities for children of all ages during wet weather. On-site is a pleasant heated outdoor pool with a grassy, shaded relaxation area; it is free to campers but is also open to outsiders on payment so can be busy in season.

Three heated toilet blocks provide washbasins in cubicles, a unit for disabled visitors and two bathrooms for children. Cosmetic studio. New beauty spa. Solar heated unit for dishwashing and laundry. Gas supplies. Motorhome services. Shop. Restaurant/bar with takeaway. Swimming pool (25x12.5 m; 10/5-10/9). Sports field. Adventure playgrounds. Bicycle and e-bike hire. Minigolf and 'pit-pat' (crazy golf played at table height with billiard cues). Activity programme. Crafts room. WiFi (charged). Dogs are not accepted in July/Aug.

Key Features

- Pets Accepted
- Disabled Facilities
- Swimming Pool
- Play Area
- Bar/Restaurant
- Bike Hire

Scan me for more information.

Alan Rogers Code: DE34050
100 accommodations
150 pitches
GPS: 48.77910, 8.73111
Post Code: D-75378

Bad Liebenzell, Baden-Württemberg

www.alanrogers.com/de34050
info@campingpark-bad-liebenzell.com
Tel: 070 529 34060
campingpark-bad-liebenzell.com

Open (Touring Pitches):
All Year

Bad Liebenzell

Privately owned, this former municipal site is attractively situated on the outskirts of the pleasant little spa town of Bad Liebenzell in the northeast Black Forest. The 250 pitches (150 for touring units) all have 16A electricity and are neatly arranged in rows on flat grass between hedges, trees and the good access roads. This is a well run and orderly site. The site is often full in high season when a reservation is advisable (if not reserved arrive early). There may be some noise from the nearby roads and railway. There is direct access to an excellent, large, heated swimming pool complex which is free to campers. This includes swimming pools, a wave pool and a long slide. There is also a children's pool and grassy sunbathing area and several tennis courts.

Two toilet blocks are well maintained with washbasins mostly in cabins in two blocks, showers mainly in the end building. Provision for disabled visitors. Washing machines and dryers. Cooking facilities. Gas supplies. Motorhome services. Bar/restaurant and takeaway (15/4-15/09). Supermarket next door. Swimming pool complex (01/5-01/9). Café/bar by pool. Large room with TV. Tennis court. Fly fishing. Playground. WiFi entire site (charged).

Key Features

- Open All Year
- Pets Accepted
- Disabled Facilities
- Swimming Pool
- Play Area
- Bar/Restaurant
- Fishing

Scan me for more information.

Alan Rogers Code: DE32600
8 accommodations
280 pitches
GPS: 49.47380, 8.19170
Post Code: D-67098

Bad Dürkheim, Rhineland Palatinate

www.alanrogers.com/de32600
badduerkheim@knauscamp.de
Tel: 06322 61356
www.knauscamp.de

Open (Touring Pitches):
All year (reduced facilities in November).

Knaus Bad Dürkheim

This is a large, comfortable site with almost 600 pitches, half of which are for touring. Being situated in Bad Dürkheim, which claims to have the world's largest wine festival, it can understandably become quite full in high season. The site is arranged either side of a long, central arcade of growing vines and along one side of the site there is a lake. Growing trees provide some shade and electrical connections are available throughout (16A). There is some noise from light aircraft, especially at weekends. Bathing is possible in the lake, which has a mostly sandy floor. There is a little beach and non-powered boats can be launched. An activity programme offers guided tours, biking, canoeing and climbing. This is essentially a wine growing region with lots of attractive villages to visit and an almost endless variety of wines to try out.

Three large sanitary blocks are spaced out along the central avenue. They are of a high standard (private cabins, automatic taps etc) and are heated in cool weather. Laundry facilities. Gas supplies. Motorhome services. Cooking facilities. Shop. Restaurant, bar and takeaway (all year excl. Nov). Sports programme. Tennis. Playground. Sauna. Swimming and non-powered boats on lake. Fishing. Riding. Bicycle hire. Activity programme (guided tours, biking and climbing). WiFi on part of site (charged).

Key Features

- Open All Year
- Pets Accepted
- Disabled Facilities
- Play Area
- Bar/Restaurant
- Bike Hire
- Fishing
- Horse Riding

Scan me for more information.

Alan Rogers Code: DE32470
80 accommodations
160 pitches
GPS: 49.95883, 6.42385
Post Code: D-54636

Oberweis, Rhineland Palatinate

www.alanrogers.com/de32470
info@pruemtal.de
Tel: 06527 92920
www.pruemtal.de

Open (Touring Pitches):
All year.

Prümtal Oberweis

This is a most attractive and popular site set in a wooded valley alongside the River Prüm. The site has an excellent restaurant, pizzeria and takeaway and a beautiful heated swimming pool. 91 pitches are now fully serviced. There are 80 long-stay units grouped in a separate area at the western end of the site, with the touring area stretching out alongside the river. The 160 touring pitches are on grass, mostly separated by hedging and all with 16A electricity. Pitches vary in size (from 30-110 sq.m) and price, and there is shade from mature trees in most parts. The restaurant, which is also open to the public, is of very high quality with menus printed in German, Dutch and English, and a good range of meals to suit all tastes and budgets (all year). There is a separate bar, a pizzeria (Papa Razzo), plus a takeaway service.

New exceptional toilet block, existing high-quality block plus a third small block in season. Good motorhome service point. Small shop with a good range of food, drink and camping accessories (1/4-31/10). Restaurant, bar and pizzeria (all year). Swimming pool (seasonal). Adventure-style playground. Full-size soccer pitch and volleyball pitch. Children's entertainment in July/Aug. River fishing. WiFi throughout (free). Free walking and cycling route guides.

Key Features

- Open All Year
- Pets Accepted
- Disabled Facilities
- Swimming Pool
- Play Area
- Bar/Restaurant
- Fishing

Scan me for more information.

Alan Rogers Code: DE31900
300 accommodations
183 pitches
GPS: 51.29999, 8.25000
Post Code: D-59872

Meschede, North Rhine-Westphalia

www.alanrogers.com/de31900
hennesee@knauscamp.de
Tel: 02919 52720
www.knauscamp.de

Open (Touring Pitches):
All year.

Knaus Hennesee

Camping Hennesee can be found in the 'land of the 1,000 mountains', a beautiful part of Sauerland. The site is situated on the banks of Lake Hennesee which links the nature reserves of Arnsberger Wald and Homert. The site offers 183 grassy touring pitches (some slightly sloping), all with 6A Europlug and some with great views over the lake. Twenty-five pitches have water and drainage also. Hennesee is an ideal base for all kinds of water-based activities, such as windsurfing, fishing (permit needed) and swimming. English is spoken. On-site amenities include a supermarket and a café/restaurant with bistro and open-air terrace. The heated indoor swimming pool with sauna and solarium is open all year. Children will doubtless enjoy the playground and games room. In high season the entertainment team organises family activities including swimming competitions, party games and torch-lit processions.

Three toilet blocks have controllable showers, some washbasins in cabins, family showers and a baby room. Washing machines and dryers. Bar. Restaurant. Takeaway. TV room. Supermarket. Indoor swimming pool. Sauna. Massage. Sunbed. Infrared room. Bicycle hire. Electric cars for children. Fishing. Fully equipped tents and mobile homes to rent. WiFi (charged).

Key Features

- Open All Year
- Pets Accepted
- Swimming Pool
- Play Area
- Bar/Restaurant
- Bike Hire
- Fishing

Scan me for more information.

Alan Rogers Code: DE32100
2 accommodations
200 pitches
GPS: 51.07529, 7.85323
Post Code: D-57462

Olpe-Sondern, North Rhine-Westphalia

www.alanrogers.com/de32100
info@biggesee.com
Tel: 02761 944111
biggesee.freizeit-oasen.de

Open (Touring Pitches):
All Year.

Camping Biggesee

Situated on a gentle, south-facing slope that leads down to the water's edge of the Biggesee, Feriencamp Biggesee blends in well with its wooded surroundings. The 200 touring pitches, all with electricity, are arranged in circles at the top part of the site and on a series of wide terraces lower down. They are grassy with some hardstanding. From the lower part of the site, there is access through a gate to a large open meadow that ends at the water's edge where swimming is permitted. The attractive Biggesee, with arms branching out into the surrounding hills, is a watersports paradise where virtually all forms of watersports are available. These include schools for sailing, diving and windsurfing. Close by, hundreds of kilometres of paths and cycleway lead along the lakeside and through the surrounding forests.

Excellent heated sanitary facilities are in two areas. New building with cabins for hire. Many washbasins in cabins and special showers for children. Facilities for babies and campers with disabilities. Laundry. Motorhome services. Cooking facilities. Shop. Restaurant. Bistro (including breakfast). Paintball. Water blob and Aqua park. Playroom and playground for smaller children. Grill hut. Fishing. Solarium and sauna. Entertainment and excursions. Dog shower.

Key Features

- Open All Year
- Pets Accepted
- Disabled Facilities
- Play Area
- Bar/Restaurant
- Skiing
- Fishing
- Horse Riding

Scan me for more information.

Alan Rogers Code: DE31970
26 accommodations
185 pitches
GPS: 50.41508, 6.71869
Post Code: D-53945

North Rhine-Westphalia, Eifel

Eifel-Camp

www.alanrogers.com/de31970
eifel-camp@freizeit-oasen.de
Tel: 026 97 282
www.eifel-camp.de

Open (Touring Pitches):
All Year

This delightful campsite offers spaciously arranged pitches on terraces set amongst lush greenery. All pitches are equipped with 220V/16 A electricity connection and the long-term pitches have access to the community antenna/common aerial. You will also find a drain and service-station for caravans and campervans, as well as well-grounded pitches for campervans. Located in the northern Eifel, Eifel-Camp is situated only a few kilometres away from Blankenheim and close to Lake Freilingen in the countryside. Situated within half an hour coming from the direction of Cologne, from Aachen, Bonn and Koblenz in less than an hour, and driving from Trier will take around 1.5 hours.

Enjoy the comforts of this award-winning camping-site with facilities including a disabled bathing unit, spacious and superb bathroom/sanitary facilities with centrally heated showers providing free unlimited hot water. You may also book individual bathing units with washbasin, shower and toilet. Washing machines and tumble dryers. The popular "Waldläufer" restaurant with sun terrace. On-site kiosk offering fresh rolls and croissants in the morning, as well as basic necessities. Playground. Leisure club " Geißbock-Stadel" on the first floor of the sanitary building offering various options for guests, e.g. as a lounge or recreation room, but it can also be used for mini-club activities, the mini-disco, indoor sports activities or cinema shows. An open barbecue facility with a separate fireplace on the outskirts of the campsite, or a small complete BBQ-cabin in the upper part of the "mountain pasture" offering room for up to 24 people. There are also two BBQ-cabins (additional-charge).

Key Features

- Open All Year
- Pets Accepted
- Disabled Facilities
- Play Area
- Bar/Restaurant
- Bike Hire

Scan me for more information.

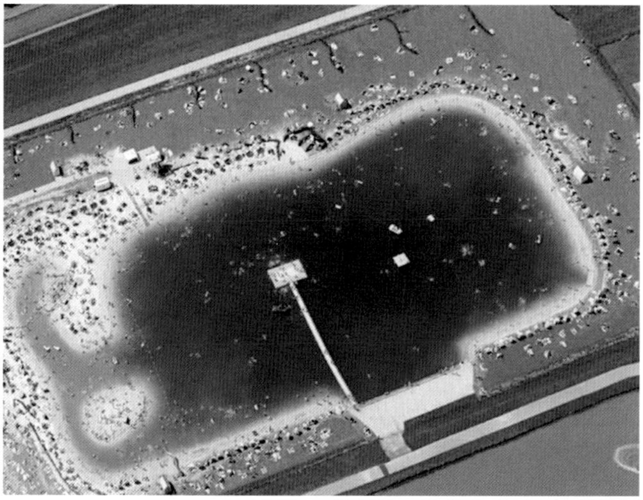

Alan Rogers Code: DE28350
250 accommodations
110 pitches
GPS: 53.58333, 8.37028
Post Code: D-26969

Burhave, Lower Saxony

www.alanrogers.com/de28350
burhave@knauscamp.de
Tel: 04733 1683
www.knauscamp.de

Open (Touring Pitches):
2 April - 15 October.

Knaus Burhave

Knaus Campingpark Burhave actually comprises three campsites: one for seasonals, one for motorhomes and an area for tourers (where dogs are welcome) with a separate tent field. It is on the North Sea peninsula of Butjadingen, in close proximity to the Wadden Sea National Park. The 110 motorhome pitches are neither marked nor numbered, but all have 16A electricity, water and drainage, and most enjoy good views over the beach. The whole site is rather open and can become a suntrap in hot weather. There is an enclosed area with an artificial lake for safe swimming, where beach chairs can be hired. Burhave Strand is an excellent location for a beach holiday, but also for walking and cycling through beautiful verdant countryside. Close to the site (200 m) is a 'Spielscheune', an indoor playground, while the Nordsee Blue Lagoon with its water castle, pirate ship and slide is within walking distance. On-site there is a beach café with fish stand and open-air terrace with good views. Other possibilities for eating and drinking can be found in the village of Burhave.

Three toilet blocks, one older style and one prefabricated, have some washbasins in cabins, controllable hot showers, baby room and excellent children's section. Facilities for disabled visitors. Washing machine and dryer. Bar with terrace and takeaway. Beach volleyball. Basketball. WiFi (charged).

Key Features

- Pets Accepted
- Disabled Facilities
- Beach Access
- Play Area
- Bike Hire
- Fishing

Scan me for more information.

Alan Rogers Code: DE30250
104 accommodations
375 pitches
GPS: 52.48555, 7.99003
Post Code: D-49597

Lower Saxony, Osnabrück

Alfsee Erlebnispark

www.alanrogers.com/de30250
info@alfsee.de
Tel: +49 (0)5464 92 120
www.alfsee.de

Open (Touring Pitches):
All Year

Alfsee has plenty to offer for the active family and children of all ages. It is a really good base for enjoying the many recreational activities available here on the lake. The smaller lake has a 780 m. water ski cableway (on payment) and there is also a separate swimming area with a sandy beach. The Alfsee itself is now a nature reserve. Many birdwatching excursions are organised by the site. Improvements to this already well equipped site continue. There are now over 750 pitches (many long stay but with 375 for touring units) on flat grass, all with 16A electricity, with some shade for those in the original area. A new camping area provides 290 large pitches. A member of Leading Campings group.

Five excellent heated sanitary blocks with family bathrooms (to rent), baby rooms and laundry facilities. Cooking facilities. Dishwashers. Motorhome services. Gas supplies. Shop, restaurants and takeaway (high season). Watersports. Playground, new indoor play centre (on payment) and entertainment for children. Entertainment hall. Grass tennis courts. Trampoline. Minigolf. Go-kart track. Games room. Fishing. Bicycle and E-bike hire. Free WiFi throughout.

Key Features

- Open All Year
- Pets Accepted
- Disabled Facilities
- Swimming Pool
- Play Area
- Bar/Restaurant
- Bike Hire
- Fishing

Scan me for more information.

Alan Rogers Code: DE30850
38 accommodations
85 pitches
GPS: 52.99987, 10.51612
Post Code: D-29525

Westerweyhe/Uelzen, Lower Saxony

Uhlenköper Camping

www.alanrogers.com/de30850
info@uhlenkoeper-camp.de
Tel: 05817 3044
www.uhlenkoeper-camp.de

Open (Touring Pitches):
All year.

The Körding family have owned this site since 2001 and have recently been joined by their son and his family to further improve the site. Their efforts are evident with electricity connections, water taps and 85 touring pitches. Of these, 40 are fully serviced with 16A electricity, water and drainage. The pitches are arranged in seven grassy areas, each taking eight to ten units, with a separate field to one side for cyclists. Pitches are 80-100 sq.m. with shade from high bushes and some trees. To the rear of the site are some rental and private static caravans. The site also features some genuinely innovative glamping options. In May the site celebrates the Schützenfestival, a traditional German shoot with revolvers and rifles with a party afterwards and traditional local dishes. In September, this whole region celebrates the Heidebluten festival where a new Moor Queen and her opponent, the Heideböck, are chosen.

Sanitary facilities are provided in the reception building where good amenities include British style toilets, free hot showers and washbasins in cabins. Facilities for disabled visitors. A second, older block to one side has toilets and a laundry. Motorhome services. Bar/restaurant, small shop for basics and a takeaway (all 1/3-31/12) and a library. Internet. Swimming pool (1/6-31/8). Basic playground. Playing field. Canoe hire. Animal farm. Some entertainment organised. Torch useful.

Key Features

- Open All Year
- Pets Accepted
- Disabled Facilities
- Swimming Pool
- Play Area
- Bar/Restaurant
- Skiing
- Bike Hire

Scan me for more information.

Llanddwyn Island, Anglesey >

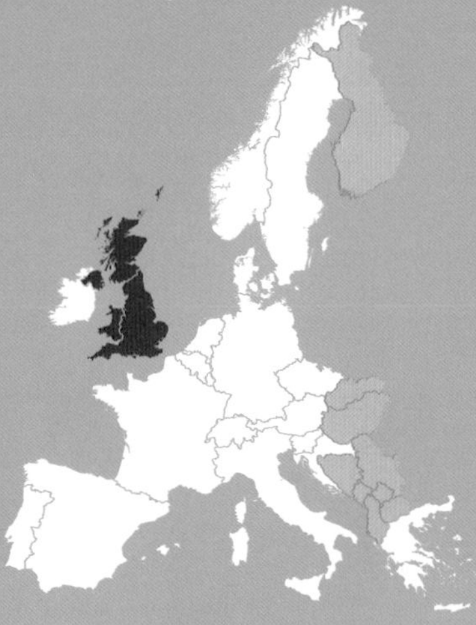

Capital London
Currency British Pound (£)
Language English
Time Zone GMT
Telephone Code 00 44

Tourist Website
visitbritain.com

Climate Varied and hard to predict but generally mild in the summer with temperatures into the high 20s and cooler and wetter in the winter months.

Public Holidays New Year's Day, Good Friday, Easter Monday, Early May Bank Holiday 6 May, Spring Bank Holiday 27 May, Summer Bank Holiday 26 August, Christmas Day, Boxing Day.

Motoring Driving is on the left and imperial measurements for road signs are used. The speed limit on motorways is 70mph. When using motorways never use the hard shoulder unless instructed to or if you break down (in this situation turn on your hazard lights). Tailgating is illegal as is drink driving, smoking in the car with under 18s present and using your mobile phone while driving unless it is hands-free.

See campsite map page

480

Eastern England A perfect mix of gentle countryside and sleepy villages, it's an unspoilt region with endless skies, inland waterways and traditional beach resorts.

Western England A region of contrasts, with windswept moorlands and dramatic cliffs towering above beautiful sandy beaches.

Wales Wales boasts a diverse landscape, from lakes, mountains, rivers and valleys to beautiful coastlines and rolling wooded countryside.

Scotland From gentle rolling hills and rugged coastlines, to dramatic peaks punctuated with beautiful lochs, Scotland is an untamed land steeped in history.

Northern Ireland From wild coastlines to green valleys, rugged mountains and shimmering lakes, to the natural phenomenon of the Giant's Causeway, Northern Ireland is crammed full of sights.

View all campsites in Great Britain
alanrogers.com/northern-ireland
alanrogers.com/scotland
alanrogers.com/england
alanrogers.com/wales

Great Britain

The United Kingdom offers a wealth of extraordinary landscapes set against the backdrop of rich and vibrant history. In terms of character and stunning scenery, it offers an unsurpassed choice of holiday activities from coast to country.

Northern England A beautiful and varied region of rolling hills and undulating moors, along with a wealth of industrial heritage and undiscovered countryside. The Yorkshire Moors, the Cumbrian lakes, -the Northumbrian ancient forts and fairytale castles, these are all highlights not to be missed.

Southern England Rich in maritime heritage and historical attractions, the southern region comprises tranquil English countryside replete with picture postcard villages, ancient towns, formidable castles and grand stately homes, coupled with a beautiful coastline, white-faced cliffs and lively seaside resorts.

Heart of England Spanning central England, from the ancient borders of Wales in the west across to Lincolnshire on the east coast, the Heart of England is rich in glorious rolling countryside, magnificent castles and fine stately homes.

Alan Rogers Code: UK0190
3 accommodations
37 pitches
GPS: 50.32759, -4.62515
Post Code: PL23 1QH

Polruan-By-Fowey, Cornwall

Polruan Holidays

www.alanrogers.com/uk0190
polholiday@aol.com
Tel: 01726 870263
www.polruanholidays.co.uk

Open (Touring Pitches):
1 April - 27 September

Polruan is a rural site in an elevated position on the opposite side of the river to Fowey and 200 metres from the Coastal Path. There are marvellous sea views. This is a well maintained, delightful little site with just 37 touring pitches and three holiday caravans to let. The holiday homes are arranged in a neat circle, with a central area for seven adults-only tourer pitches on gravel hardstanding, all with 16A electricity and one fully serviced. An adjacent meadow has 15 pitches for motorhomes and tents, all with power and a third area has ten tent-only pitches (eight with electricity). This park is in a popular tourist area, within walking distance down a steep hill to the village and the passenger ferry to Fowey. A raised picnic area gives more views across the estuary to Fowey. A member of the Countryside Discovery group.

The fully equipped, heated toilet block has modern, controllable showers large enough for an adult and child. Laundry room. Range of recycling bins. Reception with a small terrace and shop for everyday items. Gas. Microwave. Hot drinks machine and freezer for ice packs. Sloping field area with swings for children. Max. 2 dogs. Free phone charging. WiFi throughout (free).

Key Features

- Pets Accepted
- Play Area

Scan me for more information.

Alan Rogers Code: UK0220
26 accommodations
611 pitches
GPS: 50.38498, -5.12893
Post Code: TR8 5PW

Newquay, Cornwall

www.alanrogers.com/uk0220
bookings@trevornick.co.uk
Tel: 01637 830531
www.trevornick.co.uk

Open (Touring Pitches):
5 April - 30 September

Trevornick Holiday Park

Trevornick, once a working farm, is a busy and well run family touring park providing an extensive range of amenities, close to one of Cornwall's most beautiful beaches. A modern reception with welcoming staff sets the tone for your holiday. The park is well managed with facilities and standards monitored continuously. It has grown to provide pitches for caravanners and campers, 36 very well equipped Eurotents, there are 26 static caravans with decking areas (new in 2018) The 600 large grass pitches (589 with the option of semi-hardstanding, water, grey waste drainage,16A electricity and TV connection) are laid out on five level fields and two terraced areas. There are few trees but some excellent views. This site is also a member of the Best of British group.

Five modern shower/toilet blocks, latest with heated floor. Two family bathrooms, disabled toilet. Laundry block including washers/dryers/ironing/handwash facilities. Well stocked Farm Shop and Hire Shop including Bike Hire. Bars (with TV), a restaurant, café and takeaway. Kids and adult entertainment programmes (seasonal). Kids activities (seasonal). Outdoor heated pool, children's paddling pool. Tranquility Spa, jacuzzi, solarium, and sauna. Adventure Forest Trail, Wild Tribe kids club and outdoor park. Amusement arcade and toddlers indoor soft play. Stunning Par 3 Golf Course, 18-hole Pitch and Putt and newly added Mini Golf. Plus three fully-stocked coarse fishing lakes. Free site wide Wifi.

Key Features

- Pets Accepted
- Disabled Facilities
- Swimming Pool
- Play Area
- Bar/Restaurant
- Bike Hire
- Fishing
- Golf

Scan me for more information.

Alan Rogers Code: UK0681
7 accommodations
110 pitches
GPS: 51.20484, -4.06417
Post Code: EX34 9SH

Ilfracombe, Devon

www.alanrogers.com/uk0681
enquiries@millpark.com
Tel: 01271 882647
www.millpark.com

Open (Touring Pitches):
31 March - 31 October

Mill Park

Mill Park is a sheltered touring caravan and camping site set in an attractive wooded valley on the North Devon Coast. It has a shop, a takeaway, games room, laundry, and has many other useful facilities such as gas-changing and ice pack freezing. Several glamping options are available on-site, including three bell tents and three glamping pods. There is also an on-site pub. It's surrounded by attractive woodland and is an ideal family site as it's just a short walk to quiet beaches, both sand and pebble. Equally close by is the unspoilt and breathtaking beauty of Exmoor and the nearest village, Berrynarbor is just a five-minute walk from the site. This village dates back from the sixteenth century and earlier. There is a quaint old country pub, village stores and post office. Buses also pass by the site regularly. They cater very well for families and couples, and they do all possible to create a friendly, relaxed atmosphere.

2 Separate shower blocks - both recently refurbished and kept impeccably clean, onsite bar, well-stocked shop, fishing lake, small river flowing through the park, children's play area, games room, book swap, games library, free Internet in bar and games room. Close to beaches, secluded and quiet, very peaceful.

Key Features

- Pets Accepted
- Disabled Facilities
- Play Area
- Bar/Restaurant
- Fishing

Scan me for more information.

Alan Rogers Code: UK0802
25 accommodations
40 pitches
GPS: 50.54490, -4.08417
Post Code: PL19 9JZ

Tavistock, Devon

www.alanrogers.com/uk0802
jane@langstonemanor.co.uk
Tel: 01822 613371
www.langstonemanor.co.uk

Open (Touring Pitches):
21 March - 31 October

Langstone Manor Park

Situated on the southwest edge of Dartmoor, this holiday park has been developed in the grounds of the old Langstone Manor house. The touring pitches are tucked into various garden areas with mature trees and flowering shrubs, or in the walled garden area with views over the moor. In all, there are 40 level grass pitches which vary in size (35 with 16A electricity). A new camping area is popular and has been terraced with open views over farmland and the moor. You pass by some holiday caravans on the way to reception and the touring pitches, where you will also find some holiday cottages and flats to rent.

The facilities provided are to a very high standard and include a bathroom and private cabins. Laundry. Changing mats for babies are in both the men's and ladies' rooms. A private bathroom is available. Basic supplies kept in reception (order bread the day before). Bar & restaurant serving evening meals. Games room. Play area. Outdoor table tennis. Camping pods for hire.

Key Features

- Pets Accepted
- Disabled Facilities
- Play Area
- Bar/Restaurant

Scan me for more information.

Alan Rogers Code: UK2350
110 pitches
GPS: 50.88392, -1.73470
Post Code: BH24 3QT

Ringwood, Hampshire

www.alanrogers.com/uk2350
enquiries@redshoot-campingpark.com
Tel: 01425 473789
www.redshoot-campingpark.com

Open (Touring Pitches):
1 March - 31 October

Red Shoot Camping Park

Red Shoot is set in the heart of the New Forest, on four acres of level and slightly sloping grass meadows. A simple, rural retreat with panoramic views of the surrounding countryside and forest, it is very popular in high season. A cattle grid at the entrance keeps the New Forest animals outside the park. There are 110 good sized pitches, 50 with 10A electricity, served by a gravel access road. There is no site lighting, so a torch would be useful. The adjacent Red Shoot Inn (separate ownership) serves meals and brews its own real ales – Forest Gold and Tom's Tipple. There are ample opportunities for walking, cycling and naturalist pursuits in the area. Local attractions include watersports at the New Forest Water Park near Ringwood, a Doll Museum in Fordingbridge, cider making in Burley, and Breamore House just north of Fordingbridge. Nearby Ringwood has a market on Wednesday.

The toilet and shower facilities have been upgraded to a high standard with underfloor heating, a family shower room with baby bath and changing area. Well equipped laundry room. Good unit for disabled visitors. Very well stocked, licensed shop with fresh bread and croissants. Bar. Fenced adventure-style playground.

Key Features

- Pets Accepted
- Disabled Facilities
- Play Area
- Bar/Restaurant

Scan me for more information.

Alan Rogers Code: UK2445
12 accommodations
30 pitches
GPS: 50.63645, -1.40722
Post Code: PO30 4DA

Brighstone, Isle of Wight

Grange Farm Brighstone Bay

www.alanrogers.com/uk2445
grangefarmholidays@googlemail.com
Tel: 01983 740296
www.grangefarmholidays.com

Open (Touring Pitches):
1 March - 31 October.

This is a small, family-run working farm, with many unusual, friendly animals including Alpacas, pigs, goats, pony, horse, water buffalo, donkey, poultry etc. and small pets. Level pitches (some with electricity) are available for tents, caravans, campers and motorhomes; hardstanding with water is also available. Those looking for accommodation rental options can choose from pods, mobile homes or cottages. This is one of the few unspoilt, non-commercialised coastal sites with unpolluted sea air, situated on the beautiful south-west coast, with easy access to a sandy beach and picturesque views of the Chine and Brighstone Forest. The whole area is ideal for cycling, fishing, fossil hunting, and is a walkers paradise.

Heated sanitary facilities. Washing machines, dryers and irons. Shop (all season). WiFi throughout (charged - free in accommodation). Local Pub & shops 15 minutes walk in Brighstone Village. Large Indoor swimming pool 10 minutes drive away in Freshwater (childrens pool/diving board etc.) Launch onsite (they get quite a few canoe arrivals).

Key Features

- Pets Accepted
- Beach Access
- Play Area
- Fishing

Scan me for more information.

Alan Rogers Code: UK1510
2 accommodations
47 pitches
GPS: 51.33658, -2.59718
Post Code: BS39 5TZ

Bishop Sutton, Somerset

www.alanrogers.com/uk1510
enquiries@bathchewvalley.co.uk
Tel: 01275 332127
www.bathchewvalley.co.uk

Open (Touring Pitches):
All year.

Bath Chew Valley

A small and secluded garden site for adults only, Bath Chew Valley has been developed with much tender love and care by the Betton family, who are rightly proud of their David Bellamy Gold award. Hardstanding pitches are sited amongst colourful beds of flowers, shrubs and trees. Cars are tucked away on the nearby car park, providing a tranquil and restful atmosphere. An area of woodland is adjacent with an enclosed dog walking area called Puppies' Parade. The warden will assist you in placing your caravan. There are 30 spacious, fully serviced pitches, all with 16A electricity connections. Two timber lodges are available to rent and are proving very popular, so must be booked in advance. The site is affiliated to the Caravan and Motorhome Club. A member of the Best of British group.

The refurbished, heated toilet block , provides all the fittings that make life comfortable – separate en-suite units each with WC, basin and shower. One unit has facilities for disabled visitors. Useful utility room with sinks, coin-operated washer/dryers and ironing facilities, service washes are also available. Free use of freezer. Motorhome services. Internet access. WiFi over site (charged). Car hire. Max. 2 dogs.

Key Features

- 18+ Adults Only
- Open All Year
- Pets Accepted
- Disabled Facilities

Scan me for more information.

Alan Rogers Code: UK2572
39 accommodations
187 pitches
GPS: 51.54594, -0.90504
Post Code: RG9 2HY

Henley-On-Thames, Oxfordshire

www.alanrogers.com/uk2572
info@swissfarmhenley.co.uk
Tel: 01491 573419
www.swissfarmcamping.co.uk

Open (Touring Pitches):
1 March - 30 November

Swiss Farm Touring Site

Nestling at the foot of the Chiltern Hills and just a short stroll from Henley-on-Thames, Swiss Farm is ideally located for those seeking either a relaxing or an active break. The site can offer quiet, communal-style pitches or the more family orientated field type. Of the 187 pitches, 156 have 10A electricity, 62 are hardstandings, and 55 are fully serviced with 16A electricity and a TV point. A large central area contains 39 seasonal pitches. This park boasts a heated outdoor, supervised pool, bar and patio barbecue. Reception includes a small shop selling basic provisions. There is an adventure-style wooden children's play area. Not open December to March. Just ten minutes walk on a footpath is Henley-on-Thames, and there is a bus stop at the site entrance providing services to Wycombe, Marlow, Reading and Henley. Trains from nearby Twyford station take you directly to London's Paddington Station in 40 minutes.

Two fully equipped toilet blocks. One private bathroom. Free showers. Facilities for disabled campers. Baby facilities. Launderette. Basic shop in reception for camping essentials. Bar. Supervised swimming pool. Play area. Patio barbecue. Coarse fishing. WiFi. Dogs welcome in low season only.

Key Features

- Pets Accepted
- Disabled Facilities
- Swimming Pool
- Play Area
- Bar/Restaurant
- Fishing

Scan me for more information.

Alan Rogers Code: UK3250
20 accommodations
160 pitches
GPS: 51.65398, -0.00652
Post Code: E4 7RA

Chingford, London

www.alanrogers.com/uk3250
sewardstonecampsite@leevalleypark.org.uk
Tel: 02085 295689
www.visitleevalley.org.uk

Open (Touring Pitches):
1 March - 31 January

Lee Valley - Sewardstone

This attractive site provides an excellent base from which to visit London, having both easy access to the M25 and excellent public transport links into the centre of London. Close to Epping Forest in the heart of the Lee Valley, this site is on a hillside overlooking the King George reservoir in an enjoyable and relaxed setting. Like its sister sites, it is understandably very popular with overseas tourers. With capacity for 160 units, the site is mostly level, with several bush sheltered avenues and plenty of trees throughout providing shade. There are 65 pitches with hardstanding and 80 with 10A electricity. American motorhomes are welcome. Just outside the gate is a bus stop (May-September; reception have full details of good value Travelcard schemes). The bus (no. 215) will take you to Walthamstow Central Underground station from where a frequent service runs to central London. Alternatively, you can park at South Woodford or Chingford stations and use the train for London visits. Accommodation is available to rent. Staff are charming and helpful.

Two recently refurbished blocks offer good facilities (one is heated in low season). Good en-suite room for disabled visitors. Baby changing area. Laundry. Motorhome services. Well stocked shop. Takeaway food van 3 times a week. Gas available. Playground. Accommodation to rent. WiFi (charged).

Key Features

- Pets Accepted
- Disabled Facilities
- Play Area

Scan me for more information.

Alan Rogers Code: UK2915
66 pitches
GPS: 50.81358, 0.32448
Post Code: BN24 5NG

Pevensey, East Sussex

www.alanrogers.com/uk2915
enquiries@fairfieldsfarm.com
Tel: 01323 763165
www.fairfieldsfarm.com

Open (Touring Pitches):
End-March - End-October.

Fairfields Farm

Part of a working, family-run farm, this is a simple, peaceful park which is ideally located to enjoy the Sussex countryside and coast, just a short distance from Eastbourne. A single, rectangular meadow is split by a line of attractive silver birch trees and provides 66 large grass pitches, all but four with electricity connections. The farm and its rural landscape stretch towards the sea at Pevensey Bay. Beyond the camping field, there is a duck pond with grassy surrounds and picnic benches, pens with numerous small animals and pets and a pleasant walk to a fishing lake.

The single, central toilet block is traditional in style and very clean. An adjacent building houses showers and toilets for disabled visitors. Laundry facilities. Well stocked farm shop selling local produce. Small animals and pets. Fishing lake (licence required). WiFi throughout (free). Vans, commercial or sign-written vehicles are not accepted.

Key Features

- Pets Accepted
- Disabled Facilities
- Fishing

Scan me for more information.

Alan Rogers Code: UK3290
70 pitches
GPS: 51.78996, 0.98460
Post Code: CO5 8FE

Colchester, Essex

www.alanrogers.com/uk3290
havefun@fenfarm.co.uk
Tel: 01206 383275
www.fenfarm.co.uk

Open (Touring Pitches):
13 March - 28 October

Fen Farm Campsite

Tents were first pitched at Fen Farm in 1923, and since then the park has 'grown rather than developed' – something of which owners Ralph and Wenda Lord and their family are proud. There are approximately 120 pitches (many seasonal) with 70 available for touring. They are all unmarked, on level grass and within four fields that have a spacious feel to them. An area for 90 privately owned holiday homes is separate and screened from the touring area. All pitches have 10A electricity connections, and three have hardstanding and are fully serviced. A limited number of seasonal pitches are available on the smaller field, with outstanding views and direct access to the beach. This is an attractive well laid out site with trees and two ponds. The site provides facilities for launching boats from the seashore, and it is popular with water-skiers and windsurfers. Jet skis are not allowed. There are also many opportunities for walking, either inland or along the beach.

The very good toilet block in the main touring field includes a family room and shower/toilet for disabled visitors. Laundry room. Gas supplies. Two play areas. Caravan and boat storage. WiFi throughout (charged).

Key Features

- Pets Accepted
- Disabled Facilities
- Beach Access
- Play Area
- Sailing

Scan me for more information.

Alan Rogers Code: UK3055
300 pitches
GPS: 51.20073, 0.39333
Post Code: TN12 6PY

Paddock Wood, Kent

The Hop Farm Campsite

www.alanrogers.com/uk3055
touring@thehopfarm.co.uk
Tel: 01622 870838
www.thehopfarm.co.uk

Open (Touring Pitches):
1 March - 30 September.

Set in 400 acres of the Garden of England, The Hop Farm Touring & Camping Park is a popular family visitor attraction. There are plenty of activities to entertain children, including adventure play areas (indoor and outdoor), a driving school, funfair rides, the Magic Factory and the Great Goblin Hunt. This is also the venue for many special events throughout the summer, including music festivals & shows. To one side, overlooking all this activity and the attractive cluster of oasts is the touring park which provides over 300 grass and hardstanding pitches on flat, open fields. Electricity (16A) and water are available. There is also plenty of space for tents. The main toilet block is clean and provides straightforward facilities, these are supplemented by prefab units when events bring extra campers. Entry to the visitor attraction is half price for caravanners and campers and includes the Shires Restaurant and the Happy Hopper's café. This park particularly suits those looking to enjoy the visitor attraction or attend one of the events.

Brand new state-of-the-art shower and washrooms have been added to the site to enhance guest experiences, providing a luxurious touch to their stay. Small shop (in reception) for essentials. Free entry for campers and caravanners to the Family Park with restaurant and café. Nature walks. Boat launching. Fishing. Dogs accepted but not permitted inside the visitor attraction. Activities and entertainment at the visitor attraction.

Key Features

- Pets Accepted
- Disabled Facilities
- Play Area
- Bar/Restaurant
- Fishing

Scan me for more information.

Alan Rogers Code: UK4081
120 pitches
GPS: 52.18347, -1.72987
Post Code: CV37 9SE

Stratford-Upon-Avon,
Warwickshire

www.alanrogers.com/uk4081
info@stratfordtouringpark.com
Tel: 01789 201063
www.stratfordtouringpark.com

Open (Touring Pitches):
Mid-March - 31 October.

Stratford Touring Park

The site is an integral part of Stratford racecourse, which has been hosting horse racing since 1755. It is located right on the edge of Stratford-upon-Avon, just one mile from its centre. All the pitches are level and set after the home straight. There are 120 touring pitches, all on level ground, of which 74 have 16A electric hookups. Stratford Racecourse Touring Park is set in the rural Warwickshire countryside, not far from the gently flowing river Avon. It is only a 20 – 30-minute pleasant walk to discover all the Shakespearean Tapestry that historic Stratford upon Avon has to offer, as well as the beautiful surrounding area. Well signposted from all major roads, the site is accessible to the largest of vehicles; it also boasts a separate area for rallies with optional room hire.

Facilities are housed within the grandstand. They comprise refurbished showers and toilets, washing up sinks and a coin-operated launderette (takes old £1 coins, available from Reception) limited facilities for disabled visitors, Calor gas sales and electric hookups.

Key Features

Pets Accepted

Scan me for more information.

Alan Rogers Code: UK3895
20 accommodations
130 pitches
GPS: 52.74443, -0.90892
Post Code: LE14 2TD

Melton Mowbary, Leicestershire

www.alanrogers.com/uk3895
info@eyekettlebylakes.com
Tel: 01664 565900
www.eyekettlebylakes.com

Open (Touring Pitches):
All year.

Eye Kettleby Lakes

Set in the rolling Leicestershire countryside, this six-acre site with its eight lakes is a fishermen's paradise. The two adults only touring areas comprise of 130 spacious, level, touring pitches set around three small lakes. 116 of these are hardstanding super pitches with 16A electricity, water and drainage. The toilet blocks are of an exceptionally high standard with individual en-suite shower rooms, and the facilities for disabled visitors are large and well-appointed with underfloor heating. Twelve luxury lodges, each with its own hot tub, are available to rent, as well as eight camping pods. There is an intimate bar and a restaurant that serves breakfast and afternoon teas. Entertainment on some weekends.

Four superbly fitted, heated toilet blocks with free hot water and individual en-suite rooms. Laundry room. Large, well appointed wet room with en-suite facilities and hairdryer for disabled visitors. Dishwashing in heated room. Motorhome services. Shop. Bar with TV and free WiFi (open daily and evenings). Breakfast (daily 08.00-10.00). Takeaway food delivered. Small games area with pool table. Fishing. Bicycle hire. Dog shower. Dog walk. Cycle hire.

Key Features

- 18+ Adults Only
- OPEN 365 Open All Year
- Pets Accepted
- Disabled Facilities
- Bar/Restaurant
- Bike Hire
- Fishing

Scan me for more information.

Alan Rogers Code: UK3903
132 pitches
GPS: 52.72402, -0.63288
Post Code: LE15 7FN

Oakham, Rutland

Rutland Camping Park

www.alanrogers.com/uk3903
info@rutlandcaravanandcamping.co.uk
Tel: 01572 813520
rutlandcaravanandcamping.co.uk

Open (Touring Pitches):
All year.

Paul & Ruth Hinch and staff run this family-owned site situated in the heart of England's smallest county – Rutland. The family continue to invest in this excellent site, with an indoor swimming pool and seven luxury lodges to rent opened recently. The pitches (120 for touring units, 12 for tents and 12 seasonal) have limited shade and are not fenced. There are two separate pitching areas, one reserved for adults and another for families and a Rally field. Electricity (10A) and have full services, and hardstanding is provided on 61 pitches. The site is beside the village of Greetham (with a footpath from the site), through which the Viking Way and other trails meander. Seven log cabins are available to rent, one of which is dog-friendly.

Two modern heated and excellent toilet blocks. Family bathrooms, Baby changing facility. Facilities for disabled visitors. Laundry. Motorhome services. Two Elsan points. Small shop (essentials only, bread and papers to order). Gas and camping gas. Heated indoor swimming pool (charged). Play area. Small games room. Picnic tables. Security barrier (£10 deposit for card). WiFi throughout (charged). Extensive dog walk. Torches useful. The onsite café(open Thursday to Monday) offers snacks, meals, pizzas and fish and chips.

Key Features

- Open All Year
- Pets Accepted
- Disabled Facilities
- Swimming Pool
- Play Area

Scan me for more information.

Alan Rogers Code: UK3576
6 accommodations
58 pitches
GPS: 52.49817, -3.95770
Post Code: PE15 0TY

Doddington, Cambridgeshire

www.alanrogers.com/uk3576
info@fieldsendfishing.co.uk
Tel: 01354 740199
www.fieldsendwater.co.uk

Open (Touring Pitches):
All Year

Fields End Caravan Park

Fields End Water Caravan Park attracts many visitors year-round. Enthusiastic anglers will find fishing for all levels; ramblers can enjoy the flat, expansive Fenland countryside, and those who just want to sit back and relax can do so in beautiful and natural surroundings thanks to their adult-only policy and the fact that they are not near any major roads or under any flight paths. 33 exclusive caravan pitches can be found in the Main Park along with the reception/shop, which sells bait suitable for the on-site lakes, tea/coffee and some useful supplies, snacks and sweets. An additional 18 pitches can be found in the "Paddock". Affiliated with the Caravan and Motorhome Club. The campsite is dog-friendly with lots of opportunities for walking around the 5-acre woods.

Reception. Shop. Fishing lakes. Accommodation to rent. WiFi (chargeable). BBQ's allowed. Dogs allowed. Laundry facilities available.

Key Features

- Adults Only
- Open All Year
- Pets Accepted
- Disabled Facilities
- Fishing

Scan me for more information.

Alan Rogers Code: UK3475
138 pitches
GPS: 52.81255, 0.49388
Post Code: PE35 6EZ

Sandringham, Norfolk

Sandringham Estate (CAMC)

www.alanrogers.com/uk3475
UKSitesBookingService@camc.com
Tel: 01553 631614
www.caravanclub.co.uk

Open (Touring Pitches):
Open all year.

The site is in a delightfully secluded spot, within the grounds of the Royal Estate in Norfolk. Visitors will love the tranquillity offered by this woodland site where pitches are set in a clearing among trees. Away from the site, nature and RSPB reserves, as well as sandy beaches including Hunstanton and Brancaster will keep all family members entertained. Sandringham House is the most famous residence of the Royal Family, it is usually closed during the Queen's holiday (end of July and beginning of August), but during the remaining months between Easter and October, the House, Museum and grounds are fully open to visitors, as is the Country Park. Flower Show-June, Game & Country Fair-September, Christmas Craft Fair-November. Many woodland paths on the estate to explore.

Two toilet blocks have washbasins in cubicles and facilities for children and visitors who are disabled. Laundry. Information room. Late night arrivals area. Motorhome service point. Chemical toilet point. Children's play area. Recycling facilities Dog walk. Footpath into the estate. WiFi (charged). BBQs allowed gas, electric and charcoal. Gas sales. T.V. aerial booster system. Bus stop at the entrance. Supermarket 4 miles. American Motorhomes and Twin axle caravans accepted. No arrivals before 12 noon. Non-members may join on-site and save £12/night.

Key Features

- Open All Year
- Pets Accepted
- Disabled Facilities
- Play Area

Scan me for more information.

Alan Rogers Code: UK3385
11 accommodations
160 pitches
GPS: 52.44636, 1.02514
Post Code: NR16 2HE

Banham, Norfolk

www.alanrogers.com/uk3385
info@applewoodholidays.co.uk
Tel: 01953 715319
www.applewoodholidays.co.uk

Open (Touring Pitches):
01 February - 31 December

Applewood Country Park

Whether you're looking to explore Norfolk's many historic sights and lively market towns, set out for an adventure to take in the beautiful countryside and stunning coastline or simply want to relax, Applewood Countryside Park is your perfect choice of campsite. A tranquil, family-friendly caravan park and campsite set within 13-acres of grassy parkland, it caters for all. Spacious pitches with electric hook-up are separated by mature laurel hedges allowing plenty of privacy. The park then has a large central area with unmarked pitches for those who do not need electricity. There is a further area with pitches which can be booked exclusively and a large field too, perfect for rallies and larger groups. Six cosy glamping pods and five luxury en-suite Shepherd's Cabins are also available for hire.

Launched in April 2019, Applewood now boasts 8-new contemporary private shower rooms, complete with underfloor heating and adjustable water temperature. Two separate toilet buildings provide clean and adequate facilities. Exclusive hook-up points and shower and toilet facilities for disabled visitors. Washing machine and dryer. Gas supplies. Rally field. Children's play area. Free WiFi. Dogs welcome at no extra charge. Secure storage facility.

Key Features

- Pets Accepted
- Disabled Facilities
- Play Area

Scan me for more information.

Alan Rogers Code: UK5360
79 pitches
GPS: 53.58880, -3.04400
Post Code: PR8 3ST

Southport, Mersey

www.alanrogers.com/uk5360
info@willowbankcp.co.uk
Tel: 01704 571566
www.willowbankcp.co.uk

Open (Touring Pitches):
14 February - 31 January.

Willowbank Touring Park

Well situated for the Sefton coast and Southport, Willowbank Holiday Home & Touring Park is set on the edge of sand-dunes amongst mature, -windswept trees. Entrance to the park is controlled by a barrier, with a pass-key issued at the excellent reception building which doubles as a sales office for the substantial, high-quality caravan holiday home development. There are 79 touring pitches, 30 on gravel hardstandings, 16 on grass and a further 33 pitches, all with 10A electricity; these are on grass hardstanding using an environmentally friendly reinforcement system. Large units are accepted by prior arrangement. The owners are very well supported by the reception team, which has considerable experience in managing the touring park. There could be some noise from the nearby main road. This is a good area for cycling and walking with the Trans-Pennine Way being adjacent. The attractions of Southport with its parks, gardens, funfair and shopping are approximately five miles away. The area is famous for its golf courses including the Royal Birkdale championship links. Latest arrival time is 21.00.

The purpose built, heated toilet block is of a high standard including an excellent bathroom for disabled visitors, although the showers are rather compact. Baby room. Laundry. Motorhome services. Play area. Field for ball games. Beauty treatments. WiFi throughout (charged).

Key Features

- Pets Accepted
- Disabled Facilities
- Play Area

Scan me for more information.

Alan Rogers Code: UK3851
126 pitches
GPS: 53.04414, -1.62705
Post Code: DE6 3JL

Ashbourne, Derbyshire

Carsington Water (CAMC)

www.alanrogers.com/uk3851
UKSitesBookingService@camc.com
Tel: 01335 370903
www.caravanclub.co.uk

Open (Touring Pitches):
March 15th - November 4th.

Nestled within an attractive pine plantation, Carsington Water Club Site in Ashbourne is beautifully landscaped, with pitches in open clearings separated by trees. This gives visitors privacy and quiet, which many appreciate. Improvements to the toilet block and facilities, including a new drying room, were undertaken in recent years. Carsington Reservoir, a major attraction in the area, is conveniently adjacent to the site. A15 minute walk will bring you to an opportunity for fishing, sailing, windsurfing and a children's playground. The caravan site is a perfect base for walkers and cyclists wishing to explore the beautiful scenery of Dovedale and the surrounding countryside. The local villages, all with excellent pubs and restaurants offering hearty food, are within two to three miles. Don't forget to look out for examples of Derbyshire's homegrown art - "Well Dressing" - which happens in many villages from May to September. N.B. Non-members may join on-site and save £12/night.

A single Toilet Block provides facilities for visitors who are disabled and children. BBQs allowed: charcoal, gas, electric. Dishwashing area. Dog walk. Dog Shower. Motorhome Service Point. Laundry. Small shop. Information Room. WiFi all site (charged). TV fair. Children's play area. Twin Axel Caravans accepted. American Motorhomes accepted. Pets allowed. Calor Gas sales. No tents allowed. Late night arrivals area. Security barrier. Fish & Chip Van – Friday. Pizza Van – Saturday.

Key Features

- Disabled Facilities
- Play Area

Scan me for more information.

Alan Rogers Code: UK4750
3 accommodations
20 pitches
GPS: 54.02577, -1.90983
Post Code: BD23 6DJ

Skipton, North Yorkshire

www.alanrogers.com/uk4750
info@howgill-lodge.co.uk
Tel: 01756 720655
www.howgill-lodge.co.uk

Open (Touring Pitches):
1 April - 31 October.

Howgill Lodge

Howgill Lodge is a traditional family park set in the heart of the Yorkshire Dales with 20 seasonal pitches but no touring pitches. Arranged on a sloping hillside, the terraced pitches have fantastic views. It is a small park catering for the needs of walkers, tourers and people who like just to relax. The whole area is a haven for both experienced walkers or the casual rambler, without having to move your car. The 20 seasonal pitches all at the upper part of the park are on hardstanding and have 10A electricity connections. Picnic tables and chairs are provided. There are two four-bed mobile homes available to rent. The reception also houses a small shop which sells most of the basics, including fresh foods. Pretty villages abound in the area, all with attractive inns and nearby Embsay has the Dales Railway with steam trains.

Heated toilet facilities are at the entrance, close to reception. Showers are large and adjustable. Fully equipped laundry room with four additional unisex showers. Outdoor washing lines are provided. Two small blocks housing WCs are lower down the site. Shop. No play area. Fishing licences are available from reception.

Key Features

Pets Accepted

Scan me for more information.

Alan Rogers Code: UK4607
44 pitches
GPS: 54.00304, -1.09076
Post Code: YO32 2RH

York, North Yorkshire

Willow House

www.alanrogers.com/uk4607
info@willowhouseyork.co.uk
Tel: 0190 4750060
willowhouseyork.co.uk

Open (Touring Pitches):
Open all year

Willow House comprises a small adult only campsite, a certified location (CL) for the Caravan and Motorhome Club, a farm café, beauty parlour and dog pampering shop. Seasonal caravans occupy the vast majority of the 39 hardstandings, but a few are available for tourers. Booking is essential, and access details will be left in the Unstaffed reception. The CL site has five hardstandings with electricity and facilities near reception perhaps 100 yards along the access road. This simple site has a dog walking area at the rear of the caravan park near the ponds. As an adult only site, it offers peace and quiet and easy access to York. The farm café offers light meals and snacks and quiches made to order. The caravan pitches are linear along a central grass area with no screening.

The sanitary block for the caravan park offers 4 wet rooms with shower, WC and washbasin. There are also 2 further WCs. The facilities for the CL site are near reception. Camping pods are available to rent.

Key Features

- 18+ Adults Only
- Open All Year
- Pets Accepted
- Disabled Facilities
- Bar/Restaurant

Scan me for more information.

Alan Rogers Code: UK5655
200 accommodations
44 pitches
GPS: 54.19240, -2.77002
Post Code: LA7 7BS

Milnthorpe, Cumbria

Fell End Caravan Park

www.alanrogers.com/uk5655
enquiries@pureleisuregroup.com
Tel: 01524 781453
www.pure-leisure.co.uk/fell-end

Open (Touring Pitches):
All year.

Open all year round, Fell End Caravan Park is surrounded by woodland and set in the heart of the countryside close to Arnside and Silverdale. There are 44 level, pitches for caravans and motorhomes; some allocated for seasonal use, arranged on hardstandings surrounded by mature trees and shrubs. Marked and numbered, all have 10A electricity and the possibility of Freeview TV hook-up. There are no tent pitches. The park's primary interest is in over 200 privately owned caravan holiday homes and camping which are positioned around the park, some high on the hillside, although these are well screened — an excellent leisure complex offers an indoor pool and gym, and a bar and the restaurant. The site's sister park, Hall More, is just half a mile down the road and offers fishing in its well-stocked trout lake with good open plan pitches.

The toilet block is near the touring pitches, with well equipped showers and private cabins, facilities for disabled visitors (key from reception) and dishwashing facilities. There is a fully equipped laundry. Bar, café and takeaway (all year). Indoor heated swimming pool, steam room and gym. Well equipped adventure play area. Amusement arcade.

Key Features

- Open All Year
- Disabled Facilities
- Swimming Pool
- Play Area
- Bar/Restaurant

Scan me for more information.

Alan Rogers Code: UK5780
4 accommodations
70 pitches
GPS: 55.13763, -2.25990
Post Code: NE48 2JY

Bellingham, Northumberland

www.alanrogers.com/uk5780
Bellingham.Site@thefriendlyclub.co.uk
Tel: 01434 220175
campingandcaravanningclub.co.uk

Open (Touring Pitches):
28 February - 4 January.

Bellingham (C&CC) Site

In the English Borders, this site is an ideal base for outdoor life in the Northumberland National Park and for exploring the east. The compact campsite provides 70 level pitches on grass and hardstanding, all with 16A electricity. There are four camping pods for hire. This is a Club site, but non-members are welcome, as are children and pets. Bellingham, a traditional Northumbrian village, is within easy strolling distance and offers a heritage centre, shops, pubs, cafés and restaurants. A local bus stops at the site entrance. Walk to Hareshaw Linn waterfall or visit the Kielder Water and Forest Park, nine miles to the west. Hadrian's Wall is a similar distance to the south.

Excellent sanitary facilities. The ladies, finished in pine, provides washbasins in cubicles, controllable showers and a free hairdryer. The unit for men has been recently tiled and has dishwashing and laundry facilities. Reception offers tourist information, basic food supplies, camping equipment, gas and battery charging. Fridges for hire. An additional building with new heated recreation/TV room, dining area, kitchen, family shower room, other WCs, drying room and indoor games area. Play area. Glamping pods are available.

Key Features

- Pets Accepted
- Disabled Facilities
- Play Area

Scan me for more information.

Alan Rogers Code: UK6690
150 pitches
GPS: 53.29142, -3.64656
Post Code: LL22 8HG

Colwyn Bay, Conwy

www.alanrogers.com/uk6690
stay@bronywendon.co.uk
Tel: 01492 512903
www.bronywendon.co.uk

Open (Touring Pitches):
All Year

Bron-Y-Wendon

Bron-Y-Wendon Touring Caravan Park is right by the sea between Abergele and Colwyn Bay on the beautiful North Wales coast. This is a quiet park which, by its own admission, is not really geared up for the family unit - although there is a playground. The park is maintained to the highest standards and caters for a large number of seasonal caravans on pitches with gravel bases which are kept very tidy. There are a further 65 grass-based, and 85 hardstanding touring pitches, all with 16A electricity and tarmac access roads, 75 also with water and wastewater. All pitches have coastal views, and the sea and beach are just a short walk away. Trailer tents are accepted, but not other tents.

Two main toilet blocks, both with heating, provide excellent facilities including three shower blocks, separate from the toilets and washbasins. Third smaller, but roomier, shower block with underfloor heating. Good facilities for disabled visitors. Laundry with washing machines and dryers. Gas supplies. WiFi (charged). Access to coastal cycle paths.

Key Features

- OPEN 365 Open All Year
- Pets Accepted
- Disabled Facilities
- Play Area
- Skiing

Scan me for more information.

Alan Rogers Code: UK6380
142 pitches
GPS: 52.74987, -4.08036
Post Code: LL42 1RR

Barmouth, Gwynedd

www.alanrogers.com/uk6380
enquiries@trawsdir.co.uk
Tel: 01341 280999
www.trawsdir.co.uk

Open (Touring Pitches):
1 March - 6 January.

Trawsdir Caravan Park

With sea views from almost every pitch and with a backdrop of the Welsh hills, Trawsdir Touring Caravan & Camping Park has something for everyone, both young and old. Entrance and exit via the site barrier, and access to the facilities are by a key fob. A well-equipped children's play area with safety surface is close to reception. Of the 142 touring pitches, 70 are for tents (48 with electricity) while the remaining 72 are fully serviced and can take RVs. The campsite has a large dog walking field and from the corner of the campsite is a little walk to the Wayside Inn, avoiding the main road. Facilities are shared with the sister site across the road, which has a private beach. The site managers will assist with positioning your unit if required. A member of the Best of British group.

Two toilet blocks are equipped to a very high standard, however one is kept in reserve for when cleaning is being done, except at the busiest times. Facilities for disabled visitors with good access (Radar key). Baby changing facilities in both male and female toilets. Fully equipped laundry. Shop. Playground. WiFi (charged).

Key Features

- Pets Accepted
- Disabled Facilities
- Beach Access
- Play Area

Scan me for more information.

Alan Rogers Code: UK6330
84 pitches
GPS: 52.52992, -3.02970
Post Code: SY15 6EB

Montgomery, Powys

www.alanrogers.com/uk6330
enquiries@daisy-bank.co.uk
Tel: 01588 620471
www.daisy-bank.co.uk

Open (Touring Pitches):
All Year

Daisy Bank Caravan Park

For adults only, this pretty, tranquil park in the Camlad Valley has panoramic views and is an ideal base for walkers. Attractively landscaped with traditional English flower beds and many different trees and shrubs, this small park has been carefully developed. The Welsh hills to the north and the Shropshire hills to the south overlook the three fields which provide a total of 84 pitches. The field nearer to the road (perhaps a little noisy) is slightly sloping, but there are hardstandings for motorhomes, while the second field is more level. All pitches have 16A electricity, water and wastewater drainage and TV hook-up. Camping pods are also available for hire.

Two well equipped, heated toilet blocks now incorporate modern, en-suite units and facilities for disabled visitors. One has four en-suite units and two WCs. Covered dishwashing area. Laundry facilities. Shop in reception (honesty policy at certain times). Gas supplies. Barbecues. Small putting green (free loan of clubs and balls). Bicycle hire. Small library. WiFi.

Key Features

- 18+ Adults Only
- OPEN 365 Open All Year
- Pets Accepted
- Disabled Facilities
- Bike Hire

Scan me for more information.

Alan Rogers Code: UK5955
70 pitches
GPS: 51.99325, -3.78023
Post Code: SA20 0RD

Llandovery, Carmarthenshire

www.alanrogers.com/uk5955
enquiries@erwlon.co.uk
Tel: 01550 721021
www.erwlon.co.uk

Open (Touring Pitches):
All year.

Erwlon Caravan Park

Just outside Llandovery and on the edge of the Brecon Beacons National Park, Erwlon is an attractive and welcoming campsite. Of the 110 pitches, seven are used for privately owned caravan holiday homes, 33 have seasonal caravans, and 70 are for touring units. Fifty are on hardstanding with electricity connections, and 12 have water and drainage as well. There is a flat field for tents at the bottom of the park with some electrical outlets; an open-sided, covered area for eating, food preparation and bicycle storage is at the planning stage. The site has a relaxed atmosphere where consideration for others minimises the need for formal rules. It is ideal for young families, walkers, cyclists and fishers. Gold mines and the National Showcaves Centre for Wales (including dinosaur park) are within an easy drive. A member of the Best of British group.

New heated toilet block with washbasins in cabins, four family rooms (basin, shower, toilet) and a room for families and disabled visitors which includes a baby unit. Combined, well equipped laundry and dishwashing room. Motorhome services. Fridge freezer. Fishing. WiFi over site (charged).

Key Features

- Open All Year
- Pets Accepted
- Disabled Facilities
- Play Area
- Fishing

Scan me for more information.

Alan Rogers Code: UK5925
61 pitches
GPS: 51.49155, -3.20313
Post Code: CF11 9XR

Cardiff

www.alanrogers.com/uk5925
cardiffcaravanpark@cardiff.gov.uk
Tel: 02920 398362
www.cardiffcaravanpark.co.uk

Open (Touring Pitches):
All year.

Cardiff Caravan Park

Run by the city council, this popular site is set within acres of parkland, one mile from the city centre, ideal for visiting the many attractions of the city of Cardiff. The campsite has 61 touring pitches which are on a relatively open area, with 43 on a grasscrete surface with 16A electric hook-ups and the remainder on grass. There is a public right of way through the site. Security is good with an on-site warden 24 hours a day and infrared security cameras constantly scanning the whole area. The County Cricket Ground, Welsh Institute of Sport, the Millennium Stadium, Cardiff City FC, Cardiff Castle, museums and many other attractions are within walking distance. The recently redeveloped Cardiff Bay area is a 2.5-mile cycle ride (a good city centre cycle route map is available from reception), or there is a bus service from just outside the gate.

Two heated buildings, each with key code entry systems. The one by reception has a laundry with washer and dryer, and facilities for disabled campers. Both have controllable hot showers. Café near reception run by Pedal Power (a cycling charity). Baby facilities. Bicycle hire (the site specialises in bicycles adapted for disabled visitors).

Key Features

- Open All Year
- Pets Accepted
- Disabled Facilities
- Bike Hire

Scan me for more information.

Alan Rogers Code: UK6060
80 pitches
GPS: 51.56148, -3.03341
Post Code: NP10 8TW

Newport

Tredegar House (CAMC)

www.alanrogers.com/uk6060
UKSitesBookingService@camc.com
Tel: 01633 815600
www.caravanclub.co.uk

Open (Touring Pitches):
All year.

This immaculate Caravan & Motorhome Club site is ideally situated for breaking a journey or for more extended stays. It can accommodate 80 units, all with 16A electricity hook-up and 64 with gravel hardstanding, four fully serviced. Seven pitches are on grass and a further four on grass but no space for awnings. An additional grass area is allocated for tents, with its use limited to families and couples – single-sex groups are not accepted. The site itself is set within the gardens and park of Tredegar House, a 17th-century house and country park, which is open to the public to discover what life was like 'above and below stairs.' The park entrance gates are locked at dusk so contact the site reception for details of latest arrival times. Some road noise may be expected at times, but otherwise, this is an excellent site.

The sanitary block is of an excellent standard with a digital lock system. It includes washbasins in cubicles. Facilities for disabled visitors. Baby and toddler bathroom. Laundry. Good motorhome service point. Calor gas is available. The National Trust's Tredegar House visitors' centre with tea rooms, gift shop and craft workshops (open Easter-Sept) is close by. Adventure play area in the park. WiFi (charged).

Key Features

- Open All Year
- Pets Accepted
- Disabled Facilities
- Play Area

Scan me for more information.

Alan Rogers Code: UK6920
40 accommodations
45 pitches
GPS: 55.05735, -3.25762
Post Code: DG11 3DR

Lockerbie,
Dumfries and Galloway

www.alanrogers.com/uk6920
cressfieldcaravanpark@gmx.com
Tel: 01576 300702
www.cressfieldcaravanpark.co.uk

Open (Touring Pitches):
All year.

Cressfield Caravan Park

Just north of the border, Cressfield is an all-year park situated in undulating countryside near the village of Ecclefechan. There is a large caravan holiday home presence on-site, but it is peaceful and well maintained, with a mixture of touring and seasonal pitches. The park is landscaped with 85 hardstanding and grass pitches, 45 occupied by seasonal caravans, which are connected by tarmac or gravel roads and 16A electricity hook-ups are provided. The site is located at the foot of the Brownmoor Forestry Commission Woods, which offer walking, mountain biking and birdwatching, as well as panoramic views over the unspoilt countryside. The park has no shop, but Ecclefechan village, the birthplace of Robert Carlyle, is only 400 yards away and the adjacent hotel offers meals. For the more active there are seven golf courses nearby and opportunities for coarse or game fishing.

The modern heated toilet block is central with well-equipped showers, washbasins in cubicles and was in 4 separate suites (£1) with hairdryers (metered). Toilet and washbasin, plus a separate shower area for disabled visitors. Well equipped laundry room. Gas supplies. Well equipped fenced play area. Sports field with goalposts (not in wet weather or Nov-March).

Key Features

- Open All Year
- Pets Accepted
- Disabled Facilities
- Play Area

Scan me for more information.

Alan Rogers Code: UK7000
152 pitches
GPS: 55.80392, -4.04673
Post Code: G71 8NY

Glasgow, North Lanarkshire

www.alanrogers.com/uk7000
UKSitesBookingService@camc.com
Tel: 01698 853300
www.caravanclub.co.uk

Open (Touring Pitches):
All year.

Strathclyde (CAMC) Site

The 1,200-acre Strathclyde Country Park is a large green area less than 15 miles from the centre of Glasgow. This Caravan and Motorhome Club site features 107 all-weather, large, flat hardstanding pitches all with 16amp electricity. There are 12 serviced pitches. Space for 45 tents (Seasonal), all off tarmac roads. The warden's accommodation and toilet blocks are attractively clad in wood to blend in with their surroundings. This site is suitable as a stopover or for a longer holiday (max. 21 days) and it is ideal as a base for visiting the numerous attractions in and around Glasgow. As the site is close to the motorway, there may be some traffic noise.

Two toilet blocks with all facilities. Enclosed sinks for dishwashing and food preparation. Provision for babies and disabled visitors. Laundry facilities. Motorhome services. Shop in reception sells basic provisions. Play area for young children. Woodland walk. WiFi (charged). Calor gas sales. Dog walk. Information Room. Late night arrivals area. American Motor Homes accepted. Caravan & Motorhome storage. Twin Axle Caravans accepted. Pets allowed.

Key Features

- Open All Year
- Pets Accepted
- Disabled Facilities
- Play Area
- Bike Hire

Scan me for more information.

Alan Rogers Code: UK7840
120 pitches
GPS: 56.47757, -5.39875
Post Code: PA37 1RU

Oban, Argyll and Bute

www.alanrogers.com/uk7840
northledaig@btconnect.com
Tel: 01631 710291
www.northledaigcaravanpark.co.uk

Open (Touring Pitches):
End-March - Start Nov.

North Ledaig Caravan Park

North Ledaig Caravan Park is one of the best locations on Scotland's west coast. A wonderful 30-acre park that has been awarded the David Bellamy Conservation Award, it is situated on a 2 mile sand and shingle beach on Ardmucknish Bay. Here sailing, water sports and bathing can be enjoyed by all the family. Some pitches at the caravan site are almost on the water's edge, and all of them face the sea, offering a panoramic view to the beautiful Isle of Mull. The location is ideal for children with an adventure playground on site. Keep an eye out for the bin raiding otters!

BBQs allowed, Disabled facilities include an accessible shower room, Dishwashing area, Dog walking area on-site, Drive over waste disposal for motorhomes. A Camperclean machine is available for a small fee. Hardstanding motorhome pitches are all level. Electric hook-up available, Family washroom, Gas for sale, Late arrivals area with electric hook-up, Laundry facilities, Motorhome service point. On-site mini-market selling essentials including bread and milk with full disabled access.

Key Features

- Disabled Facilities
- Beach Access

Scan me for more information.

Alan Rogers Code: UK7830
174 pitches
GPS: 56.80452, -5.07392
Post Code: PH33 6SX

Fort William, Highland

Glen Nevis Caravan Park

www.alanrogers.com/uk7830
holidays@glen-nevis.co.uk
Tel: 01397 702191
www.glen-nevis.co.uk

Open (Touring Pitches):
15 Mar. - 31 Oct.

Just outside Fort William, in a most attractive and quiet situation with views of Ben Nevis, this spacious park is used by those on active pursuits as well as sightseeing tourists. It comprises eight quite large fields, divided between caravans, motorhomes and tents. The 174 large touring pitches, many with hardstanding (steel pegs required,) are marked with wooden fence dividers, all with 16A electricity and 80 also have water and drainage. The park becomes full in the peak months, but there are vacancies each day. If the reception is closed (after hours), you can site yourself.

Four modern toilet blocks with showers (extra showers in two blocks) and units for visitors with disabilities. An excellent block in Nevis Park (one of the eight camping fields) has some washbasins in cubicles, showers, further facilities for disabled visitors, a second large laundry room and dishwashing sinks. Family Room. Motorhome services. Shop (Easter-mid Oct). Barbecue area and snack bar (End of May - Mid September). Play area on bark (Was being refurbished when we visited). WiFi over site (charged, free in Bar). Bar/ Restaurant. Fishing. Pets allowed. Electric bicycles delivered to site. Gas Sales. No security barrier. 10 Camping Pods. TV signal good. Information at Reception. Bus stop at the entrance. Chemical toilet disposal point. Twin axel caravans accepted. Dog exercise area.

Key Features

- Pets Accepted
- Disabled Facilities
- Play Area
- Bar/Restaurant
- Skiing
- Fishing

Scan me for more information.

Alan Rogers Code: UK7920
6 accommodations
19 pitches
GPS: 58.22738, -6.39254
Post Code: HS2 0DR

Stornoway, Isle of Lewis

www.alanrogers.com/uk7920
info@laxdaleholidaypark.com
Tel: 01851 706966
www.laxdaleholidaypark.com

Open (Touring Pitches):
1 March - 31 October.

Laxdale Holiday Park

Whilst not in the most scenic of locations, this good park is well placed for touring. Surrounded by trees, it is on the edge of Stornaway (ferry port) and is well laid out with a tarmac road running through the centre. A level area has 19 touring pitches, all with electricity hook-ups (10A), plus five for tents, and a grassy area (no electricity) for tents gently slopes away to the trees and boundary. There is a choice of rental accommodation on offer: caravans, wigwams, a lodge, a bungalow and a bunkhouse. The site is centrally situated in an ideal spot for touring the Isle of Lewis with easy access to all parts of the island.

The well maintained and modern sanitary block is heated and raised above the hardstanding area. Access is via steps or a gravel path to the ramp. Good (but narrow) showers with dividing curtain (on payment). Well equipped laundry with washing machine, dryer, iron and board, sink and clothes line. Telephone. WiFi in reception (charged). Glamping style pods are available to rent.

Key Features

- Pets Accepted
- Disabled Facilities

Scan me for more information.

Alan Rogers Code: UK7950
42 pitches
GPS: 58.95443, -3.30041
Post Code: KW16 3DN

Stromness, Orkney

Point of Ness

www.alanrogers.com/uk7950
leisure.culture@orkney.gov.uk
Tel: 01856 873535
www.orkney.gov.uk

Open (Touring Pitches):
1 April - 30 September

This quiet site is in an idyllic position bounded by the sea on one side (an entrance to the harbour). It is sheltered by the land from the open sea and has views to the mountains and the island of Hoy. There is a rocky beach close by and walks from the site. There are 27 pitches (12 with 10A electricity hook-ups) on this level, firm grassy site, protected from the small drop to the sea by a low fence. Access to the steps to the sea is via a gate in the fence. While being located at one end of Orkney, it is still easy to visit the Churchill Barriers and the Italian Chapel as well as the closer Maes Howe and Skara Brae sites. Regular ferries come into Stromness from Thurso. Do not be surprised if the seals come to watch you. Ferries to other islands go from various ports and it is sometimes necessary to book in advance.

The well maintained traditional style toilet block has good sized showers (on payment) with curtains separating the changing area. Well equipped laundry. Lounge for campers is at one end of the block.

Key Features

- Pets Accepted
- Disabled Facilities
- Beach Access

Scan me for more information.

Alan Rogers Code: UK8410
229 accommodations
50 pitches
GPS: 54.03086, -6.06887
Post Code: BT34 4LW

Newry, Co. Down

www.alanrogers.com/uk8410
info@chestnuttholidayparks.com
Tel: 028 4176 2653
www.chestnuttholidayparks.com

Open (Touring Pitches):
Easter - Mid September.

Chestnutt Holiday Park

Chestnutt Holiday Park is one of the best in the southernmost corner of Northern Ireland. There are two areas designated for touring units, one on each side of the entrance road and all pitches have electricity, light, water and waste. The park is surrounded by dramatic scenery and unspoilt countryside and is an attractive choice for a beach-based holiday. The adjacent beach, with lifeguard, tennis court, small football pitch and play park will keep youngsters happy all day. The backdrop of the Mourne Mountains to the north gives the area shelter. Since the introduction of more facilities for children, Easter is becoming popular at this site. The long sandy beaches of the Cranfield peninsula have attracted tourists for about a century. The Blue Flag beaches of picturesque Carlingford Lough have become popular with Ulster caravanners and increasingly with tourists.

Each touring section has its own toilet block with token operated showers. The large well equipped laundry (also token operated), toilets and full facilities for disabled campers have been completely refurbished. Shop and restaurant (open Easter weekend, July/Aug). Takeaway (open as restaurant and also weekends in low season). Tennis court. Small football pitch. Play area. Adventure summer camps (8-16 year olds). Saturday club (5-14 year olds). WiFi throughout (charged).

Key Features

- Pets Accepted
- Disabled Facilities
- Beach Access
- Play Area
- Bar/Restaurant

Scan me for more information.

Alan Rogers Code: UK8310
31 pitches
GPS: 54.88819, -5.84523
Post Code: BT40 2QG

Larne, Co. Antrim

Carnfunnock Country Park

www.alanrogers.com/uk8310
carnfunnock@midandeastantrim.gov.uk
Tel: 028 2826 2471
www.carnfunnock.co.uk

Open (Touring Pitches):
End-March - Early October.

In a magnificent parkland setting overlooking the Irish Sea and Scotland, what makes this touring site popular are its scenic surroundings and convenient location. It is 3.5 miles north of the market town of Larne on the famed Antrim Coast Road. It offers 31 level super pitches, including three extra-long pitches, all with hardstanding, water, 16A electricity, drainage, individual pitch lighting and ample space for an awning. The site has a neat appearance with a tarmac road following through to the rear where several pitches are placed close together in a circular position with allocated space for tents. Run by the Borough Council and supervised by a manager, the surrounding Country Park is immaculately kept. The Visitor Centre includes a gift shop and information about local attractions and the restaurant/coffee shop is pleasant and looks towards the sea. Spending time around the parkland, you will find a walled time garden with historic sundials, a maze, forest walk, children's adventure playground, putting green, nine-hole golf course, wildlife garden and miniature railway. There is also a summer events programme.

Key Features

- Pets Accepted
- Disabled Facilities
- Play Area
- Bar/Restaurant
- Golf

A small building beside the entrance gates houses the toilet facilities (entry by key) which have had a major refurbishment and are kept very clean. Shower units, a family bathroom and facilities for disabled visitors. Baby room. Shop (Easter - 31 October). Restaurant and takeaway. WiFi throughout.

Scan me for more information.

Santorini at sunset >

Capital Athens
Currency Euro (€)
Language Greek
Time Zone EET (GMT+2)
Telephone Code 00 30

Tourist Website
visitgreece.gr

Climate Mediterranean climate with plenty of sunshine, mild temperatures and limited amount of rainfall.

Shops Varied. In high-season 8am to 2pm Mon, Wed and Sat, 8am to 2pm and 5pm to 9pm Tues, Thurs and Fri.

Banks 8.30am to 2.30pm Mon to Thurs, 8am to 2pm Fri.

Accessible Travel Although improving, much of Greece is difficult to navigate for wheelchair users and those who are less able.

Travelling with children Athens has plenty of green spaces and historical attractions. Crete is great for its sandy beaches. The Greek culture is all about sharing so restaurants will always be accommodating towards children. Make sure to bring mosquito repellant.

See campsite map page

481

Public Holidays New Year's Day, Epiphany, Ash Monday, Independence Day (25 Mar), Good Friday, Easter Sunday, Easter Monday, Labour Day (1 May), Whit Sunday, Whit Monday, Assumption, Ochi Day (28 Oct), Christmas Day, Boxing Day.

Motoring Speed limits are 100-120 km/h on highways and 50 km/h in residential areas unless otherwise marked. An international driver's licence is required, and you should carry this with you at all times. Road signs are written in Greek and repeated phonetically in English. Road tolls exist on two highways in Greece, one leading to Northern Greece and the other to the Peloponnese.

Environmental Policies There are two Low Emission Zones implemented in Athens, one affects the city centre and the other covers the larger metropolitan area. If current targets are met, diesel vehicles will be banned from the city by 2025. Plastic, glass, paper and cardboard can be recycled but more rural areas lack necessary sorting facilities.

View all campsites in Greece
alanrogers.com/greece

Greece

Greece is made up of clusters of islands with idyllic sheltered bays and coves, golden stretches of sand with dunes, pebbly beaches, coastal caves with steep rocks and volcanic black sand and coastal wetlands. Its rugged landscape is a monument to nature with dramatic gorges, lakes, rivers and waterfalls.

Nestling between the waters of the Aegean, Ionian and Mediterranean seas, Greece has over 13,000 km of coastline. A largely mountainous country, its backbone is formed from the Pindus range, which extends as far as Crete, the largest of Greece's 6,000 islands, themselves peaks of the now submerged landmass of Aegeis.

Mount Olympus in the north of the country, known from Greek mythology as the abode of the gods, is the highest mountain (2,917 m).

The Greek islands have something to offer every visitor – the vibrant nightlife of Mykonos, the 'honeymoon' island of Santorini; Rhodes, where the modern city sits alongside the medieval citadel, and Corfu with its Venetian and French influences. The mainland is home to some of the most important archaeological sites, including the Acropolis, the Parthenon and Delphi.

Alan Rogers Code: GR8590
10 accommodations
66 pitches
GPS: 38.00861, 23.67194
Post Code: GR-12136

Attica, Peristeri-Athens

www.alanrogers.com/gr8590
info@campingathens.com.gr
Tel: 210 581 4114
www.campingathens.com.gr

Open (Touring Pitches):
All year.

Camping Athens

Camping Athens is an all-year site, located to the west of the city and convenient for visiting Athens. The site prides itself on friendly Greek hospitality and offers 66 touring pitches, all with 16A electricity connections. The pitches are of a reasonable size and are generally well shaded. Smaller pitches are available for tents. The two toilet blocks are of modern design and well maintained. To visit the city, there is a bus stop opposite the site entrance. The site's restaurant is most welcoming after a day's sightseeing, and a selection of Greek starters, helped along by cool wine, can be thoroughly recommended. Before coming to Athens, be sure to plan your visit programme in advance. The city can be hot during mid afternoon in summer and the traffic may be heavy. The public transport system (bus/tram/metro etc) works well, so don't plan to drive into the city yourself.

Two modern toilet blocks. Washing machines. Shop. Bar. Takeaway food and restaurant (all May-Oct). Excursions can be arranged. Barbecues and open fires are forbidden. Free WiFi over site.

Key Features

- Open All Year
- Pets Accepted
- Bar/Restaurant

Scan me for more information.

Alan Rogers Code: GR8150
88 accommodations
215 pitches
GPS: 39.99598, 23.88168
Post Code: GR-63072

Central Macedonia, Tristinika

Camping Iza

www.alanrogers.com/gr8150
izacamping@gmail.com
Tel: 237 505 1235
www.iza.gr

Open (Touring Pitches):
1 May - 30 September.

Sithonia is the middle of three peninsulas on Halkidiki and is a popular Greek tourist destination with a good motorway south from Thessaloniki to Neos Moudania. Camping Iza is one of the larger sites on Sithonia and therefore has more facilities than many smaller sites. Behind a good sandy beach and amongst mainly olive and willow trees, the 215 pitches are clearly marked, and some have high screens to offer some shade. Only the two front rows have sea views. Many people visit the area to see Mount Athos and the monasteries on Agio Oros, the third peninsula. This is a closed area and opens only to a limited number of visitors (men over the age of 18 only) each day with prior approval. However, numerous boat trips are available to take you around this interesting historical area.

Three toilet blocks include showers, WCs and washbasins. Laundry with washing machines and ironing boards. Motorhome services. Beach bar. Shop. Restaurant. Sandy beach. Fishing, boating and swimming. Dogs are not accepted.

Key Features

- Beach Access
- Bar/Restaurant
- Fishing

Scan me for more information.

Alan Rogers Code: GR8220
9 accommodations
100 pitches
GPS: 39.28555, 20.38983
Post Code: GR-48060

Epirus, Parga

www.alanrogers.com/gr8220
info@campingvaltos.gr
Tel: 268 403 1287
www.campingvaltos.com

Open (Touring Pitches):
1 May - 30 September.

Camping Valtos

Valtos Camping lies two kilometres west of the picturesque village of Parga and just 60 m. from the beautiful sandy beach at Valtos. This is a small, friendly site with a shop, bar and restaurant. The 100 touring pitches here are of various sizes, all with electricity connections (16A). There is little grass but good shade is supplied by mulberry, lemon and olive trees. Access to the site is quite narrow and owners of larger motorhomes will need to be careful. The 35-minute walk up over the castle hill and the steep descent through the narrow, shop-lined alleys of Parga yields magnificent views, especially from the castle walls. Popular excursions from here include the islands of Antipaxos and Paxos with its blue caves, and Anthousa, a sleepy village high in the mountains. A water taxi service connects with Parga.

Two toilet blocks, one modern and one refurbished. Washing machine. Motorhome services. Shop, bar, takeaway and restaurant (all May-Sept). Caravans for rent.

Key Features

- Pets Accepted
- Beach Access
- Bar/Restaurant
- Fishing
- Sailing

Scan me for more information.

Alan Rogers Code: GR8230
13 accommodations
80 pitches
GPS: 39.50979, 20.22141
Post Code: 46100

Thesprotia, Igoumenitsa

www.alanrogers.com/gr8230
camping@drepano.gr
Tel: 26 65 02 69 80
www.drepano.gr

Open (Touring Pitches):
All year.

Drepano Igoumenitsa

Sitting just 5km from the port of Igoumenitsa, on a beautiful peninsula surrounded by lush greenery and close to the sandy beach of Drepano, this basic but well-cared-for site caters well for both tent users and caravanners. There are 80 pitches of varying sizes, some with hardstanding, most with electricity, some with shade and almost all with excellent sea views.
The surrounding region offers a good selection of attractions including the port city of Igoumenitsa, historic citadel of Parga and boat trips to the island of Corfu. The location makes this campsite an ideal choice for those travelling from Italy, with direct connections available to Ancona, Bari, Brindisi and Venice. Connections are also available to Corfu, Lefkimi, Paxoi, Patras & Cephalonia (Seasonal.)

Sanitary block is modern, well maintained and very clean with hot water and showers. Facilities for disabled campers are in the same block, wet-room style layout. Motorhome services. Washing machine. Fridge rental. Mini-market. Restaurant. Takeaway. Bar. Children's playground. Bikes for hire. Tennis court. Fishing. Beach volleyball. Beach access. Dogs allowed. WiFi (throughout, free).

Key Features

- Pets Accepted
- Disabled Facilities
- Beach Access
- Bar/Restaurant
- Bike Hire
- Fishing

Scan me for more information.

Alan Rogers Code: GR8335
42 pitches
GPS: 37.64519, 21.62285
Post Code: GR-27065

Peloponnese, Olympia

www.alanrogers.com/gr8335
Tel: 262 402 2314
www.campingdiana.gr

Open (Touring Pitches):
All year.

Camping Diana

Camping Diana is a small site with 42 pitches, 15 of which are under dense tree cover and are only suitable for tents. The remaining pitches are located off a steep concrete road in small open areas and pitch size will be small at best. Access for large caravans could be problematic. There are three pitches at the entrance suitable for large motorhomes and caravans over 8 meters. There are 3 other larger pitches on-site for outfits over 8 meters. Each has a 10A electricity supply nearby. Despite being rather dated, it is a pleasant site and located very close to the archaeological site of ancient Olympia with its museums and other attractions. The town of Olympia is about a 10-minute walk from the campsite and is home to the UNESCO World Heritage site of the same name. The archaeologically important site was home to the ancient Olympic Games and the Olympic flame is still lit in modern Olympia before embarking on its journey to the host country every four years.

The single toilet block is dated, but clean. Washing machine. Small mini-market selling essentials and fresh bread. Swimming pool. Snack bar serving breakfast, snacks, drinks & coffee. Bar. WiFi.

Key Features

- Open All Year
- Pets Accepted
- Swimming Pool
- Bar/Restaurant

Scan me for more information.

Alan Rogers Code: GR8255
200 pitches
GPS: 39.71318, 21.61528
Post Code: GR-42200

Thessaly, Kalambaka

www.alanrogers.com/gr8255
tsourvaka@yahoo.gr
Tel: 243 202 2293
www.campingkastraki.com

Open (Touring Pitches):
All year.

Vrachos Kastraki

The region of Meteora is named after the impressive rock formations which rise out to the plain of Thessaly and which now have ancient monasteries clinging to their summits. Camping Vrachos Kastraki is ideally placed to visit this unusual landscape, as it is situated in a valley surrounded by mountains and huge, natural sculptures. There are around 200 pitches, many quite small and suitable only for tents. Electricity is said to be available for all, but in some cases cables would have to cross the roads. Individual pitches are not marked and you may pitch where you like. There is plenty of shade from mature almonds, acacias and poplars. There is a warm welcome on arrival, which immediately helps the visitor unwind after the journey through the mountain passes. The site owners can advise on the numerous places of interest to visit. For the adventurous visitor, rock climbing, abseiling, canoeing and mountain biking can be organised from the site. Those less actively inclined can relax and enjoy the sunshine and the view from beside the pool. The restaurant, which is open all year, is very good value. The site also provides a covered barbecue area and excellent cooking facilities with three designated picnic areas.

Key Features

- Open All Year
- Swimming Pool
- Play Area
- Bar/Restaurant

Two modern sanitary blocks provide British style WCs and open washbasins. Laundry room. Cooking facilities with picnic areas. Shop. Bar, restaurant and snack bar. Outdoor swimming pool (seasonal). Play area.

Scan me for more information.

Alan Rogers Code: GR8425
14 accommodations
75 pitches
GPS: 38.80439, 20.71436
Post Code: GR-31100

Ionian Islands, Lefkada

www.alanrogers.com/gr8425
info@campingkariotes.com
Tel: 264 507 1103
www.campingkariotes.gr

Open (Touring Pitches):
Mid April - End October.

Camping Kariotes Beach

The island of Lefkada is one of the few Ionian islands that you can access without using a ferry. This campsite is 500 m. from the beach on the main road south (slight traffic noise). There are 75 pitches amongst tall olive trees, but only about 15 places are suitable for caravans or motorhomes. A small, simple restaurant is opened on-demand, so speak early to the owners if you want to eat there. Kariotes village has a small supermarket and three tavernas in a square about 300 m. from the site. To reach the island, you will probably go through the tunnel and then cross the unique bridge. If the klaxon goes it is worth parking to watch the bridge swing into action to allow access for boats. Around 5 hours from Athens, Lefkada town (2km from the site) is large and you can find most things there, but the rest of the island is rural and quiet.

Two toilet blocks include the usual facilities. Laundry facilities. Bar and restaurant (hours subject to demand). Swimming pool (seasonal). WiFi.

Key Features

- Swimming Pool
- Bar/Restaurant

Scan me for more information.

Alan Rogers Code: GR8385
7 accommodations
48 pitches
GPS: 39.67635, 19.72528
Post Code: GR-49083

Ionian Islands, Corfu

www.alanrogers.com/gr8385
paleocamping@gmail.com
Tel: 266 304 1204
www.campingpaleokastritsa.com

Open (Touring Pitches):
Mid May - Mid October

Paleokastritsa

Paleokastritsa is a popular holiday resort on Corfu and is definitely one of the most scenic spots on the island. The resort has several beaches and coves, from large sandy beaches to small secluded bays – something for everyone. There is a small harbour/marina 2 km. from the campsite where it is possible to berth your boat. The coastline in the area is ideal for sailing and the sea is excellent for snorkelling and diving with the spectacular underwater rock formations. For those looking for a camping experience under the shade of olive trees, this is the perfect spot. Apart from the basics, and the friendliness of the family who owns it, it has nothing to offer but that is one of its charms. One of the few signs in English said 'Don't throw away your old bread – we can give it to the chickens' and that gives an indication of the owner's attitude. Shops, bars and restaurants are all within walking distance and the road from Corfu town, 19 km. away, is good and avoids the island's infamous narrow, steep zigzags.

Two clean toilet blocks include showers (hot water), WCs, washbasins, razor and hairdryer points and sinks for laundry. Separate covered kitchen area. Indoor cooking area (facilities not supplied) and indoor dining area. Charcoal barbecue only.

Key Features

Play Area

Scan me for more information.

Clifden, Roundstone and Connemara >

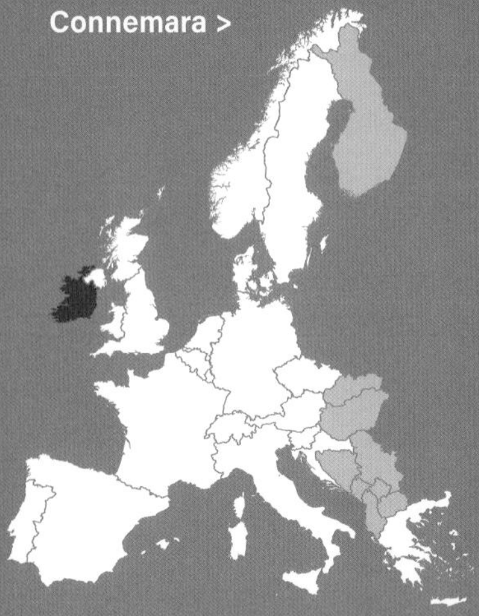

Capital Dublin
Currency Euro (€)
Language English and Irish
Time Zone GMT
Telephone Code 00 353

Tourist Website
ireland.com

Climate Oceanic climate. Summers are cool to mild with temperatures rarely exceeding 25C. Winters are cold but not freezing, and often rainy.

Shops 9.30am to 6pm Mon to Sat (to 8pm Thurs in cities), noon to 6pm Sun.

Banks 10am to 4pm weekdays (to 5pm Thurs).

Accessible Travel All new buildings are wheelchair-friendly. In cities, most buses have low-floor access. Trains are accessible (contact in advance).

Travelling with children
Children are welcomed in Ireland, although family facilities aren't always accessible in rural spots. Most restaurants accept children although some high-end establishments may not. Children under five travel free on all public transport.

See campsite map pages

480

Public Holidays New Year's Day, St Patrick's Day, Easter Monday, May Day, June Bank Holiday (first Monday in June), August Bank Holiday (first Monday in August), October Bank Holiday (last Monday in October), Christmas Day, Boxing Day.

Motoring Driving is on the left-hand side and roads are generally well maintained. Tolls exist in the Republic, generally paid at the barrier. Speed limits are 50 km/h in built-up areas, 120 km/h on motorways. Signposts are in both Gaelic and English in most areas (where Irish is the primary language signage is in Gaelic).

Environmental Policies There are currently no Low Emission Zones enforced in Ireland. Recycling is widespread and Ireland has some of the highest recycling rates in Europe. Metal (no aluminium foil or trays), plastic, paper and cardboard are all recycled via kerbside collections or recycling stations in cities and towns. Glass should be taken to local bottle banks to be recycled.

View all campsites in Ireland
alanrogers.com/ireland

Ireland

Ireland is made up of four provinces: Connaught, Leinster, Munster and Ulster, comprising 32 counties, 26 of which lie in the Republic of Ireland.

Famed for its folklore, traditional music and friendly hospitality, the Republic of Ireland offers spectacular scenery contained within a relatively compact area. With plenty of beautiful areas to discover, and a relaxed pace of life, it is an ideal place to unwind.

Ireland is the perfect place to indulge in a variety of outdoor pursuits while taking in the glorious scenery. There are plenty of waymarked footpaths which lead through woodlands, across cliffs, past historical monuments and over rolling hills. The dramatic coastline, with its headlands, secluded coves and sandy beaches, is fantastic for watersports or for just simply relaxing and watching the variety of seabirds that nest on the shores.

The Cliffs of Moher, in particular, is a prime location for birdwatching and Goat Island, just offshore, is where puffins make their nesting burrows.

In the south the beautiful Ring of Kerry is one of the most visited regions. This 110 mile route encircles the Inveragh Peninsula and is surrounded by mountains and lakes. Other sights include the Aran Islands, the Rock of Cashel and the bustling cities of Dublin, Galway and Cork.

Alan Rogers Code: IR8695
55 pitches
GPS: 54.27242, -8.60448

Co. Sligo, North West

Strandhill Caravan Park

www.alanrogers.com/ir8695
strandhillcvp@eircom.net
Tel: 071 916 8111
sligocaravanandcamping.ie

Open (Touring Pitches):
Easter - 25 September.

This seaside park is located on 20 acres of undulating grass on a sandy base, with natural protection from the coastal breezes of the famous Strandhill beach. There are 55 hardstanding pitches for caravans and motorhomes, with electricity and ample water points, and two camping areas for tents, one with views of the sea and the second more sheltered. Throughout the site, many hollows provide ideal pitches for tents. Strandhill, world recognised as a surfing Mecca, also offers activities for all the family. There are miles of sandy beach and dunes, and the Knocknarea Mountain is a popular choice for walkers.

The toilet block (keys provided on deposit) is clean and fresh with hot showers (token €1.50), electric hand dryers and hairdryer. New reception building, including a TV room, games room, campers' kitchen, laundry and a well-equipped facility for disabled visitors. WiFi over part of the site (charged). Automatic gate and door control.

Key Features

- Pets Accepted
- Disabled Facilities
- Beach Access

Scan me for more information.

Alan Rogers Code: IR9080
64 pitches
GPS: 53.01390, -6.92560

Co. Kildare, Heart

Forest Farm

www.alanrogers.com/ir9080
forestfarm@eircom.net
Tel: 059 863 1231
www.accommodationathy.com

Open (Touring Pitches):
All year.

This site makes an excellent stopover if travelling from Dublin to the southeast counties. It is also ideally placed to visit local places of interest including the Shackleton exhibition, the Japanese Gardens and the Irish National Stud. Part of a working farm, the campsite spreads to the right of the modern farmhouse, which also provides B&B and holiday apartments. The owners have cleverly utilised their land to create a site which offers 64 unmarked touring pitches on level ground. Of these, 32 are for caravans, all with electricity and ten with hardstanding, and 32 places are available for tents. Full Irish breakfasts are served at the farmhouse, and farm tours are arranged on request. The park is signed on the R418 and approached by a 500-metre avenue of tall pines.

The centrally located, red brick toilet block is heated and double glazed. Spacious shower unit for disabled visitors. Family room with shower and WC. Laundry room. Campers' kitchen with fridge/freezer, cooker, table and chairs. Comfortable, large lounge/games room (a TV can be provided). Sandpit and picnic tables.

Key Features

- OPEN 365 Open All Year
- Pets Accepted
- Disabled Facilities

Scan me for more information.

Alan Rogers Code: IR9130
42 pitches
GPS: 53.06924, -6.22269

Co. Wicklow, Heart

www.alanrogers.com/ir9130
info@dublinwicklowcamping.com
Tel: 012 818 163
dublinwicklowcamping.com

Open (Touring Pitches):
27 April - 3 September.

Roundwood Caravan Park

In the heart of the Wicklow mountains, the hospitable owner of this park maintains high standards. It is neatly laid out with rows of trees dividing the different areas and giving an attractive appearance. There are 42 hardstanding pitches for caravans and motorhomes, some sloping, all with electricity (16A), plus 30 pitches for tents, arranged off tarmac access roads. There are excellent walks around the Varty Lakes and a daily bus service to Dublin city. Close by are the Wicklow Mountains and the Sally Gap, Glendalough, Powerscourt Gardens, plus many other places of natural beauty. Apart from its scenic location, this site is well placed for the ferry ports.

The sanitary block is kept clean, with adequate washing and toilet facilities, plus spacious showers on payment (€ 1). Good laundry facilities, but ask at reception as machines are not self-service. Motorhome services. Campers' kitchen and dining room. TV room. Adventure playground. WiFi (charged). Bicycle hire.

Key Features

- Pets Accepted
- Play Area
- Bar/Restaurant
- Bike Hire

Scan me for more information.

Alan Rogers Code: IR8960
60 pitches
GPS: 53.44815, -7.88992

Co. Westmeath, Heart

www.alanrogers.com/ir8960
athlonecamping@eircom.net
Tel: 090 647 8561
www.athlonecamping.com

Open (Touring Pitches):
Mid-April - End September.

Athlone - Lough Ree East

This touring park is alongside the Breensford river, screened by trees but reaching the water's edge. The park is discreetly located behind Ballykeeran's main street. The top half of the site is in woodland, and after the reception and sanitary block, Lough Ree comes into view, and the remaining pitches run down to the shoreline. There are 60 pitches, most on hardstanding and all with 6A electricity. With fishing right on the doorstep, there are boats for hire locally, and the site has private mooring buoys, plus a dinghy slip and harbour. A restaurant and 'singing' pub are close.

The toilet block is clean, and the recently refurbished ladies' toilets, unisex showers (€ 1) and facilities for disabled visitors are all excellent. Dishwashing sinks outside. Laundry room (wash and dry € 8). A wooden chalet houses a pool room with open fire and campers' kitchen (no cooking facilities).

Key Features

- Pets Accepted
- Disabled Facilities
- Play Area
- Fishing
- Sailing

Scan me for more information.

Alan Rogers Code: IR9240
30 pitches
GPS: 52.64270, -7.22199

Co. Kilkenny, South East

www.alanrogers.com/ir9240
info@kilkennycamping.com
Tel: 086 89 08 845
kilkennycamping.com

Open (Touring Pitches):
1 March - 15 November.

Kilkenny - Treegrove Camp

This park appeals to many because of its proximity to the impressive and historic town of Kilkenny. The site is terraced with the lower terrace to the right of the wide-sweeping driveway laid out with 30 hardstanding pitches for caravans. All pitches have 10A electricity hook-ups, and plenty of water points are to be found. There are 13 full-service pitches. On the higher level is a grass area for hikers and cyclists, with further caravan and tent pitches sited on grass near the elevated sanitary block. There is some road noise, which can be distracting.

Family room with shower, WC and washbasin which can be used by disabled campers. Laundry room. Open, covered kitchen for campers with fridge, worktop, sink and electric kettle adjoins a comfortable games/TV room with pool table, and easy chairs. Bicycle hire. Riding. Tents to rent. Free WiFi.

Key Features

- Pets Accepted
- Disabled Facilities
- Bike Hire
- Horse Riding

Scan me for more information.

Alan Rogers Code: IR9300
100 pitches
GPS: 52.51686, -6.23785

Co. Wexford, South East

Morriscastle Strand

www.alanrogers.com/ir9300
info@morriscastlestrand.com
Tel: 053 913 0124
morriscastlestrand.com

Open (Touring Pitches):
Early April - End September.

Whether you use this park as a stopover, to or from Rosslare Port, or choose it for a more extended stay, you will find it to be a quiet relaxing location. Situated minutes from the pretty village of Kilmuckridge it offers well maintained and clean facilities. The 100 pitches are numbered and marked by concrete slabs, each with electricity (10A) and drainage point. Spacing can be a little tight in high season when the park gets very busy. There are 145 privately owned caravan holiday homes on-site, but these are unobtrusive and kept separate by tall hedging. The entrance to the touring park is to the right of reception by way of a tarmac drive. This leads to the secluded, gently sloping, grass pitches which enjoy an open aspect. They overlook marshland which attracts wild geese and ducks, while the sea brings in crabs, eels and fish.

Two sanitary blocks, one opened for the high season, include showers, WCs and facilities for disabled visitors. Launderette. Motorhome services. Good night lighting. Shop, snacks and takeaway in high season. Games room (from June). Two tennis courts. Play area. Dogs are only accepted in certain areas.

Key Features

- Disabled Facilities
- Play Area

Scan me for more information.

Alan Rogers Code: IR9560
40 pitches
GPS: 51.75881, -10.09112

Co. Kerry, South West

Wave Crest Caravan Park

www.alanrogers.com/ir9560
wavecrest@eircom.net
Tel: 066 947 5188
www.wavecrestcamping.com

Open (Touring Pitches):
All year.

It would be difficult to imagine a more dramatic location than Wave Crest on the Ring of Kerry coast. Huge boulders and rocky outcrops tumble from the park entrance on the N70 down to the seashore which forms the most southern peninsula on the Ring of Kerry. There are spectacular southward views from the park across Kenmare Bay to the Beara peninsula. Sheltering on grass patches in small coves that nestle between the rocks and shrubbery, are 40 hardstanding pitches and 23 on grass offering seclusion. Electricity connections are available (13A). A unique feature is the TV room, an old stone farm building with a thatched roof. Its comfortable interior includes a stone fireplace heated by a converted cast iron marker buoy. Caherdaniel is known for its lively little pubs and distinguished restaurant. The Derrynane National Park Nature Reserve is only a few kilometres away, as is Derrynane Cove and Bay.

Two blocks house the sanitary and laundry facilities and include hot showers on payment (€ 1). Small shop, restaurant and takeaway service (June-Sept). Small play area. Fishing and boat launching. WiFi throughout (charged). Boat trips from the site.

Key Features

- Open All Year
- Pets Accepted
- Beach Access
- Play Area
- Bar/Restaurant
- Fishing
- Sailing

Scan me for more information.

Alan Rogers Code: IR9515
7 accommodations
6 pitches
GPS: 51.66875, -9.26105

Co. Cork, South West

Top of the Rock Pod Páirc

www.alanrogers.com/ir9515
david@topoftherock.ie
Tel: 028 31547
topoftherock.ie

Open (Touring Pitches):
All year (excl. Christmas and own holidays).

This family site is located in the heart of West Cork, near Ireland's Atlantic coast amid nine miles of beautiful walking trails in an area rich in folklore, history and culture. The working farm provides a space to pitch tents (six 6A Europlug electricity sockets and water) and a purpose-built quarter of an acre for six camper vans (no caravans), on gravel, with full access to facilities. There are seven pods to rent, dispersed throughout the farm, their design inspired by early Christian structures. A well-placed centre to explore a beautiful rural environment of farmland, woodland, water, flora and fauna.

Sanitary facilities with provision for disabled visitors (showers 5 mins. for € 1). Laundry room with drying area, dryer and washing machine. Self-catering campers' kitchen with fridge, cookers, kettles etc. Breakfast delivered to pitches. Campfire area. Playground. Grass area for football and volleyball. Games room with table tennis, pool (€ 1), board games. Barbecue and grill for hire. WiFi in reception (free).

Key Features

- Open All Year
- Pets Accepted
- Disabled Facilities
- Play Area

Scan me for more information.

Alan Rogers Code: IR8760
28 pitches
GPS: 53.86000, -9.29000

Co. Mayo, West

www.alanrogers.com/ir8760
mail@carrowkeelpark.ie
Tel: +353 (0)94 903 1264
www.carrowkeelpark.ie

Open (Touring Pitches):
1 April - 1 October

Carrowkeel Caravan Park

What appeals most about this campsite is its quiet, 'heart of the countryside' location and well-kept appearance. Attractively laid out amidst undulating grass areas, trees and shrubs are 28 touring pitches on hardstanding (16A electricity) and a designated area for 30 tents. Adjacent to the camping area stand several buildings which are gradually being refurbished. These house reception, shop, a clubhouse serving meals and takeaway food, also a campers' kitchen and games room. For children, there is a play area, and for fishers, the Clydagh River borders this 3.5-acre site.

A reasonably modern toilet block standing in an elevated position on-site, provides open style washbasins, preset showers in cabins with curtains and seats. Toilet units for disabled visitors. Laundry room (laundry service option, small charge). Campers' kitchen. Shop and clubhouse for meals and takeaway (all season). Play area. River fishing. WiFi throughout (free).

Key Features

- Pets Accepted
- Disabled Facilities
- Play Area
- Bar/Restaurant
- Fishing

Scan me for more information.

Alan Rogers Code: IR8870
49 pitches
GPS: 53.25680, -9.10491

Co. Galway, West

Salthill Caravan Park

www.alanrogers.com/ir8870
info@salthillcaravanpark.com
Tel: 091 523 972
www.salthillcaravanpark.com

Open (Touring Pitches):
1 April - 29 September.

Salthill Caravan Park was first opened in 1960 and has been run by the O'Malley family ever since. The park comprises five acres of mobile homes and a three-acre campsite, near the water's edge. The park has superb views over Galway Bay and has access to a shingle beach, just 100 m. distant. The 49 touring pitches are grassy and open, all with 10A electrical connections and 35 hardstanding. Adjacent to the site, there is a pleasant coastal pathway which leads to Galway City and sandy beaches (800 m). Off-site, there is a friendly pub (200 m) and a large, well-stocked supermarket (600 m). Salthill beach is actually several sandy Blue Flag beaches separated by rocky outcrops. Windsurfing, kayaking and paddleboarding are all popular, and courses are available nearby. The Galway Atlantiquaria is Ireland's premier aquarium and boasts more than 170 species of freshwater and marine life. Galway City is renowned for its Arts festival in July when the city welcomes over 100,000 visitors for a varied programme of visual art, music, theatre and dance.

One toilet block in the middle of the touring pitches also contains a washing machine and dryer (€ 5 each), sinks (hot water charged). Showers by reception (on payment). Limited facilities for disabled visitors. Limited grocery items in reception. Children's playground. Games room. WiFi throughout (free).

Key Features

- Pets Accepted
- Play Area

Scan me for more information.

Portofino, Amalfi Coast >

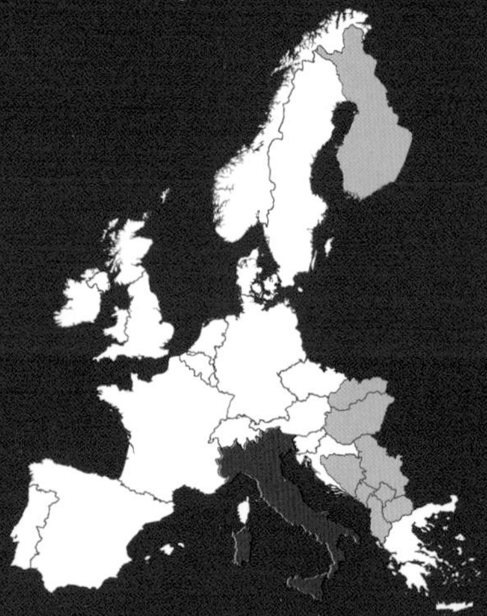

Capital Rome
Currency Euro (€)
Language Italian
Time Zone CET (GMT+1)
Telephone Code 00 39

Tourist Website
italia.it

Climate The south enjoys hot summers and mild, dry winters whilst the north is cooler with heavy snow in winter.

Shops Varied. In high-season 9am to 1pm and 3.30pm to 7.30pm Mon to Sat, some also open Sunday.

Banks 8.30am to 1.30pm and 2.45pm to 4.30pm weekdays.

Accessible Travel Not as well-equipped for wheelchair users as some of its European neighbours. Awareness is growing and museums/galleries offer reduced rates with ID.

Travelling with Children Very kid-friendly. Beaches are generally safe. State-run attractions are often free to EU citizens under 18 years of age. Few restaurants open before 7.30pm. Pizzerias usually open earlier.

See campsite map page

482

Public Holidays New Year's Day, Epiphany, Easter Sunday, Easter Monday, Liberation Day (25 Apr), Labour Day (1 May), Republic Day (2 Jun), Assumption, All Saints, Immaculate Conception, Christmas Day, Boxing Day.

Motoring Tolls are payable on the autostrada network. If travelling distances, save time by purchasing a 'Viacard' from pay booths or service areas. An overhanging load, e.g. a bicycle rack, must be indicated by a large red/white hatched warning square. Failure to do so will result in a fine.

Environmental Policies Italy has several Low Emission Zones with differing rules and time periods which are determined by the local authorities and monitored by cameras and vehicle number plate recognition systems. Recycling varies greatly from region to region but generally metal, plastic, glass, paper and cardboard are widely recycled.

View all campsites in Italy
alanrogers.com/italy

Italy

Italy, once the capital of the Roman Empire, was unified as recently as 1861, thus regional customs and traditions have not been lost. Its enviable collections of art, literature and culture have had worldwide influence and continue to be a magnet for visitors who flock to cities such as Venice, Florence and Rome.

In the north, the vibrant city of Milan is the fashion capital of the world and home to the famous opera house, La Scala, as well as Da Vinci's 'The Last Supper.' It is also a good starting-off point for the Alps; the Italian Lake District, incorporating Lake Garda, Lake Como and Lake Maggiore; the canals of Venice and the lovely town of Verona.

The hilly towns of central Italy are especially popular, with Siena, San Gimignano and Assisi among the most visited. The historic capital of Rome with its Colosseum and Vatican City is not to be missed.

Naples is an ideal base for visiting Pompeii and the breathtaking scenery of the Amalfi coast but the city also has a charm of its own – winding narrow streets and crumbling façades inset with shrines sit alongside boutiques, bars and lively street markets, amid chaotic traffic and roaring scooters.

Alan Rogers Code: IT62150
13 accommodations
150 pitches
GPS: 45.58855, 7.34293
Post Code: I-11012

Cogne, Valle d'Aosta

Camping Lo Stambecco

www.alanrogers.com/it62150
info@campeggiolostambecco.it
Tel: 0165 741 52
www.campeggiolostambecco.it

Open (Touring Pitches):
20 May - 20 September.

Lo Stambecco (the Alpine ibex) is tucked away deep in the Gran Paradiso National Park. After an enthralling scenic mountain drive, you will reach this small site with breathtaking views of the mountains and glaciers. The grass pitches are informally arranged on slopes and terraces (levelling aids are useful) and all have great views. Electricity is available (3A Europlug; long leads useful). Clean crisp air, beautiful views, the rushing clear mountain stream and the delightfully informal atmosphere make this a destination site. You decide whether to hike, bike, raft or simply relax and let it all soak in. The Gran Paradiso National Park with its flora and fauna is a must for exploration, and the scenery alone makes the journey worthwhile. The very friendly English-speaking owner will gladly assist in arranging all manner of Alpine and adventure activities. Waking up to the sound of birdsong, and watching the sunrise and set on the snow-clad mountain peaks are pleasures for all at this site. Walks in the upper part of the site may be rewarded by spotting the deer-like camoscio or even the Alpine ibex. The village has traditional bars and restaurants, and the little church is a delight.

The two toilet blocks are mature but clean. WCs are a mixture of Turkish and British style. Baby baths to borrow. Washing machine. Motorhome services. Bar and lounge with games and library. Torches useful. WiFi (free).

Key Features

- Pets Accepted
- Disabled Facilities
- Bar/Restaurant
- Skiing

Scan me for more information.

Alan Rogers Code: IT62419
20 pitches
GPS: 45.82331, 8.41398
Post Code: I-28028

Pettenasco, Piedmont

Camping Royal

www.alanrogers.com/it62419
info@campingroyal.com
Tel: 0323 888 945
www.campingroyal.com

Open (Touring Pitches):
1 March - 30 November.

It would be difficult to find a more beautiful lake than Orta, surrounded by wooded hills and mountains and fringed with ancient towns and villages. Camping Royal, family owned and run, sits on a hillside overlooking the lake. There are 60 pitches, 20 for touring, set on level terraces, each with 5A Europlug and a water point nearby. Although professionally managed, this site has maintained the typical relaxed informality for which Italy is famous. Popular with campers from all over Europe, many return year after year. Nothing seems to be too much trouble to ensure a memorable stay.

Refurbished toilet block has hot showers (20c tokens) and a mixture of British and Turkish style toilets. New wet room for disabled campers by reception. Washing machine and dryer. Laundry and dishwashing sinks. Fridges. Shop with takeaway pizzas. Bar. New swimming pool. Playground. Football field. Room with games, library, cooking hobs and TV. Children's activities (daily in July/August) and some entertainment for adults. Shuttle bus to San Giulio in season (€2 return). Bicycle, scooter and car hire arranged. Internet cabin. WiFi (charged).

Key Features

- Pets Accepted
- Disabled Facilities
- Swimming Pool
- Play Area
- Bar/Restaurant
- Skiing
- Bike Hire

Scan me for more information.

Alan Rogers Code: IT64160
58 accommodations
65 pitches
GPS: 44.22625, 9.55020
Post Code: I-19013

Deiva Marina, Ligúria

Camping la Sfinge

www.alanrogers.com/it64160
info@campinglasfinge.com
Tel: 0187 825 464
www.campinglasfinge.com

Open (Touring Pitches):
Mid March - Early November.

La Sfinge is peacefully located in the famous area of Cinque Terre and stylish Portofino, in a landscape of pine and acacia trees, with some panoramic views. Most of the 65 touring pitches are located at the lower level with tent pitches on pleasant terraces, some with views. There are permanent residents on the site but they are separated from the touring pitches. A set evening meal is prepared at a good price with barbecues in high season. There is a free private shuttle service to the beach and to the railway station to explore the region. The owners are diligent, keen to please and speak good English. There is a pleasant atmosphere at this small, uncomplicated site just 3 km. from the sea. It would particularly suit those who like different types of watersports.

Clean and modern sanitary facilities including a locked WC for disabled visitors. Washing machines, spin dryers and ironing area. Communal fridge. Small but comprehensive shop. Snack bar producing evening menu. Sports ground and safe play area for children. Free mobile phone charging facility. International phone. Animation for children at weekends in July/Aug. 27 tents for hire. Bus service to beach. No electric barbecues. Free WiFi over site.

Key Features

- Pets Accepted
- Disabled Facilities
- Play Area
- Bar/Restaurant

Scan me for more information.

Alan Rogers Code: IT64024
107 accommodations
45 pitches
GPS: 43.90876, 8.07049
Post Code: I-18013

Diano Marina, Ligúria

Camping Edy

www.alanrogers.com/it64024
info@campingedy.it
Tel: 0183 497 040
www.campingedy.it

Open (Touring Pitches):
All year.

Camping Edy is close to Diano Marina and covers an area of about 2.5 hectares. It is a steeply sloping site with panoramic views from the top-level over the surrounding olive groves. The pitches for touring units are on the lowest level on gravel with some small hedges for separation, and some are in the shade of mature olive trees. All have electricity, water and drainage. The toilet blocks are some distance and up steep roadways. A separate area is reserved for tents. Several designs of modern, fully equipped mobile homes can be rented. The convivial bar and terrace on the top level are pleasant spots to relax. The coast and town of Diano Marina are some 800 m. away, but there is a regular, free minibus service run by the campsite. The Gulf of Diano is part of the Mediterranean Sea mammals park. Boat trips allow you to get up close to whales and dolphins in the open water. Other excursions from the site include Genoa, Nice and the exotic gardens at Menton on the French border.

Laundry. Bar and snacks. Swimming pool. Multisports court. Playground. Organised entertainment. Bicycle hire. Accommodation to rent. WiFi.

Key Features

- Open All Year
- Pets Accepted
- Swimming Pool
- Play Area
- Bar/Restaurant
- Bike Hire

Scan me for more information.

Alan Rogers Code: IT62595
13 accommodations
83 pitches
GPS: 45.66667, 10.06694
Post Code: I-25049

Iseo, Lombardy

www.alanrogers.com/it62595
info@campingcovelo.it
Tel: 0309 8213 05
www.campingcovelo.com

Open (Touring Pitches):
1 April – 31 October.

Camping Covelo

Covelo has a superb lakeside location and is one of the friendliest family sites we have visited in Italy. It is three hundred metres long, with grassy pitches and mature trees. The average sized, level pitches are in rows parallel with the shores of the lake. As the site is just four pitches deep, all have excellent access to the water plus brilliant views of the mountains across the lake and the tree-clad escarpment to the rear of the site. The owners take great pride in their site, insisting on high levels of simple family-style enjoyment for their guests. Although the site is small, the creative owners of Covelo have worked wonders in getting the maximum from their site for their guests to feel relaxed and have an enjoyable holiday.

Three refurbished sanitary blocks of differing sizes provide pleasant facilities including those for disabled visitors. Baby cubicle. Motorhome services. Shop. Bar. Restaurant. Small play area. Entertainment. TV room. Big screen movies at night. Free bicycles for guests. Fishing. Boat launching. Buoys for boats. Free WiFi.

Key Features

- Pets Accepted
- Disabled Facilities
- Play Area
- Bar/Restaurant
- Bike Hire
- Fishing
- Horse Riding

Scan me for more information.

Alan Rogers Code: IT62090
59 accommodations
149 pitches
GPS: 46.41987, 11.70754
Post Code: I-38036

Pozza di Fassa, Trentino - Alto Adige

Camping Vidor

www.alanrogers.com/it62090
info@campingvidor.it
Tel: 0462 760 022
www.campingvidor.it

Open (Touring Pitches):
All year except November.

Camping Vidor - Family & Wellness Resort is a very smart, family-run site is in a beautiful mountainous setting and has the most fabulous infrastructure. The 150 pitches are of average size with 16A electricity connections, some also with water, drainage and hardstanding. Vidor has excellent facilities including a super new reception, camping shop, high-quality restaurant and pizzeria (serving local cuisine with special menus for children), and a café with terrace and lounge. There is a wellness centre with an indoor heated swimming pool with whirlpool etc. (charged), plus a superb beauty centre offering a large variety of modern treatments. This is a stunning site with all you need for a family holiday in the mountains. The support buildings on site are most attractive and use green energy. Sophisticated indoor playrooms for children and teenagers are here, a miniclub, a TV room and a cinema with a busy programme can all be accessed by lift.

Two truly excellent, hotel standard heated sanitary blocks provide hot water throughout and very good showers with private bathrooms for hire. Facilities for disabled visitors. Washing machines, drying room and dryer. Fridge and freezer. Bar/restaurant with superb views, takeaway and shop. Beauty and wellness centre, heated indoor pool and gym (charged). TV room and cinema. Indoor playrooms and miniclub. Bicycle hire. Entertainment programme. WiFi throughout (charged).

Key Features

- Pets Accepted
- Disabled Facilities
- Swimming Pool
- Play Area
- Bar/Restaurant
- Skiing
- Bike Hire

Scan me for more information.

Alan Rogers Code: IT62300
3 accommodations
157 pitches
GPS: 46.03855, 11.23698
Post Code: I-38057

Pergine Valsugana, Trentino - Alto Adige

www.alanrogers.com/it62300
info@campingclub.it
Tel: 0461 512 707
www.campingsancristoforo.it

Open (Touring Pitches):
11 May - 3 September.

Camping San Cristoforo

This part of Italy is becoming better known by those wishing to spend time by a lake in the splendid countryside, but away from the more crowded, better-known resorts. Lake Caldonazzo is one of the smaller Italian lakes but is excellent for watersports. Camping San Cristoforo is a relatively new site on the edge of the small town of the same name and is separated from the lake by a minor road, but with easy access. There are 157 pitches on flat grass with tarmac access roads, separated by shady trees. The pitches are of a good size and all have 6A electricity. The site is owners aim is to build a happy family atmosphere and the manager speaks excellent English.

The large, modern sanitary block provides some washbasins in cabins and pushbutton showers (with plenty of changing room). Facilities for disabled visitors. Washing machine and dryer. Motorhome services. No shop (but village nearby). Attractive bar/restaurant with takeaway serving reasonably priced food. Swimming pool (20x20 m) with sunbathing area and children's pool. Play area. Beach volleyball. Bicycle hire. Minigolf. Programme of activities (high season).

Key Features

- Pets Accepted
- Disabled Facilities
- Swimming Pool
- Play Area
- Bar/Restaurant
- Bike Hire

Scan me for more information.

Alan Rogers Code: IT62750
178 accommodations
266 pitches
GPS: 45.58497, 10.56582
Post Code: I-25010

San Felice del Benaco, Lake Garda

www.alanrogers.com/it62750
fornella@fornella.it
Tel: 036 562 294
www.fornella.it

Open (Touring Pitches):
23 April - 25 September.

Fornella Camping

Fornella Camping is one of the few campsites on Lake Garda still surrounded by farmed olive trees and retaining a true country atmosphere. Parts of the crisp, clean site have great lake views, others a backdrop of mountains and attractive countryside. The 266 touring pitches are on flat grass, terraced where necessary and most have good shade, all with 6/10A electricity; 101 have water and a drain as well. The remaining pitches are used for mobile homes to rent. The staff speak excellent English and Dutch. A superb lagoon pool complex is here, along with a more traditional pool. These are supplemented by a pleasant bar, and a restaurant with terrace overlooking the lakeside.

Three very clean, modern toilet blocks, well dispersed around the site, have mainly British type WCs and hot water in washbasins (some in cabins), showers and sinks. Facilities for disabled visitors. Washing machines, dryer and irons. Motorhome services. Bar/restaurant. Pizzeria and takeaway. Shop. Supervised heated swimming pools and paddling pool (all season). Tennis. Two playgrounds and entertainment for children in season. Bicycle hire (high season). Beach. Fishing. Small marina, boat launching and repairs. WiFi throughout (charged).

Key Features

- Pets Accepted
- Disabled Facilities
- Swimming Pool
- Play Area
- Bar/Restaurant
- Bike Hire
- Fishing

Scan me for more information.

Alan Rogers Code: IT62780
15 pitches
GPS: 45.56344, 10.55280
Post Code: I-25080

Manerba del Garda, Lake Garda

Camping Garden Tourist

www.alanrogers.com/it62780
info@gardentourist.it
Tel: 0365 651 428
www.gardentourist.it

Open (Touring Pitches):
Early April - Mid September.

This is a tiny, basic site with few amenities on the outskirts of Manerba del Garda, just 50 metres from a shingle beach. It has a small pool and a very old fashioned, but clean toilet block. There are just 15 level touring pitches all with 4A electricity and with shade provided by mature trees. The remaining 30 pitches are occupied by permanent caravans and accommodation for hire. The friendly young owner speaks excellent English and is keen to welcome British and Dutch visitors. There is a restaurant and bar adjoining the site and a small supermarket just 400 m. along the road. Manerba is on the less commercialised western side of Lake Garda, but it still gets very crowded in high season, so this site could provide a haven. The theme and water parks and huge hypermarkets around the southern end of the lake are still within easy reach if you fancy a change of mood!

Small traditional toilet block with stable doors and controllable showers. A mix of British and Turkish style WCs. Open washbasins, washing and laundry sinks (all with hot water) under cover. Facility for disabled visitors (moveable ramp). Washing machine. Motorhome services. Small outdoor swimming pool (1/5-15/9). WiFi. Accommodation for hire.

Key Features

- Pets Accepted
- Disabled Facilities
- Swimming Pool
- Play Area

Scan me for more information.

Alan Rogers Code: IT62600
248 accommodations
108 pitches
GPS: 45.57447, 10.54857
Post Code: I-25010

San Felice del Benaco, Lake Garda

Camping Europa Silvella

www.alanrogers.com/it62600
info@europasilvella.it
Tel: 0365 651095
www.europasilvella.it

Open (Touring Pitches):
21 April - 26 September.

This large, traditional, lakeside site is a merger of two different sites with the result that the 354 pitches (about 110 for touring units) appear randomly dispersed around the site. However, those alongside the lake are in small groups and close together; the main bar, restaurant and shop are also located at the lower level. The main area is at the top of a fairly steep hill on slightly sloping or terraced grass and has slightly larger pitches. There is reasonable shade in many parts and all pitches have 4A electricity. Nine pitches of 120 sq.m. with 10A electricity have been added. An attractive swimming pool complex also has a daytime bar and a restaurant which serves lunch and is the hub of the evening entertainment programme in high season. There is a considerable tour operator presence (160 pitches) and there are 50 bungalows, mobile homes and log cabins to rent. The site has steep slopes to the lake, so is unsuitable for campers with disabilities. The beach is suitable for swimming and has a jetty and moorings. A choice of watersports is available.

Toilet blocks include washbasins in cabins, facilities for disabled visitors and a superb children's room with small showers. Laundry. Shop. Restaurant/pizzeria. Swimming pools (11/5-13/9, hats required) with bar. Tennis, volleyball and five-a-side soccer. Playground. Bowling alley. Entertainment (every night in July/Aug). Disco for children. Bicycle hire. Tournaments. Fishing and boat launching. First aid room. WiFi on part of site (charged).

Key Features

- Pets Accepted
- Disabled Facilities
- Swimming Pool
- Play Area
- Bar/Restaurant
- Bike Hire
- Fishing

Scan me for more information.

Alan Rogers Code: IT60120
202 accommodations
298 pitches
GPS: 45.61660, 12.90655
Post Code: I-30021

Caorle, Veneto

www.alanrogers.com/it60120
info@campinglagunavillage.com
Tel: 0421 21 0165
www.campinglagunavillage.com

Open (Touring Pitches):
Mid April - Mid September.

Camping Laguna Village

Laguna Village is an unusual site located close to the lively Adriatic resort of Caorle. Three types of pitch are available here. Most pitches have 6A electrical connections, 100 are fully serviced and some have shade. It is split by the busy beach road and some long walks are required depending on your pitch. On-site amenities are impressive and include a large, lagoon-shaped swimming pool and a whirlpool. The beachside area is brilliant with safe waters and soft sand. Other amenities include an attractive restaurant/pizzeria and a well-stocked supermarket. Laguna Village is a lively site in peak season with a daily children's club and regular evening entertainment. Caorle is a delightful holiday town with narrow streets and brightly coloured, Venetian style houses. It is still an active fishing port and the beautiful seafront church dedicated to the Madonna del Angelo is still the focus of the town's annual fisherman's festival.

Laundry facilities. Motorhome services. Supermarket and bazaar. Restaurant/pizzeria. Two swimming pool complexes (from 9/5). Play area. ATM and currency exchange. Entertainment and activity programme (high season). WiFi (charged). Late arrival parking with electricity. Mobile homes to rent. Direct access to beach. Dogs are not accepted. Electric barbecues are not permitted.

Key Features

- Disabled Facilities
- Beach Access
- Swimming Pool
- Play Area
- Bar/Restaurant
- Bike Hire

Scan me for more information.

Alan Rogers Code: IT60560
82 accommodations
230 pitches
GPS: 45.19018, 12.30341
Post Code: I-30015

Sottomarina di Chioggia, Veneto

Camping Miramare

www.alanrogers.com/it60560
info@miramarecamping.com
Tel: 0414 906 10
www.miramarecamping.com

Open (Touring Pitches):
Mid April - Mid September.

Camping Miramare is a pleasant, fairly shady site with beach access, a swimming pool and a busy entertainment programme. The site is kept beautifully clean and is divided by a road with a reception on the beachside, along with most of the amenities. The other side is spacious and very peaceful with just sports amenities and a sanitary block. The 230 touring pitches are separated from the permanent units. All have 6A electricity and some have water and drainage. The beach is great, with soft sand and a lifeguard. You can hire sunshades and loungers. The restaurant offers traditional food and pizzas which can be enjoyed on the terraces overlooking the pools. Children have several play areas and there is entertainment on site all season. The swimming and paddling pool is excellent, with two diving boards and a lifeguard. The site lies close to the ancient city of Chioggia, famous for its fishing and Venice-like construction.

Three identical, modern, very clean blocks, one in the permanent campers' area. Pushbutton hot showers and mainly Turkish style toilets. Facilities for disabled visitors. Baby room. Laundry rooms. Motorhome services. Pleasant bar. Restaurant, pizzeria and takeaway, smart shop (all open all season). Excellent swimming pool and separate paddling pool (9/5-21/9). Several great play areas. Multisports court. Bicycle hire. Entertainment and children's activities (high season). WiFi over site (charged). Mobile homes to rent.

Key Features

- Pets Accepted
- Disabled Facilities
- Beach Access
- Swimming Pool
- Play Area
- Bar/Restaurant
- Bike Hire

Scan me for more information.

Alan Rogers Code: IT60050
498 accommodations
378 pitches
GPS: 45.69649, 13.45595
Post Code: I-34073

Grado, Friuli - Venézia Giúlia

www.alanrogers.com/it60050
info@villaggioeuropa.com
Tel: 043 180 877
www.villaggioeuropa.com

Open (Touring Pitches):
21 April - 18 September.

Villaggio Turistico Europa

This large, flat, high-quality site is beside the sea and has 500 pitches, with about 400 for touring units. They are all neat, clean and marked, most with shade and 6/10A electricity and 300 are fully serviced. The terrain is undulating and sandy in the areas nearer the sea, where cars have to be left in parking places. A huge, impressive aquatic park covers 1,500 sq.m. with two long slides, a whirlpool and many other features, including a pool bar. This is a very pleasant site with a spacious feel which families will enjoy. There is direct access to the beach, where local tidal activity presents a large, protected area for children to play and paddle under the gaze of the lifeguards. The beach bar is pleasant and a narrow wooden jetty gives access to deeper water and the tour boats. This is a neat, well-managed site setting high standards.

Five excellent, refurbished toilet blocks are well designed and kept very clean. Free hot water in all facilities, mostly British style WCs with excellent facilities for disabled visitors. Baby showers and baths. Washing machines. Dishwashers. Freezer. Motorhome services. Large supermarket, small general shop (all season). 3 bars and 2 restaurants with takeaway (all season). Gelateria. Swimming pools (1/5-17/9). Tennis. Fishing. Bicycle hire. Playground. Full entertainment programme in season. Miniclub. Football. Basketball. Minigolf. Archery. Watersports. Dancing lessons. WiFi (charged). Dogs are restricted to specific areas and not allowed on the beach.

Key Features

- Pets Accepted
- Disabled Facilities
- Beach Access
- Swimming Pool
- Play Area
- Bar/Restaurant
- Bike Hire
- Fishing

Scan me for more information.

Alan Rogers Code: IT60055
220 accommodations
331 pitches
GPS: 45.69467, 13.45255
Post Code: I-34073

Grado, Friuli - Venézia Giúlia

www.alanrogers.com/it60055
info@puntaspin.it
Tel: 0431 807 32
www.puntaspin.it

Open (Touring Pitches):
Early April - Mid September.

Camping Punta Spin

Punta Spin is a large, well-maintained site, set between the road and a soft sand beach. About 300 flat touring pitches vary in size (65-100 sq.m), all with 6A electricity, and with some on the beachfront (book early for these). A bicycle is an asset here to access the furthest sanitary blocks. The comprehensive amenities are clustered near the entrance and include three pools, one of which is a sophisticated paddling complex, another is covered and heated. The restaurant and bar terraces overlook the lit pools, making a great setting for dinner. This site has a distinctly Italian feel and will suit all families. A professional team organises all manner of entertainment in high season and an impressive Kids' Club is in full swing all day.

Three modernised sanitary blocks have free hot water throughout. Mostly British style toilets. Facilities for disabled campers. Washing machines and dryers. Motorhome services. Large supermarket and other shops. Bars and restaurant (April-Sept). Pizzeria. Takeaway. Three swimming pools. Beauty and fitness centre. Minigolf. Disco. Entertainment team in high season. Beach bar. Playground. Tennis. WiFi (charged). Bicycle hire. Bungalows and mobile homes for hire.

Key Features

- Pets Accepted
- Disabled Facilities
- Beach Access
- Swimming Pool
- Play Area
- Bar/Restaurant
- Bike Hire

Scan me for more information.

Alan Rogers Code: IT60730
109 accommodations
376 pitches
GPS: 44.46641, 12.28499
Post Code: I-48122

Marina di Ravenna, Emília-Romagna

Piomboni Camping Village

www.alanrogers.com/it60730
info@campingpiomboni.it
Tel: 054 453 0230
www.campingpiomboni.it

Open (Touring Pitches):
Mid April - Mid September.

The pine forest which is home to Piomboni forms part of the Po Delta National Forest and has been spared the frantic commercial development of other parts of the Adriatic coast. The site, still family-owned and run, maintains a totally natural feel with pitches located between the ancient, tall pines and younger, dividing trees. There are 376 pitches for everything from tiny tents to motorhomes up to 8 metres, all with 4-10A electricity. Access to the beach is just 100 metres from the site gate and there are large, free public areas. Road noise is negligible, and our night here was peaceful. Early in the evening, the children's singing and dancing near the restaurant makes for a happy family atmosphere. The restaurant offers fixed menus and à la carte, and is very reasonably priced. Other hostelries line the road a short walk from the site. Although there are commercial sunbed operators on the beach, there are open sections for public use.

Seven toilet blocks, two with hot and cold showers. Baby rooms. Facilities for disabled visitors. Washing machines and dryer. Dog bath. Well stocked shop. Bar, restaurant and takeaway (seasonal). Dancing and entertainments area. TV room with library. Games and play area with boules pitch. Children's activities programme. Archery. Bicycle hire. Free WiFi. Excursions arranged.

Key Features

- Pets Accepted
- Disabled Facilities
- Beach Access
- Bar/Restaurant
- Bike Hire

Scan me for more information.

Alan Rogers Code: IT66020
92 accommodations
120 pitches
GPS: 44.52366, 11.37410
Post Code: I-40127

Bologna, Emília-Romagna

www.alanrogers.com/it66020
info@hotelcamping.com
Tel: 0513 250 16
www.hotelcamping.com

Open (Touring Pitches):
9 January - 20 December.

Camping Città di Bologna

This spacious city site was established in 1993 on the edge of the Trade Fair Centre of this ancient and historic city and is very clean and modern. The 120 pitches, with 6A electricity, are numbered and marked out in a very orderly manner and shaded by trees. All pitches are on level 'grasscrete' hardstandings. There are two main areas plus a separate section for very long units. You will always find space here as there is huge over capacity. There is an unassuming restaurant and bar in a central location and the pleasant swimming pool with paddling area is very welcome after a day exploring the city. The site is excellent for an overnight stop or for longer stays to explore the most attractive and unusual city of Bologna.

Modern sanitary blocks include excellent provision for disabled visitors (with British style WCs, free showers and alarms that ring in reception). Washing machines. Motorhome services. Restaurant and bar with adjoining terrace where quality meals are offered. Large swimming pool with shallow area for children. Basic play area. Minigolf. Fitness centre. WiFi over site (first 15 mins. free).

Key Features

- Pets Accepted
- Disabled Facilities
- Swimming Pool
- Play Area
- Bar/Restaurant

Scan me for more information.

Alan Rogers Code: IT66360
151 accommodations
173 pitches
GPS: 43.25386, 10.55303
Post Code: I-57020

Bibbona, Tuscany

www.alanrogers.com/it66360
info@campinglecapanne.it
Tel: 0586 600 064
www.campinglecapanne.it

Open (Touring Pitches):
24 April - 20 September.

Camping le Capanne

Marina di Bibbona is a relatively little known resort situated a little to the south of Livorno and close to the better-known resort of Cecina. There are 324 good sized pitches, 173 for touring units, all with electricity and 40 with water and drainage. Most are well shaded by pine, olive and eucalyptus trees. The remainder of the site has a sunnier, more open setting with mobile homes or chalets belonging to the site or to tour operators. There is something for everyone here and the site has been thoughtfully designed and is well maintained. Lagoon-style pools with palm trees and extensive landscaped grass areas for sunbathing are a popular feature. The restaurant offers a reasonably priced and varied menu and there is also a brasserie and gelateria.

Three modern toilet blocks with plenty of hot water and toilets of British style. Washing machines. Shop and 'bazaar.' Bar and popular restaurant away from camping area near site entrance specialising in Tuscan cuisine. Large swimming pool and large play area. Bicycle hire. Entertainment programme in high season. Minigolf. WiFi. Golf practice field.

Key Features

- Pets Accepted
- Swimming Pool
- Play Area
- Bar/Restaurant
- Bike Hire
- Golf

Scan me for more information.

Alan Rogers Code: IT66760
105 accommodations
98 pitches
GPS: 42.77926, 10.80123
Post Code: I-58043

Castiglione della Pescaia, Tuscany

Camping Village Rocchette

www.alanrogers.com/it66760
booking@rocchette.com
Tel: 056 494 1123
www.rocchette.com

Open (Touring Pitches):
11 April - 19 October

Camping Village Rocchette can be found at the heart of the Maremma woods, 6 km. to the north of Castiglione della Pescaia. This well-maintained site includes 105 modern bungalows grouped around the high-quality facilities. The 98 flat, shady touring pitches with 6A electricity are in a separate area, further away from the facilities. A 300 m. walk will take you to the beach but the on-site pool complex here is stunning with several pools to choose from to suit all ages. Excursions are organised by the campsite and, during the high season, there is a lively entertainment programme. Castiglione is a delightful seaside town, best known for its beaches and the quality of its pizzas! This is a good starting point for excursions to the islands of the Tuscan archipelago, Elba, Giglio and Formiche, as well as Siena, Florence and Rome.

Sanitary facilities include private cubicles and facilities for disabled visitors. Laundry facilities. Supermarket and other shops, bar, restaurant and takeaway (all season). Swimming pool with whirlpools (from Mid April). Pool bar. Two children's pools. Tennis. Sports Courts (Padel - Beach Tennis/Volley). Play area. Bicycle hire. Windsurfing School. Free WiFi over part of site. Miniclub (Mid May - End August). Entertainment and activity programme (Mid May - End August). Direct but awkward access to beach 300 m. Brick Bungalows and Glamping tents (1-6 People).

Key Features

- Pets Accepted
- Disabled Facilities
- Swimming Pool
- Play Area
- Bar/Restaurant
- Bike Hire

Scan me for more information.

Alan Rogers Code: IT66088
246 accommodations
500 pitches
GPS: 43.33553, 10.46568
Post Code: I-57018

Vada, Tuscany

www.alanrogers.com/it66088
campofiori@multinet.it
Tel: 0586 770 096
www.campingcampodeifiori.net

Open (Touring Pitches):
End March - Mid September.

Camping Campo dei Fiori

Located some 35 kilometres south of Livorno and close to the Tuscany coast, this tranquil campsite offers both touring pitches and chalets to rent. The pitches are generally level with shade from established trees. All have electrical connections. The large swimming pool and children's pool are of a simple design and are supplemented by safe swimming and play in the sea, which is a short walk or cycle ride away. A well-stocked mini-market, bar and restaurant, together with evening music and entertainment for all ages provide all the essentials for a pleasant stay. Pets are permitted in the camping areas. Campo dei Fiori is close to several villages, some dating back to before 300BC, and also many popular tourist destinations. Vada, 1.5 km. from the campsite, has vast expanses of sparkling, white sand beaches and crystal clear sea. It offers many good seafood restaurants that serve locally caught fish. Romantic Florence, Pisa and Lucca can all be enjoyed on day trips, either by car or public transport.

Six sanitary blocks. Laundry. Shop. Café, bar and restaurant. Swimming pool. Play areas. Tennis. Bicycle hire. Accommodation to rent.

Key Features

- Pets Accepted
- Swimming Pool
- Play Area
- Bar/Restaurant
- Bike Hire

Scan me for more information.

Alan Rogers Code: IT66081
21 pitches
GPS: 43.83170, 10.42574
Post Code: 56017

San Giuliano Terme, Tuscany

www.alanrogers.com/it66081
info@agricampeggiolavalle.it
Tel: 331 421 4683
www.agricampeggiolavalle.it

Open (Touring Pitches):
Mid March - Mid November.

La Valle Agricampeggio

La Valle is welcoming family-run campsite, conveniently located between Pisa and Lucca in San Giuliano Terme. This small terraced campsite has 21 marked out, hard-standing pitches, all with electricity supplies. Set in an ancient quarry, this site benefits from continuing development, including a recently developed bar which serves light snacks from the region. The small pool offers welcome relief from the Tuscan sun or a sunbathing area if you prefer. A further 25 tent only pitches are also available. Pisa is just a short drive away with the attractions of the Cathedral of Santa Maria Assunta, Museo dell'Opera del Duomo being welcome alternatives to the obvious tower (comedy photographs obligatory!) The less well-known city of Lucca is a walled city with a cathedral dating back to the 13th century. A circuit of the town walls, built between 1500 and 1645 by Flemish engineers, should take about an hour

---

Open-air swimming pool (seasonal) Bar with a small shop. Free hot showers. Laundry room. Free WiFi throughout. Recreation room with satellite TV. Small children's play area. Communal BBQ area.

Key Features

- Disabled Facilities
- Swimming Pool
- Play Area
- Bar/Restaurant
- Bike Hire

Scan me for more information.

Alan Rogers Code: IT66380
800 accommodations
200 pitches
GPS: 43.04972, 10.55861
Post Code: I-57027

San Vincenzo, Tuscany

www.alanrogers.com/it66380
parkalbatros@ecvacanze.it
Tel: 0565 701 018
www.humancompany.com

Open (Touring Pitches):
23 April - 20 September.

Camping Park Albatros

Camping Albatros is situated on the historic Costa Degli Etruschi and is a huge site with something for everyone. Of the 1,000 shaded pitches (6/10A electricity), the 200 for touring are in a separate area on flat ground. All have water and drainage. The top-quality facilities and entertainment here are so good that you need not leave the site during your holiday. The extensive pools and water features are outstanding and the wide range of recreational facilities are superb. This is a great site for family holidays if you do not mind a few queues and several thousand people holidaying around you.

Two superb circular toilet blocks with brilliant rooms for children. All WCs are British style and there are hot showers and facilities for disabled visitors. Washing machines. Huge air-conditioned supermarket. Bazaar. Beauty salon. Lagoon complex with five amazing pools (one covered and heated). Central area includes two bars, two restaurants and pizzeria with large terrace with waiter service. Takeaway. Daily entertainment programme in season. Disco. Miniclub (4-12 yrs). Minigolf. New play areas (2013). Diving organised. Bicycle hire. No barbecues allowed. WiFi over site (charged). Train around site in high season.

Key Features

- Pets Accepted
- Disabled Facilities
- Swimming Pool
- Play Area
- Bar/Restaurant
- Bike Hire

Scan me for more information.

Alan Rogers Code: IT66470
14 accommodations
50 pitches
GPS: 43.35076, 12.68450
Post Code: I-06021

Costacciaro, Umbria

www.alanrogers.com/it66470
info@campingrioverde.it
Tel: 075 917 0181
www.campingrioverde.it

Open (Touring Pitches):
1 June - 30 September.

Camping Rio Verde

This is a very peaceful and straightforward campsite located in a wooded valley with plenty of shade. There are 50 informally arranged pitches with 6A electricity connections. Some pitches are a little uneven and the site slopes in parts. Amenities include a small, fenced swimming pool (with lifeguard) and a restaurant serving simple food from the region. This campsite is ideal for outdoor activity enthusiasts. The area is also excellent for hill walking and mountain biking, with a pleasant excursion possible up Monte Catria where wild horses graze on the lower slopes. Other than the attractions of the mountains, Fabriano is a picturesque little town, and there is an old Roman settlement at Gubbio.

A large, modern toilet block is a short walk. Facilities include British and Turkish style toilets and free showers. Facilities for disabled visitors (key from reception). Small shop. Restaurant. Swimming pool (mid June-Sept, hats compulsory). Play areas. Five-a-side. Riding. Chalets to rent. Communal barbecue. WiFi (free).

Key Features

- Pets Accepted
- Disabled Facilities
- Swimming Pool
- Play Area
- Bar/Restaurant
- Horse Riding

Scan me for more information.

Alan Rogers Code: IT68120
57 accommodations
275 pitches
GPS: 42.13011, 12.17353
Post Code: I-00062

Bracciano, Lazio

www.alanrogers.com/it68120
info@romaflash.it
Tel: 0699 805 458
www.romaflash.it

Open (Touring Pitches):
1 April - 30 September.

Camping Roma Flash

This pleasant site is in a superb location with magnificent views over Lake Bracciano and Castello Odescalchi. Although it was busy when we visited, it was still peaceful and relaxing. There are 275 flat, shaded pitches with 6A electricity (Europlug). A pleasant, covered restaurant offers pizza and a limited menu. Set alongside the lake with its fabulous views, the restaurant complex has a large terrace, as does a smaller indoor area. Elide speaks excellent English and will happily go out of her way to ensure guests enjoy their holiday. Many of the visitors told us that they return year after year and some stay for 8 to 12 weeks at a time, enjoying all that the Lazio region has to offer.

Two large, but tired sanitary blocks (scheduled for refurbishment) have free hot water throughout and fully adjustable showers. Facilities for disabled visitors in one block. Rooms for children. Laundry facilities. Gas supplies. Bar/restaurant/pizzeria, small shop (all open as site). Swimming pool (1/6-31/8). Play area. Watersports. Games room. Entertainment for children in high season. WiFi (charged). Excursions. Private bus to Roma San Pietro and return. Sports area.

Key Features

- Pets Accepted
- Disabled Facilities
- Swimming Pool
- Play Area
- Bar/Restaurant
- Bike Hire
- Fishing
- Sailing

Scan me for more information.

Alan Rogers Code: IT67780
428 accommodations
61 pitches
GPS: 41.77743, 12.39594
Post Code: I-00125

Roma, Lazio

Fabulous Camping Village

www.alanrogers.com/it67780
fabulous@humancompany.com
Tel: +39 06 5259354
humancompany.com

Open (Touring Pitches):
1 April - 31 October

Fabulous Camping Village is a venture by the 'Human' Company. Purchased a number of years ago, the re-developments are now complete and they have created a superb family campsite on top of a hill, midway between Rome and the sea. The site is attractively located under tall pine trees which give plenty of shade. Pitches are of varying size, all with 6/10A electricity and access is by tarmac and hardcore roads. They are frequently positioned close to the access routes so there can be a little noise. The wonderful 2 pools and jacuzzis, tennis courts and activity amenities are at the far end of the site where there are superb views towards Rome. two The amenities are by the reception and include an internet/ information area. Also here is a very large bar, entertainment area and restaurant. When we visited there were many young campers and it can become rather loud, however, on a site of this size quieter areas can be found.

Two blocks, one in traditional style in the permanent area and one new for the touring units. This block is excellent. Facilities for disabled visitors. Baby rooms. Washing machines. Motorhome services. Excellent supermarket. Restaurant/pizzeria and bar. Three swimming pools, one for paddling, with lifeguards. Play area. Tennis. Miniclub (5 yrs plus) and teenage activities. Entertainment programme for all ages. Bicycle hire. Internet. Torches useful. WiFi on part of site (charged). No charcoal barbecues permitted.

Key Features

- Pets Accepted
- Disabled Facilities
- Swimming Pool
- Play Area
- Bar/Restaurant

Scan me for more information.

Alan Rogers Code: IT68060
38 accommodations
58 pitches
GPS: 42.58140, 14.09290
Post Code: I-64025

Pineto, Abruzzo

www.alanrogers.com/it68060
into@internationalcamping.it
Tel: 085 930 639
www.internationalcamping.it

Open (Touring Pitches):
1 May - Mid September.

Camping Torre Di Cerrano

This small, very Italian, family-run site, just north of Pescara and south of Pineto, is situated between the coastal railway line and a superb sandy beach. Inevitably there is some railway noise. About 60 small pitches area available for touring units (cars parked away from pitches), all have 6A electricity and are shaded by trees which you will need to watch out for when manoeuvring. It is quieter than the larger sites that are usually found on this coast. During June to August, it is very much an Italian family site with entertainment and all sorts of fun and games on the beach. Nearby Pineto is a pleasant, small, seaside town with a small market, good restaurants and cafés and all essential shops. With a backdrop of the Gran Sasso d'Italia with its high, snow-capped peaks and with good communication links via autoroutes, it is a popular tourist area in high season. In low season, the weather is dry, warm and inviting and the excellent sandy beaches are almost deserted. There are ten mobile homes to rent.

One sanitary block provides ample toilets (British and Turkish style) washbasins and hot showers (token). Children's bathrooms and baby changing room. Good facilities for disabled visitors. Shop (1/5-15/9). Bar, restaurant and takeaway. Direct beach access. Play area. Boules. Entertainment for all (high season). Excursions organised. Mobile homes to rent. WiFi. Dogs are not accepted 1/6-30/9.

Key Features

- Pets Accepted
- Disabled Facilities
- Beach Access
- Play Area
- Bar/Restaurant

Scan me for more information.

Alan Rogers Code: IT68380
64 accommodations
60 pitches
GPS: 40.58389, 14.35194
Post Code: I-80061

Massa Lubrense, Campania

www.alanrogers.com/it68380
info@villaggionettuno.it
Tel: 081 808 1051
www.villaggionettuno.it

Open (Touring Pitches):
20 March - 2 November.

Camping Nettuno

Camping Nettuno is owned and run by the friendly Mauro family, who speak excellent English. Nestled in the bay of Marina del Cantone, it is situated in the protected area of Punta Campanella, away from the busiest tourist spots. As a result, the approach roads are difficult and narrow. This small campsite of only 60 pitches (with 4A electricity available) is spread over three levels above the pebbly beach, and there are about 60 mobile homes. Up several steps and across the road are the amenities, reception, shop and dive centre, and then above this is a restaurant with magnificent views over the bay. Pitches are informally arranged, some with a fabulous sea view (extra charge), most with shade. Because the site is tucked into the hillside pitches are small and close together, but there is plenty of cheerful assistance to find the best place. The site has two pathways to the nearby beach that, unusually, for the area involves little walking or steps.

The single central sanitary block includes facilities for disabled campers (and access via a ramp to the beach). Washing machine. Basic motorhome service point. Gas supplies. Small shop. Delightful restaurant with sea views. Bar (lively at night). Dive centre. Excursions. TV in bar area. Small play area. Free tennis arranged at court next door. Fishing. Bicycle hire.

Key Features

- Pets Accepted
- Disabled Facilities
- Beach Access
- Swimming Pool
- Play Area
- Bar/Restaurant
- Bike Hire
- Fishing

Scan me for more information.

Alan Rogers Code: IT68340
208 accommodations
350 pitches
GPS: 40.62753, 14.35736
Post Code: I-80067

Sorrento, Campania

Santa Fortunata

www.alanrogers.com/it68340
info@santafortunata.eu
Tel: 081 807 3574
www.santafortunata.eu

Open (Touring Pitches):
1 April - 25 October

Village Camping Santa Fortunata is situated on the hillside just outside Sorrento among olive and lemon groves. There is plenty of shade but low hanging branches make some of the pitches unsuitable for larger units. There is a steep tarmac approach to some but the stunning views over the bay more than compensate. Pitches are of average size with several spaces for larger units and there is a feeling of spaciousness as many are separated by trees and shrubs intersected with wooden constructed walkways. Two small beaches can be reached via long steep inclines. A daily excursion to Capri (well worth taking) departs from one of the beaches. The good-sized pool, terrace and bar are especially welcome after a day's sightseeing. Near reception is a well-stocked shop and a large restaurant with a terrace that serves a simple menu of local dishes and delicious pizza which are also available for take away.

Five sanitary blocks with adjustable hot showers. Hot water for dishwashing but not laundry sinks. Washing machines and dryers. Good restaurant/bar. Small well stocked shop. Swimming pool. Disco bar (high season). Mini farm. Boules pitch. Football and basketball court. Excursions. Bicycle and scooter hire. Car hire. WiFi.

Key Features

- Pets Accepted
- Beach Access
- Swimming Pool
- Play Area
- Bar/Restaurant
- Bike Hire
- Sailing

Scan me for more information.

Alan Rogers Code: IT68660
82 accommodations
600 pitches
GPS: 39.99832, 18.02650
Post Code: I-73014

Gallipoli, Puglia

Camping Baia di Gallipoli

www.alanrogers.com/it68660
info@baiadigallipoli.com
Tel: 083 327 3210
www.baiadigallipoli.com

Open (Touring Pitches):
1 April - 15 September.

The western shoreline of Puglia offers beaches of excellent quality, interspersed with small villages and some holiday complexes. The Baia di Gallipoli campsite is in a quiet rural area to the southwest of the town on a minor coast road. It offers 600 pitches, all with 6A electricity, under pine and eucalyptus trees. Cars are parked in a separate area and access for vehicles is strictly controlled, which gives the site a quiet, peaceful ambience. Although it is 800 m. from the beach it has solved that problem in partnership with others by providing regular shuttle buses to the beach car park. The sites jointly fund a bar and restaurant on the beach with toilets and showers. The short walk to the beach from the car park is along a timber walk, and site staff clear the beach and the pinewood behind of rubbish daily.

Five clean, modern toilet blocks have been recently refurbished and include facilities for disabled visitors, both on the site and at the beach. Motorhome services. Washing machines. Shop. Bar and restaurant. Swimming pool. Tennis. 5-a-side football. Volleyball. Bocce. Fitness trail. Bicycle, car and fridge hire by arrangement. Children's clubs (4-12 yrs, 13-17 yrs). Entertainment. WiFi in bar and pool area (free). Shuttle bus to beach.

Key Features

- Pets Accepted
- Disabled Facilities

Scan me for more information.

Alan Rogers Code: IT69158
10 accommodations
40 pitches
GPS: 37.74800, 12.49614
Post Code: I-91025

Marsala, Sicily

Camping Lilybeo Village

www.alanrogers.com/it69158
info@lilybeovillage.it
Tel: 0923 998357
www.lilybeovillage.it

Open (Touring Pitches):
All Year

Close to the coastal town of Marsala in western Sicily, best known for its fortified wine, Lilybeo Village is a small, family-friendly campsite within easy reach of the attractive coastline and the vineyards and olive groves of Trapani Province. There are just 40 spacious, grassy pitches with shade provided by mature trees. The area for motorhomes is more open, yet with some shade from olive trees. The beach of Lido Signorino is easily accessible by bicycle or car, as is the historic town of Marsala. Along the coast to the north and east are several nature reserves and archaeological sites. Marsala has an archaeological museum with a preserved Phoenician warship, as well as a range of shops, bars and restaurants and a 'cantine' selling local wines direct from the vat. From Marsala, you can take a twenty-minute boat trip to the beautiful Egadi Islands. Heading north along the Tyrrhenian coast, you can visit the salt marshes and city of Trapani, the medieval walled town of Erice, the ancient hilltop site of Segesta and, finally, bustling Palermo with its busy street markets. To the east along the Mediterranean coast are more beaches and several nature reserves and archaeological sites.

Sanitary block with hot showers and hairdryers. Washing machine, iron and ironing board. Campers' kitchen. Motorhome services. Children's pool. Football field. Bowling. Playground. Bicycle hire. Bungalows for hire. Airport transfer. Car hire. WiFi. Organised visits on Fridays.

Key Features

- Open All Year
- Pets Accepted
- Disabled Facilities
- Swimming Pool
- Play Area
- Bar/Restaurant
- Bike Hire

Scan me for more information.

Alan Rogers Code: IT69920
79 accommodations
275 pitches
GPS: 40.08400, 8.49100
Post Code: I-09073

Cuglieri, Sardinia

Camping Bella Sardinia

www.alanrogers.com/it69920
info@bellasardinia.it
Tel: 078 538 058
www.camping-bellasardinia.com

Open (Touring Pitches):
End April - Mid October

Camping Bella Sardinia is a long rectangular site with beach access at one end. Much work has taken place over recent years to improve the standards on this site. The 275 pitches are informally arranged on undulating ground under a full canopy of pines and have 6A electricity (long leads useful). There is one central drinking water point. The restaurant, which is centrally located has an attractive terrace. There is also a bar, animation area and children's playground here. The fine sand beach is accessed by a 60 m. track and there is a lifeguard in high season. The beach quickly shelves to deeper water and is ideal for watersports. An attractive swimming pool has been designed and constructed in sympathy with the wooded surrounds. It has a flume, wooden boardwalk and beach bar. Giant air-filled bouncy toys are also here. The site is large enough to offer pitches close to the action or in tranquil corners. You may enjoy the twenty-minute beach walk to the nearby village.

Two sanitary blocks, one large and one small, washbasins and hot showers. Facilities for disabled campers. Washing machines and dryers. Motorhome services. Shop. Restaurant and bar. Pizzeria/snack bar/crêperie. Beach bar. All facilities open May-Sept. Tennis. Minigolf. Bicycle hire. Excursions and entertainment (high season). No barbecues allowed, communal area only. Internet and WiFi (charged).

Key Features

- Pets Accepted
- Disabled Facilities
- Beach Access
- Swimming Pool
- Play Area
- Bar/Restaurant
- Bike Hire
- Fishing

Scan me for more information.

Alan Rogers Code: IT69600
98 accommodations
450 pitches
GPS: 41.16117, 9.40300
Post Code: I-07020

Palau, Sardinia

www.alanrogers.com/it69600
info@capodorso.it
Tel: 078 970 2007
www.capodorso.it

Open (Touring Pitches):
21 April - 26 September.

Camping Capo d'Orso

Capo d'Orso is a large, attractive, terraced site with views of the Maddalena Archipelago. Set into a hillside that slopes down to the sea, the 450 terraced pitches (40-80 sq.m) are of gravel, grass and sand, some with views over the sea and some others set alongside the beach. All have 3A electricity. Access to the pitches is good despite the rocky terrain. Cars are parked away from the pitches in high season. The very Italian restaurant at the top of the amenities building serves delicious meals and has a covered terrace giving excellent sea views. This site is suitable for families. The two beaches are delightful, with fine sand and clear waters. Good English is spoken and the staff are friendly and helpful. Capo d'Orso has an extensive entertainment programme and a huge array of activities, many with instructors on site. Look for the 'rock bear' from which the site takes its name.

Three toilet blocks are being renovated and will provide ample facilities, including hot showers, and mainly Turkish style WCs. Motorhome services. Shop. Bazaar. Bar/restaurant. Pizzeria. Takeaway. Scuba diving, windsurfing, sailing school, boat excursions, boat hire and moorings (all main season). Tennis. Entertainment programmes for children and adults. Excursions arranged in high season. Free WiFi.

Key Features

- Pets Accepted
- Disabled Facilities
- Beach Access
- Play Area
- Bar/Restaurant
- Sailing

Scan me for more information.

Alan Rogers Code: IT69845
34 accommodations
100 pitches
GPS: 38.96759, 8.97794
Post Code: I-09010

Pula, Sardinia

Camping Flumendosa

www.alanrogers.com/it69845
info@campingflumendosa.it
Tel: 070 461 5332
www.campingflumendosa.com

Open (Touring Pitches):
1 April - 1 November.

Camping Flumendosa is a 2.5 hectare site set in a leafy pine forest, just across the road from the sandy beach and shallow clear waters of the lively town of Santa Margherita di Pula, on the southern coast of Sardinia. The 100 pitches of 70 sq. m. have 8A Europlug electrical connections and water points around. With a focus on fun, relaxation and nature, this site is ideally located for a range of activities including, mountain-biking, horse riding, hiking and diving. A day could be spent at the nearby Blue-Fan Water Park or at the Pula Aerial Adventure Park. For the more archaeologically minded, a visit to the ruins of Nora, one of the most important archaeological sites on Sardinia is a must.

Toilet blocks with free hot water, laundry facilities and washing-up sinks. Shop, bar/restaurant/takeaway with a spacious terrace, pizzas and traditional recipes, outdoor swimming pool (all open all season). Charcoal barbecues permitted and communal barbecues available. Fishing. Beach. Children's play area. Baby-sitting service. Bicycle hire. WiFi (free).

Key Features

- Pets Accepted
- Disabled Facilities
- Beach Access
- Swimming Pool
- Play Area
- Bar/Restaurant
- Fishing

Scan me for more information.

Vianden valley >

Capital Luxembourg City
Currency Euro (€)
Language Letzeburgesch, French and German
Time Zone CET (GMT+1)
Telephone Code 00 352

Tourist Website luxembourg.co.uk

Climate Temperate climate. The summer often extending from May to late October.

Shops Varied. In high-season 10am to 5pm Mon to Sat, some shops in Luxembourg City open on Sunday.

Banks 8.30am to 4.30pm weekdays, closed for lunch. Some open Saturday morning.

Accessible Travel Although hilly, Luxembourg is generally wheelchair-friendly. Buses and trams are fitted with ramps, check before using trains.

Travelling with children A very family-friendly country. Many attractions are free for those under 26 years old. Most restaurants will cater for children. Trains, trams and buses are set to become free for all from March 2020.

See campsite map page

473

Public Holidays New Year's Day, Easter Monday, Labour Day (1 May), Europe Day (9 May), Ascension, Whit Monday, National Day (23 Jun), Assumption, All Saints, Christmas Day, Boxing Day.

Motoring Many holidaymakers travel through Luxembourg to take advantage of the lower fuel prices, thus creating traffic congestion at petrol stations, especially in summer. A Blue Zone area exists in Luxembourg City and various parts of the country (discs from tourist offices) but meters are also used.

Environmental Policies There are currently no Low Emission Zones enforced in Luxembourg. Recycling is widespread, but it can be a little confusing. Generally metal, plastic, drink cartons and plastic shopping bags are recycled but its best to check before adding your waste to recycling containers.

View all campsites in Luxembourg
alanrogers.com/luxembourg

Luxembourg

The Grand Duchy of Luxembourg is a sovereign state, lying between Belgium, France and Germany. Divided into two areas: the spectacular Ardennes region in the north and the rolling farmlands in the south, bordered on the east by the wine growing area of the Moselle Valley.

Most attractions are within easy reach of Luxembourg's capital, Luxembourg-Ville, a fortress city, perched dramatically on its rocky promontory overlooking the Alzette and Petrusse Valleys. The verdant hills and valleys of the Ardennes are a maze of hiking trails, footpaths and cycle routes – ideal for an activity holiday.

The Moselle Valley, famous for its sweet wines, is just across the river from Germany; its charming hamlets can be discovered by bicycle or by boat. Popular wine tasting tours take place from late spring to early autumn. Echternacht is a good base for exploring the Mullerthal region, known as 'Little Switzerland.' Lying on the banks of the River Sûre, its forested landscape is dotted with curious rock formations and castle ruins, notably those at Beaufort and Larochette. The pretty Schießentümpel cascade is worth a visit.

Alan Rogers Code: LU7780
12 accommodations
79 pitches
GPS: 50.09128, 6.02783
Post Code: L-9974

Maulusmühle, Diekirch

www.alanrogers.com/lu7780
info@woltzdal-camping.lu
Tel: 998 938
campingwoltzdal.com

Open (Touring Pitches):
Easter - 30 October.

Camping Woltzdal

Set by a stream in a valley, Camping Woltzdal is one of the many delightful sites in the Ardennes, a region of wooded hills and river valleys that crosses the borders of Belgium, France and Luxembourg. The site has 79 flat touring pitches, set on grass, amongst fir trees; all with 4A electricity and 20 of which also have water and wastewater. They are relatively open and have views of the surrounding wooded hills. A railway passes the site on the far side of the stream, but there are only trains during the day. This is a family run site with a small, friendly bar/restaurant. In the surrounding hills, there are kilometres of marked paths and mountain bike tracks for those wishing to enjoy the natural environment. For city life, a family ticket from the railway station close to the site is an economical and convenient way of visiting Luxembourg City with its museums, exhibitions and many other attractions. Details are available at reception.

The site boasts a new state-of-the-art toilet block with solar-powered water heating (access is by smart key with deposit). Large family bathrooms and facilities for disabled visitors. Laundry room. Service points for motorhomes. Reception and small shop are in the large house at the entrance where there is also a bar and a restaurant/snack bar with terrace. Children's library/activity room. WiFi throughout (charged). Play area. Boules. Mountain bike hire. Entertainment programme for children in high season.

Key Features

- Pets Accepted
- Disabled Facilities
- Play Area
- Bar/Restaurant
- Skiing
- Bike Hire

Scan me for more information.

Alan Rogers Code: LU7510
13 accommodations
151 pitches
GPS: 50.11889, 6.00152
Post Code: L-9912

Troisvierges, Diekirch

Camping Troisvierges

www.alanrogers.com/lu7510
info@visittroisvierges.lu
Tel: 99 71 41
www.camping-troisvierges.lu

Open (Touring Pitches):
1 April - 30 September

Camping Troisvierges (formerly Camping Walensbongert) is just 300 metres from all the facilities of Troisvierges, a large village with pleasant bars, restaurants and shops. The local tourist office owns the site, and the village swimming pool, with its restaurant and bar, is located at the heart of the site – campers enjoy a daily concessionary rate. The 151 level, grass touring pitches are separated by hedges and vary in size from 80-100 sq.m. They are in both open and shady areas, and all have 10A electricity. A staircase must be used to access the main sanitary block, but new well equipped disabled facilities are provided at ground level. This site, with its waymarked walks, will suit anyone who wants to enjoy the tranquillity of the countryside, although the campsite can be lively in high season. There is a bus stop within 300 m. and a railway station within 600 m. of the entrance.

Unusual rotunda style building (one flight of stairs) contains hot showers, toilets, laundry and washing up facilities. Facilities for disabled visitors at ground level (key access and unmarked door). Heated indoor and outdoor swimming pools (July/Aug), indoor pool closed 21/8-15/9. Playing field adjacent. Play area. Activity programme (July/Aug). WiFi throughout (charged).

Key Features

- Pets Accepted
- Disabled Facilities
- Swimming Pool
- Play Area

Scan me for more information.

Alan Rogers Code: LU7540
36 accommodations
110 pitches
GPS: 49.91698, 6.17850
Post Code: L-9465

Walsdorf, Diekirch

Beter-Uit Walsdorf

www.alanrogers.com/lu7540
walsdorf@beter-uit.nl
Tel: 834 464
beteruitholidayparks.com/walsdorf

Open (Touring Pitches):
Mid-March to End-August
(accommodation to 1 October).

Beter-Uit Walsdorf is a beautifully presented site, set in a quiet wooded valley. The 100+ touring pitches are set in terraces alongside a small stream. The pitches are a good size at 100 to 170 sq.m, each with mature hedges and 4/6A electricity. The site buildings are modern and very well maintained. There are 36 mobile homes for rent, and these are discreetly placed on the upper terracing. This is a very popular site which becomes lively in high season but quiet and peaceful at other times. A Christian travel group manages the site, and they have made this a delightful place to stay. Christian values are promoted throughout the campsite along with associated activities, you are welcome to participate or not, as you choose. A small bar and basic restaurant are available.

Immaculate, well equipped sanitary block with facilities for children and disabled visitors. Hot showers (first 5 minutes free). Small shop (limited hours in low season). Pleasant bar with terrace, restaurant and takeaway. Club room with TV. Full entertainment programme (July/Aug). Field for ball games. Volleyball. Trampoline. Free WiFi in restaurant.

Key Features

- Pets Accepted
- Disabled Facilities
- Play Area
- Bar/Restaurant
- Bike Hire

Scan me for more information.

Alan Rogers Code: LU7830
18 accommodations
200 pitches
GPS: 49.95387, 6.02730
Post Code: L-9663

Kautenbach, Diekirch

Camping Kautenbach

www.alanrogers.com/lu7830
campkaut@pt.lu
Tel: 00352950303
www.campingkautenbach.lu

Open (Touring Pitches):
20 January - 16 December

Kautenbach is situated in the heart of the Luxembourg Ardennes and was established over 60 years ago. Although in an idyllic location, it is less than a mile from a railway station with regular trains to Luxembourg City to the south. There are 200 touring pitches here, mostly of a good size and with reasonable shade. All pitches have electrical connections (10A). This is excellent walking country with many tracks around the site. The site managers will be happy to recommend walks for all abilities. Kautenbach has an attractive bistro style restaurant specialising in local cuisine, as well as a large selection of whiskies!

Three toilet blocks with open style washbasins and showers, baby changing. Facilities for disabled visitors (key). Laundry. Shop for basics (1/4-31/10, bread to order). Restaurant, bar/snack bar (all season). Direct river access. Fishing. Play area. Mobile homes, safari tents and camping pods for rent. Internet café.

Key Features

- Pets Accepted
- Disabled Facilities
- Play Area
- Bar/Restaurant
- Fishing

Scan me for more information.

Alan Rogers Code: LU7770
27 accommodations
76 pitches
GPS: 50.00017, 5.99106
Post Code: L-9747

Enscherange, Diekirch

www.alanrogers.com/lu7770
valdor@pt.lu
Tel: 920 691
www.valdor.lu

Open (Touring Pitches):
2 April - 29 October.

Camping Val d'Or

Camping Val d'Or is one of those small, family run, countryside sites where you easily find yourself staying longer than planned. Set in four hectares of lush meadowland under a scattering of trees, the site is divided into two by the tree-lined Clerve river as it winds its way slowly through the site. A footbridge goes some way to joining the site together and there are two entrances for vehicles. There are 76 marked, level grass touring pitches, all with electricity (6A Europlug) and with some tree shade. Cars are parked away from the pitches. There are open views of the surrounding countryside with its wooded hills. The site's Dutch owners speak good English.

Next to the reception is a heated sanitary block where some facilities are found, others including some showers are located under cover, outside. Showers are token operated. Laundry room. Gas supplies. Bar (all day in high season). Takeaway (high season except Sundays). Swimming and paddling in river. Three play areas (one with waterways, waterwheel and small pool). Bicycle hire. WiFi (free). Max. 1 dog.

Key Features

- Pets Accepted
- Play Area
- Bar/Restaurant
- Bike Hire

Scan me for more information.

Alan Rogers Code: LU7620
32 accommodations
359 pitches
GPS: 49.78472, 6.16519
Post Code: L-7465

Nommern, Luxembourg District

www.alanrogers.com/lu7620
info@nommerlayen-ec.lu
Tel: 878 078
www.nommerlayen-ec.lu

Open (Touring Pitches):
1 March - 6 November.

Europacamping Nommerlayen

Situated at the end of its own road, in the lovely wooded hills of central Luxembourg, this is a top quality site with fees to match, but it has everything! A large, central building housing most of the services and amenities opens onto a terrace around an excellent swimming pool complex with a large fun pool and an imaginative water playground. The 359 individual pitches (100 sq.m) are on grassy terraces, all have access to electricity (2/16A) and water taps. Pitches are grouped beside age-appropriate play areas and the facilities throughout the campsite reflect the attention given to families in particular. Interestingly enough, the superb sanitary block is called Badtemple, (having been built in the style of a Greek temple). A member of Leading Campings group.

A large, high quality, modern sanitary unit provides some washbasins in cubicles, facilities for disabled visitors, family and baby rooms and a sauna. Twelve private bathrooms for hire. Laundry. Motorhome services. Supermarket. Restaurant. Snack bar. Bar (all 19/3-6/11). Excellent swimming pool complex and new heated pool with sliding roof (1/5-15/9). Fitness programmes. Bowling. Playground. Large screen TV. Entertainment in season. Bicycle hire. WiFi (free over part of site).

Key Features

- Pets Accepted
- Disabled Facilities
- Swimming Pool
- Play Area
- Bar/Restaurant
- Bike Hire

Scan me for more information.

Alan Rogers Code: LU7580
17 accommodations
137 pitches
GPS: 49.74357, 6.08978
Post Code: L-7572

Mersch, Luxembourg District

www.alanrogers.com/lu7580
contact@campingkrounebierg.lu
Tel: +352 329 756
campingkrounebierg.lu

Open (Touring Pitches):
1 April - 31 October.

Camping Krounebierg

Situated on a hillside with views over the Mersch valley this is an attractive site for stopovers or more extended stays. It is close to the town of Mersch with good facilities and transport links, but the site has a pleasant rural ambience. There are 177 pitches, 137 for touring, including 12 hardstandings. All are level, grassy and of a good size, with 10A electricity, and separated by hedges. A stylish, modern building at the site entrance houses reception, shop, bar and restaurant and has an excellent elevated terrace overlooking the open-air children's pool. Everything is fresh and spotlessly clean, and we received a warm and friendly welcome from the managers. Campers can also use the town's indoor pool, adjacent to the site, at a reduced rate.

Five traditional, clean sanitary blocks are heated and have free hot showers. Facilities for disabled visitors. Well stocked shop. Modern bar and restaurant/takeaway. Outdoor paddling pool. Play area. Games room with TV. Football field. Badminton. Daily activity programme (July/Aug). Free WiFi throughout. Max 3 Dogs allowed. BBQs permitted.

Key Features

- Pets Accepted
- Disabled Facilities
- Swimming Pool
- Play Area
- Bar/Restaurant

Scan me for more information.

Alan Rogers Code: LU7370
51 accommodations
105 pitches
GPS: 49.82594, 6.34349
Post Code: L-6552

Berdorf, Grevenmacher

www.alanrogers.com/lu7370
info@camping-martbusch.lu
Tel: 790 545
camping-martbusch.lu

Open (Touring Pitches):
All year.

Camping Martbusch

Camping Martbusch is situated in woodland on the edge of the small village of Berdorf, in the 'Petit Suisse' region of Luxembourg. This area is popular with nature lovers with its rock formations, caves, gorges and breathtaking views. This three-hectare site comprises 167 pitches, with 105 for touring, set informally with seasonal pitches. All are grassy and level with 10A electricity. There is no bar or restaurant on-site, but the village is a short walk away, where a selection of hotel/restaurant options are available. There are few shops in Berdorf, so a trip to nearby Echternach must be made for groceries. The site is a favourite with Dutch campers, who return year after year.

Heated sanitary blocks with free hot showers and facilities for disabled campers. Laundry area with washing machine and dryer. Takeaway. Bicycle hire. Play area. TV room with satellite TV. WiFi (charged). Max 3 Dogs allowed. BBQs permitted. Fresh bread available from reception. Limited choice restaurant/bar (seasonal) Children's playground and crazy golf.

Key Features

- Open All Year
- Pets Accepted
- Disabled Facilities
- Play Area
- Bike Hire

Scan me for more information.

Colorful tulip fields >

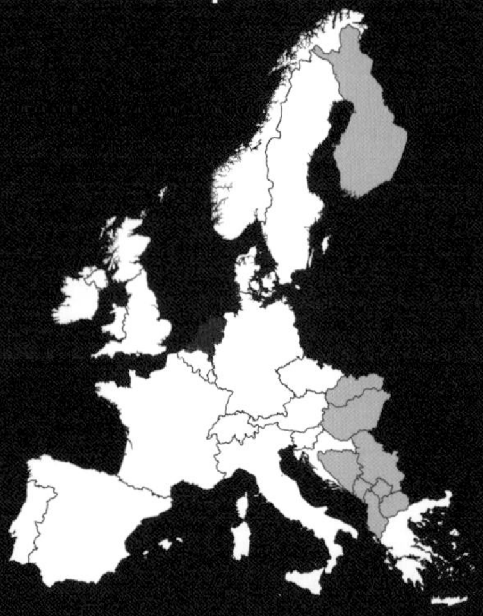

Capital Amsterdam
Currency Euro (€)
Language Dutch. French and German also widely spoken.
Time Zone CET (GMT+1)
Telephone Code 00 31

Tourist Website
holland.com

Climate Temperate with mild winters and warm summers.

Shops Varied. In high-season 10am or noon to 6pm Tue to Fri, 10am to 5pm weekends, noon to 5pm Mon. Larger supermarkets are open 8am to 8pm.

Banks 9am to 4pm weekdays and some open Sat mornings.

Accessible Travel Generally very good, especially in cities. Public buildings and transport are well equipped. WCs in restaurants can be difficult for wheelchair users.

Travelling with children
Amsterdam is one of Europe's most child-friendly cities, we recommend you stay clear of the Red Light District. Beaches are safe. Restaurants are kid-friendly, nearly all offer children's menus and colouring crayons.

See campsite map page

483

Public Holidays New Year's Day, Good Friday, Easter Sunday, Easter Monday, King's Day (27 Apr), Liberation Day (5 May), Ascension, Whit Sunday, Whit Monday, Christmas Day, Boxing Day.

Motoring There is a comprehensive motorway system but due to the high density of population, all main roads can become very busy, particularly in the morning and evening rush hours. There are many bridges which can cause congestion. There are no toll roads but there are a few toll bridges and tunnels, notably the Zeeland Bridge, Europe's longest across the Oosterschelde.

Environmental Policies Many major cities have introduced Low Emission Zones. No stickers are currently required. Check before travelling if you plan to drive through a city. Metal, plastic, paper, cardboard and drink cartons are widely recycled. Glass should be separated according to colour and taken to bottle banks. Plastic drink bottles can be taken to deposit stations.

View all campsites in the Netherlands
alanrogers.com/netherlands

Netherlands

With vast areas of the Netherlands reclaimed from the sea, nearly half of the country lies at or below sea level. The result is a flat, fertile landscape criss-crossed with rivers and canals. Famous for its windmills and bulb fields, it also boasts some of the most impressive coastal dunes in Europe.

No visit to the Netherlands would be complete without experiencing its capital city, Amsterdam, with its maze of canals, bustling cafés, museums and summer festivals.

The fields of South Holland are an explosion of colour between March and May when the world's biggest flower auction takes place at Aalsmeer.

The Vecht valley and its towns of Dalfsen, Ommen and Hardenberg are best explored by bicycle, while Giethoorn, justly dubbed the 'Venice of Holland' has to be seen from a boat. The Kinderdijk windmills on the Alblasserwaard polder are a UNESCO World Heritage Site.

The islands of Zeeland are home to beautiful old towns such as Middelburg, the provincial capital, Zierikzee, with its old harbour and the quaint old town of Veere.

Alan Rogers Code: NL6952
1175 accommodations
314 pitches
GPS: 51.72738, 3.75897
Post Code: NL-4325 DM

Renesse, Zeeland

Camping Julianahoeve

www.alanrogers.com/nl6952
julianahoeve@ardoer.com
Tel: 0111 461 414
www.julianahoeve.nl

Open (Touring Pitches):
11 March - 6 November.

A huge site with about 1,400 pitches, mainly for mobile homes and chalets, Camping Julianahoeve still retains a few pitches for touring units and tents. You cannot get much closer to the sea, and a path leads through the dunes to the beach. All the main touring pitches are large and fully serviced. Some have individual sanitary units, and others have hardstandings. Located in the sunniest area of the Netherlands, this is an ideal site for a family holiday by the beach. A member of the Ardoer group. The site has many facilities designed to make your stay as pleasant as possible - a supermarket, cafeteria with terrace, snack bar and several playfields and sports pitches. The popular beach resort of Renesse is only 15 minutes walk away. The landscape makes it ideal for cycle tours, and many towns and cities are within easy reach if you feel like a change from the beach. The indoor playground and indoor pool are both welcome additions for rainier or colder days.

Several well-appointed toilet blocks serve the site with facilities for younger children, babies and disabled visitors. Individual sanitary units are available. Launderette. Supermarket. Bar. Brasserie. Café with a terrace. Snack bar. Indoor pool complex with 60 m. water slide. Play areas. Sports pitches. Theatre with entertainment for all ages. WiFi. Dogs are not accepted. Dishwasher service available.

Key Features

- Disabled Facilities
- Beach Access
- Play Area
- Bar/Restaurant

Scan me for more information.

Alan Rogers Code: NL5560
50 accommodations
218 pitches
GPS: 51.71843, 3.76713
Post Code: NL-4325 CP

Renesse, Zeeland

Camping De Wijde Blick

www.alanrogers.com/nl5560
wijdeblick@molecaten.nl
Tel: 0111 468 888
www.molecaten.nl/wijde-blick

Open (Touring Pitches):
All Year

The Van Oost family run this neat campsite in a pleasant and personal way. It is located on the outskirts of the village of Renesse in a quiet rural spot. From May to September a free bus runs to Renesse and the beach, just 2 km. away. De Wijde Blick has 328 pitches with 218 for touring units, all with 6/10A electricity and TV connections, and 90-120 sq.m. in area. Of these, 16 have private sanitary facilities and 202 are fully serviced. There are 20 attractively arranged motorhome pitches with hardstanding, and ten special 'bike and hike' pitches for those touring without a car. Cars must be parked away from pitches. Children are welcomed by the campsite mascot, Billy Blick, and will thoroughly enjoy the large playground, the indoor activity room or an evening at the theatre. There is a good entertainment programme and an area set aside for teenagers.

Three first class, modern toilet blocks are heated, with clean facilities including washbasins in cabins, controllable showers and facilities for disabled campers. Microwave and fridge. Bath (on payment). Laundry (with pleasant waiting area). Gas supplies. Motorhome services. Shop. Restaurant/bar (15/3-31/10). Swimming pool (1/5-20/9; can be covered). Free WiFi over site. Good playgrounds. Air trampoline. Volleyball area. Open-air theatre. Bicycle hire. Activities for children. Hotel chalets to rent. Breakfast service available.

Key Features

- OPEN 365 Open All Year
- Pets Accepted
- Disabled Facilities
- Swimming Pool
- Play Area
- Bar/Restaurant
- Bike Hire

Scan me for more information.

Alan Rogers Code: NL6980
6 accommodations
68 pitches
GPS: 51.90970, 4.18536
Post Code: NL-3231 NC

Brielle, Zuid-Holland

www.alanrogers.com/nl6980
info@krabbeplaat.nl
Tel: 0181 412 363
www.krabbeplaat.nl

Open (Touring Pitches):
30 March - 27 October

Camping De Krabbeplaat

Camping De Krabbeplaat is a family run site situated near the ferry port in a wooded, recreation area next to the Brielse Meer lake. There are 448 spacious pitches, with 68 for touring units, all with 10A electricity, cable connections and a water supply nearby. A nature conservation plan exists to ensure the site fits into its natural environment. The lake and its beaches provide the perfect spot for watersports and relaxation, and the site has a harbour where you can moor your own boat. This excellent site is very convenient for the Europort ferry terminal, making it the ideal location for a stopover or for a more extended stay. Plenty of cultural opportunities can be found in the historic towns of the area, including the 'futuristic' cube houses, market hall and Euromast viewpoint and restaurant, all within easy reach.

One large and two smaller heated toilet blocks in traditional style provide separate toilets, showers and washing cabins. High standards of cleanliness. Dedicated unit for disabled campers and provision for babies. Warm water is free of charge. Dishwasher (free). Launderette. Motorhome services. Supermarket, snack bar, restaurant and takeaway (all season). Recreation room. Youth centre. Tennis. Playground and play field. Animal farm. Bicycle and children's pedal hire. Canoe, surf, pedal boat and boat hire. Fishing. WiFi over site (charged). Six cabins to rent.

Key Features

- Pets Accepted
- Disabled Facilities
- Play Area
- Bar/Restaurant
- Bike Hire
- Fishing
- Sailing

Scan me for more information.

Alan Rogers Code: NL6970
25 accommodations
120 pitches
GPS: 51.82943, 4.11618
Post Code: NL-3221 LJ

Hellevoetsluis, Zuid-Holland

www.alanrogers.com/nl6970
info@weergors.nl
Tel: +31 (0)181 312 430
www.weergors.nl

Open (Touring Pitches):
28 March - 1 November

Camping 't Weergors

A rustic style site built around old farm buildings, Camping 't Weergors has a comfortable mature feel. At the front of the site is a well-presented farmhouse which houses the reception and includes the main site services. The sanitary blocks are modern and the farm accommodates an attractive à la carte restaurant and pancake outlet. The reception includes a new minimarket from where you can order fresh bread. There are currently 120 touring pitches (plus seasonal and static places). Some of the touring pitches are exceptionally large. Each pitch has a cable TV connection and the site now has WiFi internet access. An appealing feature of this site is the lake which lies to the rear, offering a quiet corner where you might head for an evening stroll. The old centre of Hellevoetsluis is worthy of a visit and the bustling city of Rotterdam is not far.

Three sanitary blocks have showers (by card), washbasins, some in cabins, children's showers and toilets plus baby baths. Laundry facilities. Motorhome services. Small shop. Restaurant and bar (snacks) and pancakes. Tennis. Internet access. Play area. Paddling pool (15/5-15/9). Organised entertainment in high season. Fishing pond. Bicycle hire. Rally field.

Key Features

- Pets Accepted
- Disabled Facilities
- Play Area
- Bar/Restaurant
- Bike Hire
- Fishing

Scan me for more information.

Alan Rogers Code: NL5643
9 accommodations
GPS: 51.90982, 4.30964
Post Code: NL-3132 EK

Vlaardingen, Zuid-Holland

www.alanrogers.com/nl5643
info@devreemdevogel.nl
Tel: 010 341 5025
www.devreemdevogel.nl

Open (Touring Pitches):
All year.

De Vreemde Vogel

This glamping site offers overnight facilities, including breakfast, in very unusual accommodation, De Vreemde Vogel (The Strange Bird) is the creation of Davy and Petra Knijnenburg. Located in a natural setting on the edge of Vlaadingen the site reflects and combines the differing backgrounds of its owners, hotels and farming. The Ostrich, a caravan perched high above the ground with accommodation for two, The Bird House, a nest box somewhat more substantial than normal, capable of accommodating four people, the Iron Bird, an aircraft situated on the bank of the river running through the site, with beds for 4, plus many more exciting sleeping possibilities, all heated and with full sanitary facilities. Cars are parked outside the site on the adjacent public road - No touring pitches available.

Restaurant (high season) and bar (all year) with sun terrace. Buffet breakfast for 2 people (which is included in the price) served in the old farmhouse mornings, or upon request, served in your accommodation. Garden café (Wednesdays, Saturday and Sunday) serving home made cakes, fresh sandwiches and drinks. Pizza oven. Grills. Bicycle hire. Fishing. Play room. Small zoo, Play area. WiFi at reception and in the restaurant (free).

Key Features

- Open All Year
- Disabled Facilities
- Play Area
- Bar/Restaurant
- Bike Hire
- Fishing
- Golf

Scan me for more information.

Alan Rogers Code: NL5970
530 pitches
GPS: 51.33635, 5.35552
Post Code: NL-5571 TN

Bergeijk, Noord-Brabant

Camping De Paal

www.alanrogers.com/nl5970
info@campingdepaal.nl
Tel: 0497 571 977
www.depaal.nl

Open (Touring Pitches):
1 April - 31 October

A really first class, family run campsite, ideal for families with children up to 12 years old, with activities on a grand scale, yet retaining a relaxed atmosphere. Situated in 42 hectares of woodland, it has 530 touring pitches (up to 150 sq.m). The pitches are numbered and in meadows, separated by trees, with cars parked mainly on dedicated parking areas. All have 6A electricity, TV, water, drainage and a bin. There are 60 pitches with private sanitary facilities some of which are partly underground and attractively covered with grass and flowers. Each group of pitches has a small playground. There are larger adventure-style play areas, one resembling a desert with water and other activities, in a 40,000 sq.m. dune-like setting.

High quality sanitary facilities are ultra modern, including washbasins in cabins, family rooms and baby baths, all with lots of space. Facilities for disabled visitors. Launderette. Motorhome services. Underground supermarket. Restaurant (high season), bar and snack bar (all season). Indoor pool (all season, supervised in high season). Outdoor pool (May-Sept). Tennis. Play areas. Theatre. WiFi (charged). Bicycle hire. Pet zoo.

Key Features

- Pets Accepted
- Disabled Facilities
- Swimming Pool
- Play Area
- Bar/Restaurant
- Skiing
- Bike Hire

Scan me for more information.

Alan Rogers Code: NL5904
37 accommodations
31 pitches
GPS: 51.51685, 5.30783
Post Code: NL-5688 MB

Oirschot, Noord-Brabant

Camping De Bocht

www.alanrogers.com/nl5904
info@campingdebocht.nl
Tel: +31 499 550 855
www.campingdebocht.nl

Open (Touring Pitches):
All Year

De Bocht is located on the outskirts of the attractive village of Oirschot, in a rural area of woodland and fields. The site is a small but charming, family-run campsite where tents and caravans are placed between pitches containing cabins and seasonal caravans. Some pitches have shade and most are separated by hedges. Cars are parked on the pitch or on an outside parking area. Small motorhomes are welcome. The appearance of the site is very attractive and well cared for. The pitches are 100 sq.m. in size and are connected to 10A electricity and cable TV, with water and drainage. The sanitary facilities are very well cared for and were spotlessly clean on our most recent visit. An outdoor swimming pool and play equipment are available, with the possibility to eat and sit on the terrace by the accompanying bowling alley. Oirschot is a traditional Dutch village with a number of small attractions including the Vandeoirsprong brewery, Saint Petrus Basilica and small local history Museum, De Vier Quartieren.

One heated sanitary block with tidy facilities. Facilities for families. Baby room. Laundry facilities. Motorhome services. Fine restaurant. TV room. Swimming pool (1/7-31/8). Playground. Bicycle hire. Entertainments team in high season. WiFi throughout.

Key Features

- Open All Year
- Pets Accepted
- Swimming Pool
- Play Area
- Bar/Restaurant
- Bike Hire

Scan me for more information.

Alan Rogers Code: NL5920
336 accommodations
450 pitches
GPS: 51.41065, 5.27618
Post Code: NL-5512 NW

Vessem, Noord-Brabant

www.alanrogers.com/nl5920
info@eurocampingvessem.nl
Tel: 0497 591 214
www.eurocampingvessem.nl

Open (Touring Pitches):
1 April - 30 September.

Eurocamping Vessem

Eurocamping Vessem is a family run site of 50 hectares with the touring area quietly located at the bottom of the site, well away from the large outdoor swimming pool complex, playground and sports area. Of the 800 or so pitches, 450 are for tourers, they are on grass in groups surrounded by tall trees, and 400 have 6A electricity. Besides, there are 40 motorhome pitches outside of the site, (24 with power) which are open all year. The site offers a broad range of activities for children, and by carefully selecting your pitch, you can almost imagine that you are camping in the forest. The site is an excellent base for walking and cycling, and perfect for visiting the countryside of this region which is made up of forests, lakes and several beautiful villages, such as Oirschot, Vessem, Hapert and Bladel. A large lake is close at hand and is ideal for windsurfing. The Belgian border is just 10 km. away. Holland is a country full of interesting surprises for the tourist; however, full use of tourist information is usually needed to find them.

Key Features

- Pets Accepted
- Swimming Pool
- Play Area
- Bar/Restaurant
- Skiing
- Fishing

Two main sanitary blocks near site entrance and three modern units in the touring area. They contain all the usual facilities. Showers upon payment (€ 0.50). Forty double WC-only units are spread around site. Supermarket. Snack bar. Bar and large entertainment area. Swimming pool complex with paddling pool. Tennis courts. Minigolf. Football. Basketball. Beach volleyball. Sports/games activities. Entertainment programme for children in summer. Play areas. Bouncy castle. Fishing lake. WiFi (charged).

Scan me for more information.

Alan Rogers Code: NL6635
374 accommodations
300 pitches
GPS: 51.64029, 5.81053
Post Code: NL-5446 PW

Wanroij, Noord-Brabant

www.alanrogers.com/nl6635
info@debergen.nl
Tel: 0485 335 450
www.debergen.nl

Open (Touring Pitches):
1 April - 31 October.

Vakantiepark De Bergen

Brabant is an attractive holiday region within easy reach of large cities such as Den Bosch and Nijmegen. The main attraction at this well-equipped site is the large swimming lake with a restaurant, snack bar and sandy beaches. There are four grades of pitch available, ranging from the relatively simple standard pitch to top of the range comfort pitches (with 10A electricity, cable TV connections, water and drainage). Visitors need not leave the site as the shop is very well stocked, the Twinkle Club in high season keeps the children occupied, and there is entertainment for adults. Twin-axle caravans and units over 7.75 m. are not accepted. A range of chalets and mobile homes are available to rent. An extensive leisure park surrounds the site and boasts a wide range of activities, including go-karts, minigolf, pedaloes and pony rides. A section of the lake has been cordoned off and is no deeper than 2 m. During peak season, bonfires are regularly organised on the lakeside.

Several toilet blocks throughout the site are modern, heated and well maintained. Baby room and facilities for disabled visitors (key access). Laundry. Well stocked shop. Snack bars and restaurants. Fishing. Pedalos. Bicycle hire. Adventure playground. Bowling. Pony rides. Play area. Sports field. Activity and entertainment programme. Mobile homes and chalets to rent. Direct lake access (suitable for swimming). WiFi over part of site (charged).

Key Features

- Pets Accepted
- Disabled Facilities
- Swimming Pool
- Play Area
- Bar/Restaurant
- Bike Hire
- Fishing
- Horse Riding

Scan me for more information.

Alan Rogers Code: NL6513
31 accommodations
285 pitches
GPS: 50.86005, 5.77258
Post Code: NL-6325 PE

Valkenburg aan de Geul, Limburg

Camping Oriental

www.alanrogers.com/nl6513
info@campingoriental.nl
Tel: 0436 040 075
www.campingoriental.nl

Open (Touring Pitches):
11 April - 28 October.

Camping Oriental is an excellent family site located between Valkenburg and Maastricht. There is a mixture of 285 sunny and shaded touring pitches, all with 10A electricity and some with water, drainage and TV connections. There is also a selection of mobile homes for rent (all with TV). On-site amenities include a pleasant bar, a snack bar and a well-stocked shop (with fresh bread daily). There is a heated swimming pool with a retractable roof, as well as a children's paddling pool. A large sports field is ideal for football, volleyball and basketball. Valkenburg has a colourful history characterised by siege and conquest. The ancient castle ruins (destroyed in 1672) can be found close to the town centre. Two of the original town gates remain, the Berkelpoort and the Grendelpoort. More recently, the town was the base of a significant resistance movement, The Valkenburg Resistance. Nowadays, it is an important tourist destination and an excellent base for walking and cycling holidays in the southern Netherlands.

Four sanitary blocks include showers and washbasins, open and in cubicles. Facilities for disabled visitors. Baby room. Launderette. Dog shower. Shop. Bar. Snack bar. Heated and covered swimming pool. Paddling pool. Play areas. Large sports field. Zip wire. Boules. Mobile homes for rent. WiFi over part of site (charged).

Key Features

- Pets Accepted
- Disabled Facilities
- Swimming Pool
- Play Area
- Bar/Restaurant

Scan me for more information.

Alan Rogers Code: NL6518
173 accommodations
259 pitches
GPS: 51.56733, 6.06028
Post Code: NL-5855 EG

Well, Limburg

Vakantiepark Leukermeer

www.alanrogers.com/nl6518
vakantie@leukermeer.nl
Tel: 0478 502 444
www.leukermeer.nl

Open (Touring Pitches):
18 March - 29 October.

Leukermeer is a pleasant holiday park in the green surroundings of the Maasduinen, with Lakeside beaches. All 259 pitches have 10A electricity and TV connections, 225 also have fresh and wastewater connections. The pitches are grassy, level and relatively open, and are arranged in groups of six or eight in hedge and tree-lined enclosures. The site offers a wealth of water- and land-based sports facilities, as well as entertainment programmes and play areas for children. Consequently, it is an excellent site for families with children who are looking for an active holiday. Although this is a rural site, there are many interesting towns close at hand, notably Arcen and Well. Arcen is located on the Maas river and is a popular tourist attraction. It is squeezed between Germany to the east and the Maas to the west. Historic buildings include the Schanstoren (Schans Tower) and a fine castle, as well as several ancient houses. Across the German border, pretty villages such as Kevelaer and Xanten, with its cathedral and fascinating archaeological park, merit a visit.

Heated toilet blocks. Free hot showers, baby room, children's and family showers. Facilities for disabled visitors. Washing machine. Supermarket. Restaurant with terrace overlooking the marina, café and snack bar. Indoor and outdoor swimming pools and paddling pool (open to public). Marina. Bicycle and scooter rentals. Minigolf. Volleyball. Basketball. Activities and entertainment.

Key Features

- Pets Accepted
- Disabled Facilities
- Swimming Pool
- Play Area
- Bar/Restaurant
- Bike Hire
- Sailing

Scan me for more information.

Alan Rogers Code: NL6510
21 accommodations
550 pitches
GPS: 51.38296, 5.97615
Post Code: NL-5975 MZ

Sevenum, Limburg

www.alanrogers.com/nl6510
info@schatberg.nl
Tel: 0774 677 777
www.schatberg.nl

Open (Touring Pitches):
All year.

De Schatberg

In a woodland setting of 96 hectares, this friendly, family-run campsite is more reminiscent of a holiday village, with a superb range of activities that make it an ideal venue for families. Look out for the deer! A large site with 1,100 pitches and many mobile homes and seasonal or weekend visitors, there are 550 touring pitches. All have electricity (10/16A Europlug), cable, water and drainage and average 100-150 sq.m. in size. They are on rough grass terrain, mostly with shade, but not separated. Seventy-two pitches have private sanitary facilities, of which 32 also have dishwashing, fridge and gas ring, and two have a sauna and jacuzzi. The site is well situated for visits to Germany and Belgium and is easily accessible from the port of Zeebrugge. The surrounding countryside offers the opportunity to enjoy nature, either by cycling or walking. For those who prefer to stay on-site, the location is excellent with several lakes for fishing, windsurfing and swimming, plus an extensive range of activities and a heated outdoor swimming pool.

Five modern, fully equipped toilet blocks, supplemented by three small wooden toilet units to save night-time walks. Family shower rooms, baby baths and en-suite units for disabled visitors. Washing machines and dryers. Motorhome services. Supermarket. Restaurant, bar and takeaway. Pizzeria. Pancake restaurant. Indoor pool. Outdoor pool. Multisport play areas. Air trampolines. Fishing. Watersports. Bicycle hire. Games room. Bowling. Climbing park. Indoor playground. Entertainment weekends and high season. Theatre for small children. Water-ski track. Charcoal barbecues not permitted. WiFi (free).

Key Features

- Open All Year
- Pets Accepted
- Disabled Facilities
- Swimming Pool
- Play Area
- Bar/Restaurant
- Bike Hire
- Fishing

Scan me for more information.

Alan Rogers Code: NL5892
318 accommodations
89 pitches
GPS: 51.63512, 6.03420
Post Code: NL-5851 EK

Afferden, Limburg

www.alanrogers.com/nl5892
info@campingroland.nl
Tel: 0485 531 431
www.campingroland.nl

Open (Touring Pitches):
All year.

Camping Roland

Family-run Camping Roland is a quiet site in an attractive region between the River Maas and the German border. The surroundings are made up of dunes, woods, moorland and lakes. Pitches here are divided into two groups, each with its own charm. All 90 spacious, grassy pitches have 6A electricity, water, drainage and cable TV connections. Swimming, sailing, fishing, mountain biking and hiking are amongst the activities on offer here. The swimming pool features a 40 m. water slide and a large sun terrace. This region has many signed cycle routes both around the site and on the far side of the Maas, which can be reached by ferry. The formal castle gardens in nearby Arcen are highly recommended. The castle dates back to 1674 and is also home to an excellent collection of tropical plants. The MaasHopper boat is a popular day out, combining a river cruise with cycling, and can be arranged at the site reception. Just across the German border lies the pretty town of Xanten, with an abundance of Roman traces still evident. Close at hand, there are two good 18-hole golf courses.

Two well maintained, attractive sanitary blocks with showers (token). Laundry with washing machines and dryers. No facilities for disabled visitors. Shop (seasonal). Cafeteria, restaurant and bar with billiards and large screen TV (seasonal). Swimming pool with water slide and sun terrace. Fishing pond. Large playground. Sports field. Entertainment and activity programme. Tennis. WiFi over site (charged).

Key Features

- Open All Year
- Pets Accepted
- Swimming Pool
- Bar/Restaurant
- Bike Hire
- Fishing

Scan me for more information.

Alan Rogers Code: NL6526
398 accommodations
399 pitches
GPS: 51.31759, 6.02365
Post Code: NL-5988 NH

Helden, Limburg

De Heldense Bossen

www.alanrogers.com/nl6526
info@deheldensebossen.nl
Tel: 077 307 2476
www.deheldensebossen.nl

Open (Touring Pitches):
1 April - 28 October.

Camping de Heldense Bossen is a woodland site of around 30 hectares. There are 400 spacious touring pitches here. These are grassy, and all have 6/10A electricity. A selection of standard, comfort (TV connections) and super comfort pitches are available. The latter include water and drainage. A subtropical swimming pool is ideal for relaxing and having fun. It has a massive 36 m. water slide, rapids, bubble beds, and a separate infant and toddler pool. There is also a good Caribbean-themed café. Outside, is a heated 25 m. pool with a nursery and a children's pool, as well as a broad sun terrace with a lawn and play area. The large playground is excellent and includes a pond and a pull raft. Unusually, there is a small zoo and also a special area for teenagers. All around the site are miles of waymarked footpaths and cycle tracks through the woods. Nearby Roermond is a historically significant town, with a skyline still dominated by its cathedral and Munsterkerk.

Eight modern toilet blocks. Supermarket. Café/restaurant, snack bar and Caribbean café. Sub-tropical swimming pool complex. Outdoor swimming pool (late Apr-late Aug). WiFi (small charge). Mobile homes and chalets to rent.

Key Features

- Pets Accepted
- Disabled Facilities
- Swimming Pool
- Play Area
- Bar/Restaurant
- Bike Hire

Scan me for more information.

Alan Rogers Code: NL6805
9 accommodations
125 pitches
GPS: 52.08466, 5.55130
Post Code: NL-3927 CJ

Renswoude, Utrecht

www.alanrogers.com/nl6805
info@campingdegrebbelinie.nl
Tel: 0318 591 073
www.campingdegrebbelinie.nl

Open (Touring Pitches):
30 March - Mid October.

Camping De Grebbelinie

Camping Grebbelinie is a friendly, family-run, environmentally green campsite within the Utrechtse Heuvelrug National Park. The pitches are large and grassy and all have 6/10A electricity, water, drainage, WiFi and TV connections. A number of pitches run along a riverbank, with other pitches more centrally located and with shade from tall trees. There is a pleasant café/snack bar and a good playground. Opposite the site, Fort Daatselaar has an interesting history dating back to the mid 18th century and merits a visit. There are many delightful walks along the Gelderlei valley and the site owners will be pleased to recommend options. A bed and breakfast service is available here and appeals to backpackers passing through the region. Fully equipped safari tents and mobile homes are also available for hire. Camping Grebbelinie is well located for exploring the broader reach, with the Hoge Veluwe National Park within easy reach, as well as the Utrechtse Heuvelrug.

Several heated sanitary facilities, the most recent with underfloor heating, provide washbasins and showers and include provision for children and disabled visitors. Snack bar/café. Play area. Small petting zoo. Bicycle hire. Safari tents and mobile homes to rent. Bed and breakfast service. WiFi throughout.

Key Features

- Disabled Facilities
- Play Area
- Bike Hire

Scan me for more information.

Alan Rogers Code: NL6838
215 accommodations
347 pitches
GPS: 52.09272, 5.28287
Post Code: NL-3707 HW

Zeist, Utrecht

www.alanrogers.com/nl6838
info@dekrakeling.nl
Tel: 0306 915 374
www.dekrakeling.nl

Open (Touring Pitches):
End March - End September.

Allurepark De Krakeling

Allurepark De Krakeling is a spacious (22 ha) campsite with around 350 touring pitches, spread over several grassy fields. All pitches are surrounded by hedges and are supplied with 6A electricity and a cable TV connection (additional charge). There are also a number of mobile homes and chalets to rent. The site is attractively located in the middle of the Zeister forest and is a good choice for a family holiday with a wide range of facilities and a lively entertainment programme for young and old. The site enjoys a very pleasant natural setting, with plenty of routes for walking and cycling in the forest. The on-site restaurant, Bistro Jan offers a full menu or the coffee shop offers a range of snacks.

Heated toilet block with facilities for babies and disabled visitors. Laundry facilities. Motorhome services. Supermarket. Restaurant/ bar (every day in high season, weekend only in low season). Snack bar and takeaway. Games room. TV. Play area. Sports area. Entertainment programme. Hairdresser. Small petting zoo. Free WiFi. Max. 1 dog.

Key Features

- Pets Accepted
- Disabled Facilities
- Play Area
- Bar/Restaurant

Scan me for more information.

Alan Rogers Code: NL6860
715 accommodations
413 pitches
GPS: 53.15163, 4.85855
Post Code: NL-1795 JV

De Cocksdorp, Noord-Holland

www.alanrogers.com/nl6860
info@krim.nl
Tel: 0222 390 111
www.krim.nl

Open (Touring Pitches):
All year.

Camping De Krim Texel

Camping De Krim Texel is an attractive, well-maintained campsite which is open all year round and you are assured of a warm welcome. There are about 900 pitches which include 413 are for touring units and tents. All have electricity, and 179 have electricity, water and drainage; there are 100 pitches with private sanitary facilities. There are separate areas for bungalows and mobile homes. The manager tells us that Texel records the lowest rainfall and the most hours of sunshine than any other part of the Netherlands. The site is 3 km. from the northern point of Texel. There are plenty of activities – minigolf, bowling, a big playground inside and outside. The superb indoor pool complex offers sunbeds, steam baths and sauna. The outside pool has a slide. In quiet seasons, sauna and beauty evenings are arranged. There is a varied all-year activity programme.

Five excellent toilet blocks, all heated, include baby rooms, washbasins in cabins, showers (free), family showers and facilities for disabled visitors. Free dishwasher. Microwave. Motorhome services. Gas supplies. Laundry. Three restaurants and a snack bar. Large supermarket. Outdoor (seasonal) and indoor pools (all year) with slides. Sauna, massage and sunbeds. Riding. Minigolf. Bowling. Internet café. Indoor play paradise and play station. Tennis. Multisport court. Bicycle hire. Skelter track. Varied entertainment programme. Max. 2 dogs. WiFi throughout.

Key Features

- Open All Year
- Pets Accepted
- Disabled Facilities
- Swimming Pool
- Play Area
- Bar/Restaurant
- Bike Hire
- Golf

Scan me for more information.

Alan Rogers Code: NL6890
82 pitches
GPS: 52.45545, 4.64106
Post Code: NL-1985 EL

Velsen-Zuid, Noord-Holland

www.alanrogers.com/nl6890
info@campingschoonenberg.nl
Tel: 0255 52 39 98
www.campingschoonenberg.nl

Open (Touring Pitches):
1 April - 31 October.

Camping Schoonenberg

Camping Schoonenberg is a simple, family-run campsite set in the heart of an oak forest. It is surrounded by 25 hectares of wooded estates. The campsite covers 2.5 hectares and is affiliated with the Nature Campgrounds organisation. The camping areas are car-free except for loading; this makes it a very safe and friendly environment. There are 82 pitches, 23 with 4A electricity connections, most have shade and are separated by mature bushes. The twice-weekly evening bonfire is an ideal meeting place to make new friends and discuss the numerous activities nearby, many of which can be reached using hired bicycles. The surrounding area is full of nature-related opportunities, from the uncommercialised North Sea beach at Ijmuiderslag to the animal and play park of Velserbeek. World War Two bunkers and museums tell the story of this land's recent history and its current importance. With three golf courses nearby and canoe hire in Spaarnwoude, this is the ideal location for a varied and interesting holiday.

One modern shower block. Playground and campfire in tent field. Cold drinks and ice-cream available. Bicycle hire. WiFi on part of site (free). Torches useful.

Key Features

- Pets Accepted
- Skiing
- Bike Hire

Scan me for more information.

Alan Rogers Code: NL6335
2 accommodations
107 pitches
GPS: 52.10665, 6.35526
Post Code: NL-7251 KT

Vorden, Gelderland

www.alanrogers.com/nl6335
info@meulenbrugge-vorden.nl
Tel: 0575 556 612
meulenbrugge-vorden.nl

Open (Touring Pitches):
15 March - 1 November.

Camping 't Meulenbrugge

Camping 't Meulenbrugge is an open, attractive site attached to a working farm and approached by a bridge over the Baakse Brook. The emphasis at this site is centred on the enjoyment of nature, with no constructed leisure facilities. The 107 touring pitches are spacious and arranged on large grassy fields with tall trees around the edges offering some shade. All have electricity (10/16A) and Europlugs. There are also 94 serviced pitches with electricity, water and drainage and some hardstandings for awnings. Fishing is available on site in the Baakse brook and there are many marked walking and cycling trails from the site including the renowned castle route which takes in eight local castles. Cars are parked away from the pitches. In de Dennen, less than 1 km. away from the site, is a heated, outdoor swimming pool which recently won an award for the best swimming pool in the Netherlands. The site is also a stone's throw from the Parish of Kranenburg and the historic Saints' museum in the church of Kranenburg. Further afield is the beautiful port city of Zutphen, where you can wander the medieval streets and forts and visit its historic churches.

Two modern, heated toilet blocks (hot water payment card). Free use of fridge. Launderette. Motorhome services. No shop but fresh bread daily. Play area. Bicycle hire. Free bike parking. Boules pitch. Fishing. WiFi over part of site (charged). Caravans to rent.

Key Features

- Pets Accepted
- Bike Hire
- Fishing

Scan me for more information.

Alan Rogers Code: NL6285
11 accommodations
330 pitches
GPS: 52.31386, 5.92699
Post Code: NL-8166 JJ

Emst-Gortel, Gelderland

Camping De Wildhoeve

www.alanrogers.com/nl6285
info@wildhoeve.nl
Tel: +31 (0)578 66 13 24
www.wildhoeve.nl

Open (Touring Pitches):
29 March - 30 September

Camping De Wildhoeve is an excellent, welcoming, privately-owned site with many amenities of the type one would usually find on larger holiday camps. The well-maintained site is located in woodland, in the centre of the "Veluwe" region, known for its beautiful nature. There are 330 pitches and 11 accommodations. Pitches can be found in several areas, mostly in the shade of mature conifers. Partly separated by trees and bushes, the level pitches are numbered, and all have 6/10A electricity, water and drainage. A variety of outdoor activities like hiking, mountain biking and horse riding belongs to the surroundings of Emst. The Wildhoeve site also has an app, where guests can download multiple walking routes. Behind reception is an octagonal-shaped, indoor sub-tropical pool with a large water slide and fun paddling pool. Next to reception is a water adventure playground with a small beach.

Four well placed, heated blocks with toilets, washbasins (open style and in cabins) and free, preset hot showers. Special section for children with showers, washbasins and toilets. Baby room. Family shower room. Facilities for disabled children. Laundry facilities. Shop, grand café/restaurant. Snack bar. Indoor and outdoor pools with slides and paddling pool. Water adventure playground. Bicycle hire. Tennis. Open-air theatre. WiFi over site (charged). Dogs are not accepted.

Key Features

- Disabled Facilities
- Swimming Pool
- Bar/Restaurant
- Bike Hire

Scan me for more information.

Alan Rogers Code: NL6420
289 accommodations
287 pitches
GPS: 52.03477, 6.63163
Post Code: NL-7141 DH

Groenlo, Gelderland

www.alanrogers.com/nl6420
info@marveld.nl
Tel: 0544 466 000
www.marveld.nl

Open (Touring Pitches):
All year.

Marveld Recreatie

This large, high-quality holiday park lies on the outskirts of Groenlo in the Achterhoek, (Back Country) a region of the Netherlands rich in nature and history. The site is level with several separated, grassy camping fields surrounded by mature trees. There are about 200 touring pitches and a further 300 permanent holiday homes. Three main touring fields are serviced by modern, heated toilet blocks. In addition, 34 pitches have individual sanitary cabins. The site is pleasantly landscaped and, in spite of its size, does not give an impression of overcrowding. With its many recreational facilities, the campsite is ideal for family holidays. Indoor activities include two large swimming pools, tennis and squash courts and play areas. Outside, there is a whole range of children's activities, including activity programmes and treasure hunts. There is a pitch and put golf course and many cycle trails to follow.

Three modern, heated toilet blocks servicing the three touring fields include facilities for babies and disabled visitors. Individual sanitary cabins on full-service pitches. Supermarket. Restaurant and snack bar. Launderette. Hairdressing salon. Outdoor pool and sub-tropical swim paradise with covered competition pool. Tennis and squash courts. Sauna and sunbeds. Bicycle hire. Pitch and putt golf. Games field. Bowling. Fishing. Rowing. Disco. WiFi over site (charged).

Key Features

- Open All Year
- Pets Accepted
- Disabled Facilities
- Swimming Pool
- Bar/Restaurant
- Bike Hire

Scan me for more information.

Alan Rogers Code: NL6348
5 accommodations
200 pitches
GPS: 52.12822, 5.90427
Post Code: NL-7351 BP

Hoenderloo, Gelderland

Camping 't Schinkel

www.alanrogers.com/nl6348
info@veluwevakantieparken.nl
Tel: 0553 781 367
www.hetschinkel.nl

Open (Touring Pitches):
25 March - 23 October.

Camping 't Schinkel is a campsite with lots of facilities and activities, especially suitable for families with young children. It has been created with a Kingdom theme, so children will get into the fairytale atmosphere as soon as they arrive. Set in the heart of a nature reserve, on the edge of the little town Hoenderloo, it is surrounded by forests and moors. The site has a total of 200 touring pitches, all with 6-10A electricity. A part of the site is car-free. The shop, bar and restaurant were undergoing renovation when we visited. Hoenderloo has one of the three main entrances to the national park, the Hoge Veluwe, where you will find deer, wild mountain sheep and hogs. Activities for children include sports, swimming in the heated outdoor pool, cuddling the bunnies in the royal stables, showering with the monkeys or climbing the castle. There are also films available to watch, bingo and clue hunts are organised by the entertainment team.

Heated toilet block providing washbasins in cabins, controllable showers and free hot water. Family cabins and special facilities for children and babies. Launderette. Shop. Bar. Restaurant. Snack bar. Heated outdoor pool. Paddling pool. Recreation area. Indoor and outdoor play areas. Bicycle hire. Mountain bike hire. Animal farm. Butterfly garden. Sports pitches. Boules. Entertainment team in high season. Miniclub and child minding. Excursion programme (high season). First aid post. WiFi over site (charged). Walking and cycling routes.

Key Features

- Pets Accepted
- Swimming Pool
- Play Area
- Bar/Restaurant
- Bike Hire

Scan me for more information.

Alan Rogers Code: NL6390
249 accommodations
70 pitches
GPS: 52.15900, 5.96400
Post Code: NL-7361 TM

Beekbergen, Gelderland

Het Lierderholt

www.alanrogers.com/nl6390
Tel: 0555 061 458
www.lierderholt.nl

Open (Touring Pitches):
All year.

Holiday Park Het Lierderholt was established in 1951 amongst the woods of the Veluwe by the grandfather of Nico Willemsen, the current owner. The site has 110 numbered pitches of which 70 are for touring with 6A electricity, water, drainage and cable TV. The level pitches vary in size from 100-120 m^2 and are positioned in the shade. The woods are ideal for walking and cycling but there is also plenty to do on-site. Children can enjoy karaoke, aquarobics, painting of roof tiles, old traditional Dutch games and a casino for children, whilst adults can compare their strength with barrel rolling or play volleyball. After a long day of fun and activities, visitors can cool down in the swimming and paddling pools. The site also organises dance evenings, bingo and cycle trips. Nearby you will find De Apenheul in Apeldoorn (monkeys), Het Burgers Zoo and Safari park and the Dolphinarium in Hardewijk.

Modern heated toilet block with toilets, washbasins (open and in cabins) and showers. Facilities for children, family shower rooms, baby room. Facilities for disabled visitors. Laundry facilities. Motorhome services. Shop with basics. Restaurant and snack bar. Sports pitch. Tennis. Minigolf. Bicycle hire. Extensive entertainment for young and old in high season.

Key Features

- Open All Year
- Pets Accepted
- Disabled Facilities
- Swimming Pool
- Play Area
- Bar/Restaurant

Scan me for more information.

Alan Rogers Code: NL6356
292 accommodations
350 pitches
GPS: 52.36348, 5.95799
Post Code: NL-8162 NR

Epe, Gelderland

RCN Camping De Jagerstee

www.alanrogers.com/nl6356
reservation@rcn.eu
Tel: +31 85 0400 700
www.rcn.nl

Open (Touring Pitches):
All Year

De Jagerstee (literally, hunter's home) can be found at the heart of the Veluwe, the largest natural park in The Netherlands. Using the site as a base, there are many walks and cycle trips through the forests. The site's attractions are grouped around the open-air heated pool and the two touring areas are on either side. All pitches have 10A electricity and 96 are fully serviced. Rented bungalows occupy the remainder of the site. To the rear of each pitch are large trees and shrubs which provide some welcome shade on hot summer days. On-site is a large restaurant with a terrace and also a café and takeaway. There is a full range of sporting activities and an open-air theatre. An activity programme is offered in high season. From the campsite, you can explore some beautiful countryside but there are also some fine old Dutch towns, and the Kröller-Müller Museum, which holds the world's second-largest (after the Amsterdam Van Gogh museum) collection of works by Van Gogh.

Four modern toilet blocks all have family rooms and baby facilities. Launderette. Restaurant, bar, café, takeaway. Bakery and supermarket. Outdoor swimming pool. Sports hall. Open-air theatre. Play area. Minigolf. Beach volleyball. 5-a-side football pitch. Bicycle and go-kart hire. Mobile homes and chalets to rent. WiFi over site (free).

Key Features

- Open All Year
- Pets Accepted
- Disabled Facilities
- Swimming Pool
- Play Area
- Bar/Restaurant
- Bike Hire

Scan me for more information.

Alan Rogers Code: NL6470
100 accommodations
245 pitches
GPS: 52.39200, 7.04900
Post Code: NL-7591 NH

Denekamp, Overijssel

www.alanrogers.com/nl6470
info@depapillon.nl
Tel: 0541 351 670
www.depapillon.nl

Open (Touring Pitches):
29 March - 1 October.

Camping De Papillon

De Papillon is perhaps one of the best and most enjoyable campsites in the Netherlands. All 245 touring pitches are spacious (120-160 sq.m), all have electricity (4/10/16A), and TV; a further 220 have water and drainage. An impressive, new sanitary block has state-of-the-art equipment and uses green technology. There is a new entertainment centre with an outdoor auditorium for children, and the water play area by the adventure playground and covered, heated pool are among the most imaginative and exciting we have seen, making it ideal for families. The restored heathland area offers opportunities for nature lovers; there is also a large fishing lake and a swimming lake with beach area and activities. A member of Leading Campings group.

Two large sanitary buildings with showers, toilets, washbasins in cabins, facilities for babies and for disabled visitors. Laundry room. Spacious reception area with supermarket, restaurant, bar and takeaway. Heated pool with children's pool and sliding roof. Lake swimming with sandy beach. New modern adventure play area and smaller play areas. Pétanque. Bicycle hire. Fishing pond. Tennis. Pets to stroke. Max. 2 dogs. Luxury bungalows to rent (good views). New water spray park for children up to 13 yrs. Free WiFi over the whole site. Motorhome Friendly.

Key Features

- Pets Accepted
- Disabled Facilities
- Swimming Pool
- Play Area
- Bar/Restaurant
- Bike Hire
- Fishing

Scan me for more information.

Alan Rogers Code: NL6449
110 accommodations
125 pitches
GPS: 52.52053, 6.36380
Post Code: 7731 RC

Ommen, Overijssel

Resort de Arendshorst

www.alanrogers.com/nl6449
info@resort-de-arendshorst.nl
Tel: 0529 453248
www.arendshorst.nl

Open (Touring Pitches):
End March - Mid October

A most peaceful and spacious site, Resort de Arendshorst is located about 2.5 hours East of the Hook of Holland and could make a convenient stopover on the way to Germany or Scandinavia. Michael, the owner and his family, are friendly and accommodating, and the friendly staff all speak English, with an English language handbook given to guests upon arrival. The onsite restaurant and bar are popular and of high quality. The facilities are all immaculate, with hot water for showers and washing up available with a pre-paid card. Pitches are large, with many offering waste-water, electric and freshwater hookups. The area around the site is perfect for cycling, with the Fietsknoop network accessible from just outside the campsite. Local towns of Ommen, Vilsterren, Dedemsvaart, and Zwolle are all accessible through the cycle network, almost always avoiding even the most minor roads.

Modern toilet blocks. Laundry. Boating and swimming jetties. A sandy river beach. Play areas. Petting zoo. Bouncy castle. Paddling pool. Small shop for basics including fresh bread (which is baked on premises daily). Dutch fishing licenses and bait as well other fishing attributes. Bar and restaurant serving breakfast, lunch and dinner as well as take-ways. Spectacular countryside, villages, hamlets and other places of interest which are best explored by bike or on foot using the extensive walking paths and dedicated cycle lanes. Bike and canoe rental is available on site.

Key Features

- Play Area
- Bar/Restaurant
- Bike Hire
- Fishing

Scan me for more information.

Alan Rogers Code: NL5785
143 accommodations
150 pitches
GPS: 52.67598, 5.93918
Post Code: NL-8325 PP

Vollenhove, Overijssel

www.alanrogers.com/nl5785
info@akkertien.nl
Tel: 0527 241 378
www.akkertien.com

Open (Touring Pitches):
All year.

Vakantiepark 't Akkertien

Akkertien op de Voorst has about 300 pitches (150 are for tourers) on large, flat grassy fields with shade at the rear from high bushes. In circular bays, the pitches are 100-150 sq.m. all with 10A electricity, water and drainage. To the front of the site are the reception block and an area for drinks, music and recreation activities in high season. A fascinating tractor museum displays several antique tractors. A small unfenced lake for fishing and boating is by the comfort pitches. A sandy play area is available for children. Akkertien op de Voorst is in the grounds of a former farm close to the Frisian lakes and the IJsselmeer. You could visit one of the bustling lakeside resorts, such as Lemmer. Cycling around the Vollenhove area will introduce one of the more open parts of the Netherlands and the famous polders - land the Dutch reclaimed from the sea. Other possibilities include a trip to Giethoorn, better known as Dutch Venice, where you can take boat trips through the smallest canals of the Netherlands.

Two toilet blocks, central on the site and one small block to the front. Washbasins in cabins, controllable hot showers. Baby room. Facilities for disabled visitors. Laundry facilities. Motorhome services. Small shop. Bar (several nights a week in high season). Snack bar. Outdoor swimming pool (May-Sept). Lake for boating and fishing. Bicycle hire. Free WiFi over site. Club room. Playground. Entertainment team in high season.

Key Features

- Open All Year
- Pets Accepted
- Disabled Facilities
- Swimming Pool
- Play Area
- Bar/Restaurant
- Skiing
- Bike Hire

Scan me for more information.

Alan Rogers Code: NL6055
50 accommodations
300 pitches
GPS: 53.12680, 5.94618
Post Code: NL-9264 TP

Eernewoude, Friesland

www.alanrogers.com/nl6055
info@wiid.nl
Tel: 0511 539 223
www.wiid.nl

Open (Touring Pitches):
All year.

Camping It Wiid

Camping It Wiid is surrounded by water and has easy access to the famous Frisian lakes. On-site, it is possible to rent sailing boats and motorboats or you can moor your own. The site has 300 touring pitches, all with 4-16A electricity. Of these, 90 have water, wastewater and cable as well. Pitching is on level, grassy fields with shade from mature trees and hedges. There are 12 hardstanding pitches for motorhomes, all fully serviced. To the far edge of the site is a spit of land where you can camp surrounded by water, and from where there are great views over the Fokkesloot water. Cars are parked away from pitches. It Wiid has an open-air pool with a water slide and fun paddling pool. The central building is next to the water and houses a theatre, a sub-tropical pool with jacuzzi, jet stream and paddling pool and a sports hall. In high season, the site offers a full entertainment programme. At the central building is a jetty where touring boats and Skutsjes (special Frisian sailing boats) leave for tours through the Alde Feanen nature reserve.

There is one older sanitary blocks, plus two new, heated blocks with washbasins and adjustable hot showers. Baby room. Facilities for children and disabled visitors. Laundry. Motorhome services. Well stocked shop, bar/restaurant and takeaway (seasonal). Open-air pool with 65 m. water slide and fun paddling pool (seasonal). Boat rental. Sailing school. Football. Volleyball. Basketball. Fishing. Bicycle hire. Tennis. Playground. Entertainment programme in high season. WiFi throughout (charged).

Key Features

- Open All Year
- Disabled Facilities
- Swimming Pool
- Bar/Restaurant
- Skiing
- Bike Hire
- Fishing

Scan me for more information.

Alan Rogers Code: NL6075
33 accommodations
85 pitches
GPS: 53.18968, 5.55333
Post Code: NL-8800 AA

Franeker, Friesland

Camping Bloemketerp

www.alanrogers.com/nl6075
info@bloemketerp.nl
Tel: 0517 395 099
www.bloemketerp.com

Open (Touring Pitches):
All year.

Camping Bloemketerp can be found within walking distance of the interesting and historic town of Franeker. There are about 80 sheltered and good sized pitches here. These are dispersed around several camping fields. The park also has a range of holiday homes to rent. There is a well-equipped sports centre adjacent, with sub-tropical indoor swimming pool, canoe rental and bicycle hire. Campers are allowed free access to this centre (fitness, tennis, squash, racquetball, sauna and massage). The park boasts an attractive, friendly restaurant (with sun terrace) offering both a set menu and buffet options. Some road noise can be heard, but it is not too intrusive. Franeker is one of Friesland's famed Eleven Cities. The town is famous for its unique Eisinga planetarium which dates back to the 18th century. Franeker was formerly a town of great note, with the second university in The Netherlands, and home to the Duke of Saxony. Nowadays, it is a tranquil place surrounded by delightful Frisian countryside. This is best explored on foot, or by bicycle, and the site managers will be pleased to recommend routes.

One large toilet block with controllable, hot showers (€ 0.50), open style washbasins and facilities for disabled visitors. Laundry. Motorhome services. Restaurant (with buffet option). Takeaway meals. Sports centre full facilities. Play area. Ten-pin bowling. Recreation team (high season). Canoe hire. WiFi over site (charged). Accommodation to rent.

Key Features

- Open All Year
- Pets Accepted
- Disabled Facilities
- Swimming Pool
- Play Area
- Bar/Restaurant
- Bike Hire

Scan me for more information.

Alan Rogers Code: NL6057
29 accommodations
46 pitches
GPS: 53.09740, 5.94746
Post Code: NL-9215 VV

De Veenhoop, Friesland

www.alanrogers.com/nl6057
info@de-veenhoop.nl
Tel: 0512 462 289
www.de-veenhoop.nl

Open (Touring Pitches):
1 April - 31 December.

Camping de Veenhoop

Camping Veenhoop is located at the heart of Friesland in the De Alde Feanen National Park. There are about 50 pitches spread across three grassy fields with tall trees around the perimeter. All the pitches are spacious and all have electricity. The site also has its own small marina and sailing school with boat and canoe hire facilities – a great way to explore the extensive waterways of the National Park. There is a good restaurant 100 m. from the site with a terrace overlooking the river. This site is a good choice for cycling, hiking or fishing holidays. The campsite is close to the historic village of Aldeboarn. The Waag is one of the most imposing original buildings that merit a visit. The town of Beetsterzwaag, often described as the 'green pearl of Opsterland' is just 15 minutes from Veenhoop. Amongst its best-known sights are the fine house of Lycklama house and the Harinxma estate.

Clean and modern sanitary block with heating and climate control system. Launderette. Library. WiFi (free). Bicycle, canoe and boat hire.

Key Features

- Pets Accepted
- Play Area
- Bar/Restaurant
- Bike Hire
- Fishing
- Sailing

Scan me for more information.

Alan Rogers Code: NL6180
11 accommodations
210 pitches
GPS: 52.86675, 6.32018
Post Code: NL-7981 LW

Diever, Drenthe

www.alanrogers.com/nl6180
info@campingdiever.nl
Tel: 521 591 644
www.campingdiever.nl

Open (Touring Pitches):
1 April - 30 September.

Camping Diever

Camping Diever is just outside the quiet, rural village of Diever and close to the Drents-Friese Wold nature reserve. The campsite has 210 touring pitches, all with 10A electricity, and 11 camping pods arranged informally around the site, located between trees and separated by natural greenery. Some of the ground is sandy with some grass areas found, off the sandy access roads. The campsite is car-free, with parking at the entrance and electric vehicle charge points available. Innovative features include a dishwashing service which is not only efficient but an ecologically sound choice too. The heated sanitary facilities are modern and cleaned regularly, a family shower room is available. Hot water is available, with remaining credit refunded at the end of your stay. through a pre-paid card system. The village of Diever is an easy 15-minute walk, where local attractions include the open-air theatre where Shakespearean plays are performed throughout the summer. You could also visit one of the famous hunebeds (Neolithic dolmen) and the Museum of Coaches. This whole area is excellent for long walks and cycling tours. In high season, an entertainment team arranges activities, and the site organises walks through the woods with a forester.

Key Features

- Pets Accepted
- Play Area
- Bike Hire

Three toilet blocks (one heated) provide toilets, washbasins (open style and in cabins) and preset hot showers with key for hot water. Private facilities on eight pitches. Family shower. Baby room. Laundry facilities. Fresh bread and basics from reception. Recreation hall with games machine and library. Playing field. Bicycle hire. Adventure play island (parents not allowed). No charcoal barbecues. Torch useful. WiFi (charged).

Scan me for more information.

Alan Rogers Code: NL6143
8 accommodations
130 pitches
GPS: 52.80144, 6.52469
Post Code: NL-9418 TL

Wijster, Drenthe

De Otterberg

www.alanrogers.com/nl6143
info@otterberg.nl
Tel: 0593 562 362
www.otterberg.nl

Open (Touring Pitches):
1 April - 1 October.

Familiecamping De Otterberg is a well-established site in the green heart of Drenthe. It has 330 pitches including 130 for tourers. The touring pitches are on well-tended, grassy fields with shade from mature trees, the newer field to the front right being more open. All pitches have 6A electricity. Central on the site is an open-air pool which is heated to 30 degrees and has a jet stream, jacuzzi and a paddling pool with mushroom fountain. Visitors may bring their own horses to stay in the site's stables. The site has a tranquil atmosphere and offers good facilities for wheelchair users. For example, in high season the pool is reserved twice a day for disabled visitors only. Next to the pool complex is a welcoming bar/restaurant with a terrace where you can enjoy good, simple meals and where bingo and card evenings are organised. In high season there is an active animation team for youngsters and adults. Close to the site is the Dwingelerveld national park, ideal for walking and cycling.

Three toilet blocks, (1 main and 2 smaller) with toilets, washbasins (open style and in cabins) and preset hot showers (5 minutes free hot water). Bathroom with jacuzzi (charged). Family shower room. Baby room. Facilities for disabled visitors (with alarm). Washing machines and dryers. Shop with fresh bread (daily in season). Bar/restaurant with TV and snack bar. Pool with jet stream, jacuzzi and paddling pool. Games room. Internet point. Riding stables with new indoor hall. Sports field. Minigolf. Fishing. Entertainment team in high season.

Key Features

- Pets Accepted
- Disabled Facilities
- Swimming Pool
- Play Area
- Bar/Restaurant
- Fishing
- Horse Riding

Scan me for more information.

Alan Rogers Code: NL6168
25 accommodations
60 pitches
GPS: 52.87610, 6.61250
Post Code: NL-9433 TJ

Zwiggelte, Drenthe

www.alanrogers.com/nl6168
nfo@campingmiddendrenthe.nl
Tel: 0593 370 022
campingmiddendrenthe.nl

Open (Touring Pitches):
28 March - 25 October.

Camping Midden Drenthe

Camping Midden Drenthe is a pretty site located in woodland and fields in the heart of the rural province of Drenthe. The site has 60 spacious and grassy pitches, all with electricity, arranged on large grassy fields. Some pitches offer shade and most are overlooked by tall trees. The site is ideal for young children, with a small farm (home to rabbits, chickens and goats), a good, spacious play area and a family room with games. Just five minutes from the site is Lake Loomeer, a natural lake with a sandy beach, perfect for swimming. On the border of Friesland and Drenthe is one of the largest nature reserves in the Netherlands. There are over 60,000 hectares of woodland, heathland, river valleys, nature and equestrian trails to explore, not to mention countless marked cycling and walking routes to choose from.

Modern sanitary blocks, well lit at night, with facilities for babies and disabled visitors. Launderette. Breakfast service. Children's farm. Family games room. Playground. Pétanque pitch. Bicycle hire. WiFi (free).

Key Features

- Pets Accepted
- Disabled Facilities
- Play Area
- Bike Hire

Scan me for more information.

Alan Rogers Code: NL6104
7 accommodations
77 pitches
GPS: 52.95440, 7.13805
Post Code: NL-9551 VT

Sellingen, Groningen

Camping De Bronzen Eik

www.alanrogers.com/nl6104
recepttie@debronzeneik.nl
Tel: 0599 322 006
www.debronzeneik.nl

Open (Touring Pitches):
All year.

This site is perfect for families with young children and those who enjoy cycling and walking in a peaceful and natural environment. Camping De Bronzen Eik is a small family, friendly campsite with 65 fully equipped pitches, all with 6A electricity, water and drainage. Twelve pitches are without electricity and there are a further five fields available for tents, ideal for group camping. There is free use of the heated, municipal swimming pool nearby. The restaurant with a terrace offers an extensive menu ranging from a cup of coffee and a snack to à la carte dishes. Just a stone's throw from the Westerwolde nature reserve, there are over 200 km. of walking, cycling and riding trails to choose from. There are 2,300 hectares of woodland flora and fauna waiting to be discovered, an ideal area for hide and seek and where children can play safely.

Modern sanitary block with underfloor heating, free hot showers and facilities for children. Launderette with dryers. 'FootGolf' pitch. Play area. WiFi (free).

Key Features

- Open All Year
- Play Area

Scan me for more information.

Hanseatic wharf, Bergen >

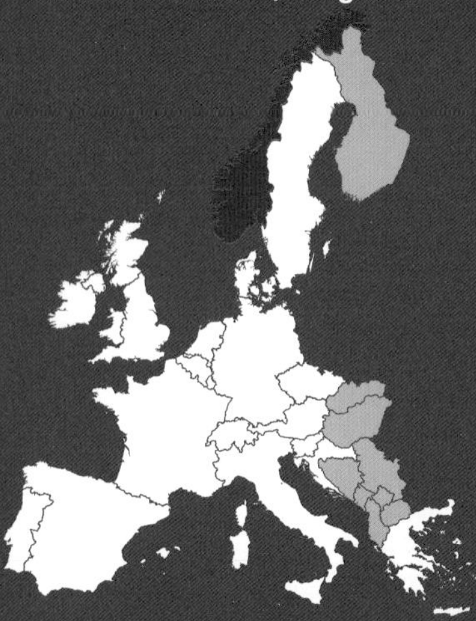

Capital Oslo
Currency Norwegian Krone (NOK)
Language Norwegian
Time Zone CET (GMT+1)
Telephone Code 00 47

Tourist Website
visitnorway.com

Climate Winters are mild on the coast, cold and snowy inland and extremely cold in the north. Summers are hot and dry with 24hr daylight.

Shops Varied. In high-season 10am to 5pm Mon to Sat. Supermarkets 9am to 11pm weekdays and until 10pm Sat.

Banks 8am to 4pm weekdays.

Accessible Travel Generally well equipped for disabled visitors, especially in cities. Public transport and street crossings are good but planning ahead is always a smart idea.

Travelling with children A great country for children. Oslo is home to many parks and museums but not all attractions are children-friendly. Attractions are often free for under 6s and discounted for under 16s.

See campsite map page

486

Public Holidays New Year's Day, Maundy Thursday, Good Friday, Easter Sunday, Easter Monday, Labour Day (1 May), Constitution Day (17 May), Ascension, Whit Sunday, Whit Monday, Christmas Day, Boxing Day.

Motoring Roads are generally uncrowded around Oslo and Bergen. Be prepared for long tunnels and hairpins bends. Certain roads are forbidden to caravans (check the tourist website). Vehicles must have sufficient road grip and in winter it may be necessary to use winter tyres with or without chains. Vehicles entering Oslo and Bergen must pay a toll and other tolls are levied on certain roads.

Environmental Policies Oslo and Bergen both enforce Low Emission Zones. No stickers are currently required. Plastic is widely recycled. Items contained in plastic bottles are subject to a small deposit which can be redeemed at bottle deposit stations when the bottle is finished with. Metal and glass are not as widely recycled.

View all campsites in Norway
alanrogers.com/norway

Norway

A land full of contrasts, from magnificent snow-capped mountains, dramatic fjords, vast plateaux with wild untamed tracts, to huge lakes and rich green countryside. With nearly one-quarter of the land above the Arctic Circle, Norway has the lowest population density in Europe.

Norway is made up of five regions. In the heart of the eastern region, Oslo has everything one would expect from a major city, and is the oldest of the Scandinavian capitals. The west coast boasts some of the world's most beautiful fjords, with plunging waterfalls and mountains.

Trondheim, in the heart of central Norway, is a busy university town with many attractions, notably the Nidarosdomen Cathedral. The sunniest region is the south, its rugged coastline with white wooden cottages is popular with Norwegians and ideal for swimming, sailing, scuba diving and fishing.

The north is the Land of the Midnight Sun and the Northern Lights. It is home to the Sami, the indigenous people of Norway, whose traditions include fishing, hunting and reindeer herding. The scenery varies from forested valleys and narrow fjords to icy tundra, and there are several cities worth visiting including Tromsø, with the Fjelheisen cable car, Polaria aquarium with bearded seals, and the Arctic Cathedral.

Alan Rogers Code: NO2380
10 accommodations
35 pitches
GPS: 61.14466, 6.62180
Post Code: N-6894

Sogn og Fjordane, Western Fjords

www.alanrogers.com/no2380
post@tveitcamping.no
Tel: 57 69 66 00
tveitcamping.no

Open (Touring Pitches):
15 May - 15 September.

Tveit Camping

Located in the district of Vik on the south shore of Sognefjord, 4 km. from the small port of Vangsnes, Tveit Camping is part of a small working farm and it is a charming neat site. Reception and a kiosk open most of the day in high season and there is a phone to summon assistance at any time. Three terraces with wonderful views of the fjord provide 35 pitches with 30 electricity connections (10A) and there are also site owned cabins. On the campsite, you will find a restored Iron Age burial mound dating from 350-550 AD, whilst the statue of 'Fritjov the Intrepid' towers over the landscape at Vangsnes. The fjord is some four kilometres wide at the campsite and over a kilometre deep. Within reach is a sightseeing ferry journey from Gudvangen, and a mountain railway at Flåm. Worth visiting are the Kristianhus Boat and Engine Museum, the traditional Gamalost cheese making in Vik, and in Fjærland, across the fjord, you can find the Norwegian Glacier Museum. It is also possible for families to do easy hikes on the glacier at Nigardsbreen, something more challenging on Jostedalsbreen above Fjaerland.

Modern, heated sanitary facilities provide showers on payment, a unit for disabled visitors, kitchens with facilities for cooking, and laundry facilities (hot water on payment). Motorhome services. Kiosk (15/6-15/8). TV rooms. Playground. Trampoline. Harbour for small boats, slipway and boat/canoe hire. Fishing and fish preparation area. Free WiFi over site. Bicycle hire. Comprehensive tourist information.

Key Features

- Pets Accepted
- Disabled Facilities
- Beach Access
- Play Area
- Bike Hire
- Fishing

Scan me for more information.

Alan Rogers Code: NO2452
4 accommodations
41 pitches
GPS: 62.49444, 7.75833
Post Code: N-6300

Møre og Romsdal, Western Fjords

Trollveggen Camping

www.alanrogers.com/no2452
post@trollveggen.no
Tel: 71 22 37 00
www.trollveggen.no

Open (Touring Pitches):
10 May - 20 September.

The location of this site provides a unique experience – it is set at the foot of the famous vertical cliff of Trollveggen (the Troll Wall), which is Europe's highest vertical mountain face. The site is pleasantly laid out in terraces with level grass pitches. The facility block, four cabins and reception are all very attractively built with grass roofs. Beside the river is an attractive barbecue area where barbecue parties are sometimes arranged. This site is a must for people who love nature. The site is surrounded by the Troll Peaks and the Romsdalshorn Mountains with the rapid river of Rauma flowing by. Close to Reinheimen (home of reindeer) National Park and in the beautiful valley of Romsdalen, you have the ideal starting point for trips to many outstanding attractions such as Trollstigen (The Troll Road) to Geiranger or to the Mardalsfossen waterfalls. In the mountains, there are nature trails of various lengths and difficulties. The campsite owners are happy to help you with information.

One heated toilet block provides washbasins, some in cubicles, and showers on payment. Family room with baby bath and changing mat, plus facilities for disabled visitors. Communal kitchen with cooking rings, small ovens, fridge and sinks (free hot water). Laundry facilities. Motorhome services. Car wash facility. Barbecue area (covered). Playground. Duckpond. Fishing. Free WiFi over the site. Old Trollveggen Station Master's apartment for hire by arrangement (Apr-Nov).

Key Features

- Pets Accepted
- Disabled Facilities
- Play Area

Scan me for more information.

Alan Rogers Code: NO2585
41 accommodations
200 pitches
GPS: 59.38828, 9.26325
Post Code: N-3812

Telemark, South

Norsjø Ferieland

www.alanrogers.com/no2585
post@norsjo-ferieland.no
Tel: 35 95 84 30
www.norsjo-ferieland.no

Open (Touring Pitches):
1 May - 1 October

Norsjø Ferieland is a campsite where camping meets boating and the local residents, all set in a very pleasant environment. This is an ideal campsite for those who love water sports. It is usually bustling, with peak days seeing thousands of visitors, so there is always something new to see. There is a large area for camping with a tent, caravan or motorhome. Enjoy a meal in beautiful surroundings at Norsjø Ferieland's own restaurant with both indoor and outdoor facilities. The restaurant is located next to the small shop and service facilities, overlooking the water. Well-being is the keyword here, with green lawns and bulging flower beds. For lovers of adrenaline sports, the 550m. long Norsjø Cable Park is one of the best in Europe, catering for wakeboarders and waterskiers of all abilities. A children's playground is found near the restaurant.

Heated sanitary facilities for children and the disabled. Individual shower-WC cubicles. Baby room. Chemical toilet disposal point. Laundry with sinks, washing machines and dryers. Cooking facilities for groups and individuals. Fresh bread and groceries are available in high season. Shop. Bar. Restaurant. Pizzeria. Takeaway meals. Communal barbecue area. Freezers are available. Canoe and pedal boat hire. Fishing. Sailing. Snorkelling. Windsurfing. Waterskiing (courses available). Own boats accepted. Jetty. Kids club (English). Crazy golf. Bouncy castle. Multisports field. Trampoline. Volleyball. Boules. Climbing wall. Television.

Key Features

- Pets Accepted
- Disabled Facilities
- Play Area
- Bar/Restaurant
- Fishing
- Sailing

Scan me for more information.

Alan Rogers Code: NO2610
31 accommodations
260 pitches
GPS: 58.68839, 7.80175
Post Code: N-4741

Aust-Agder, South

Neset Camping

www.alanrogers.com/no2610
post@neset.no
Tel: 37 93 42 55
www.neset.no

Open (Touring Pitches):
All year.

On a semi-promontory on the shores of the 40 km. long Byglandsfjord, Neset is a well run, friendly site ideal for spending a few active days, or as a shortstop en route north from the ferry port of Kristiansand (from Denmark). Neset is situated on well kept, grassy meadows by the lake shore, with water on three sides and the road on the fourth. There are over 250 unmarked pitches with electricity and cable TV, and 40 hardstandings for motorhomes. The main building houses reception, a small shop and a restaurant with fine views over the water. The campsite has a range of activities to keep you busy, and the excellent hardstandings for motorhomes look out onto the lake. Byglandsfjord offers good fishing (mainly trout) and the area has marked trails for cycling, riding or walking in an area famous for its minerals. Samples of these can be found in reception, and day trips to specialist exhibitions at the Mineralparken (8 km) are possible. Walking and cycling routes abound and cycles and mountain bikes can be hired from Neset.

Three modern, heated sanitary blocks have showers (on payment), en-suite family rooms, washing up facilities and kitchen. Facilities for disabled campers in one block. Motorhome services. Restaurant and takeaway (15/6-15/8). Shop (1/5-1/10). Playground. Lake swimming, boating and fishing. Trampoline. Bouncy cushion. Outdoor fitness. Beach volleyball. Barbecue area and hot tub (winter). Boat, canoe and pedalo hire. Elk safaris arranged. Climbing, rafting and canoeing courses arranged (linked with Trollaktiv). Cross-country skiing (winter). Car wash. Free WiFi.

Key Features

- Open All Year
- Pets Accepted
- Disabled Facilities
- Play Area
- Bar/Restaurant
- Fishing
- Sailing

Scan me for more information.

Alan Rogers Code: NO2577
14 accommodations
40 pitches
GPS: 60.61879, 8.22088
Post Code: N-3577

Buskerud, East

www.alanrogers.com/no2577
informasjon@birkelund-camping.com
Tel: 45 29 78 41
birkelund-camping.com

Open (Touring Pitches):
All Year

Birkelund Camping

Birkelund camping has been certified since 2013 with the Norwegian "Miljøfyrtårn" environmental mark and is a quiet family campsite with lots of space and excellent facilities. The campsite is located in an old, cultural landscape with agricultural traditions and summer mountain farms. The campsite can be used as a base for various tours by car, motorcycle or bicycle. It's the perfect location for climbing, mountain biking, fishing or hiking holidays. Spend your free time fly fishing in the Storåni river where fish are abundant. The river is 500 m from the campsite and fishing rods are available from reception. At Birkelund camping there is room for 40 caravans, campers and tents.14 cabins are available to rent.

---

2 heated sanitary buildings with toilets, showers, washbasins and washing cabins. Kitchen where you can cook, eat, play boardgames or watch TV. Books in the kitchen can be borrowed or exchanged. Washing machine and dryer in the laundry room. The use of EasyBe dishwashers are free. Cross-country skiing and alpine skiing is possible in the vicinity of the campsite. Bicycles, mountain bikes and the sauna at the campsite are complimentary. Small playground. Trampoline. Table tennis. Volleyball/badminton court. Boules court. Fire pit with barbecue facility at the campsite and a number of barbecues that you can hire. Free WiFi throughout the campsite.

Key Features

- Open All Year
- Pets Accepted
- Swimming Pool
- Play Area
- Skiing
- Bike Hire

Scan me for more information.

Alan Rogers Code: NO2545
74 accommodations
50 pitches
GPS: 61.28025, 10.36095
Post Code: N-2636

Oppland, East

www.alanrogers.com/no2545
rustberg@pluscamp.no
Tel: 61 27 77 30
www.rustberg.no

Open (Touring Pitches):
All year.

PlusCamp Rustberg

Conveniently located beside the E6, 23 km. from the centre of Lillehammer, this attractive terraced site provides a comfortable base for exploring the area. Like all sites along this route, it does suffer from road and train noise at times, but the site's facilities and nearby attractions more than compensate for this. There are 110 pitches with 50 available for touring units (all with 16A electricity). Most are reasonably level and some gravel hardstandings are available for motorhomes. A small, open-air, heated swimming pool has a water slide. Lillehammer, host to the 1994 Olympic Winter Games, has a pleasant pedestrian precinct and Mailhaugen outdoor museum. We recommend a visit to the latter and pay parking for the day, it is cheaper (minimum time three hours). At Øyer and Hunderfossen (10 km) you will find a road museum, fairytale park and the more adventurous can ride the Olympic bobsleigh track.

Heated, fully equipped sanitary facilities include washbasins in cubicles, showers on payment and free saunas. Two good family bathrooms. Unit for disabled visitors. Campers' kitchen and dining room with microwave oven and double hob. Laundry. Motorhome services. Solarium (on payment). Kiosk for basics and café (both 1/6-31/8). Swimming pool and slide (1/5-31/8, weather permitting). Minigolf. Playground. WiFi (free).

Key Features

- Open All Year
- Pets Accepted
- Disabled Facilities
- Swimming Pool
- Play Area
- Bar/Restaurant
- Skiing
- Horse Riding

Scan me for more information.

Alan Rogers Code: NO2432
13 accommodations
80 pitches
GPS: 68.77278, 16.57712
Post Code: N-9411

Troms, North

www.alanrogers.com/no2432
postmaster@harstad-camping.no
Tel: 77 07 36 62
harstadcamping.no

Open (Touring Pitches):
1st May- Mid October.

Harstad Camping

In a delightful setting with fine views, Harstad Camping has space for 120 units as it slopes down to Vågsfjorden with on-site fishing and boating. This well established, popular site near Harstad, provides an excellent base on Hinnøya, the largest island in Norway. The 80 touring pitches are unmarked but a flat area by the water's edge provides most of the site's 46 electricity hook-ups (16A). These pitches are sought after and a mid afternoon arrival may gain a level pitch with electricity. This site is ideal for those looking for a scenic view and a bustling town nearby with a variety of activities on offer.

Two sanitary units, one modern and unisex with showers (on payment) and two en-suite WC with washbasins. Older unit is separate sex, each with showers (on payment), toilets and washbasins (some in individual cabins for ladies). Room for disabled visitors with key from reception. Laundry room (tokens required). Kitchen with hot plates, tables and chairs. Reception (08.00-23.00 high season) sells drinks, ices, postcards etc. Fishing. Bicycle hire. WiFi (charged).

Key Features

- Pets Accepted
- Disabled Facilities
- Beach Access
- Play Area
- Bike Hire
- Fishing
- Sailing

Scan me for more information.

Alan Rogers Code: NO2435
23 accommodations
40 pitches
GPS: 69.97968, 23.46810
Post Code: N-9505

Finnmark, North

www.alanrogers.com/no2435
solvangcamp@hotmail.com
Tel: 78 43 04 77
www.solvangcamping.no

Open (Touring Pitches):
1 June - 31 August.

Solvang Camping

This is a restful little site with a welcoming atmosphere. It is set well back from the main road, so there is no road noise. The site overlooks the tidal marshes of the Altafjord, which are home to a wide variety of birdlife, providing ornithologists with a grandstand view during the long summer evenings bathed by the Midnight Sun. The 40 pitches are on undulating grass amongst pine trees and shrubs and are not marked, although there are 16 electricity hook-ups (16A). Out of season, the site provides holidays for children and carers. Places of interest in the area are Alta Museum with its ancient rock carvings, and the Alta Canyon, the largest in Europe, with the controversial Alta Hydroelectric Power Station and its 145m.Virdnejávr dam at its upper end.

Reception and sanitary facilities with underfloor heating, washbasins in cubicles, showers and a family room. Facilities for disabled visitors. Sauna. Kitchen with cooker, sinks and dining area. Washing machine and dryer. Large TV room. Football field. Play area. WiFi (free).

Key Features

- Pets Accepted
- Disabled Facilities
- Beach Access
- Play Area
- Fishing

Scan me for more information.

Colares, Portugal >

Capital Lisbon
Currency Euro (€)
Language Portuguese
Time Zone GMT
Telephone Code 00 351

Tourist Website
visitportugal.com

Climate Maritime climate. Hot summers and mild winters with comparatively low rainfall in the south, heavy rain in the north.

Shops Varied. In high-season 9.30am to noon and 2pm to 7pm weekdays, 10am to 1pm Sat. Shopping centres 10am to 10pm.

Banks 8.30am to 3pm weekdays.

Accessible Travel Access is limited but improving. Newer public buildings are required to cater for wheelchair users. Accessible parking spaces are available but are often occupied.

Travelling with children
Portugal has a lot to offer children. Lisbon has a good choice of attractions. The Algarve is one of the best destinations for kids with its long sandy beaches, zoos, water parks and boat trips.

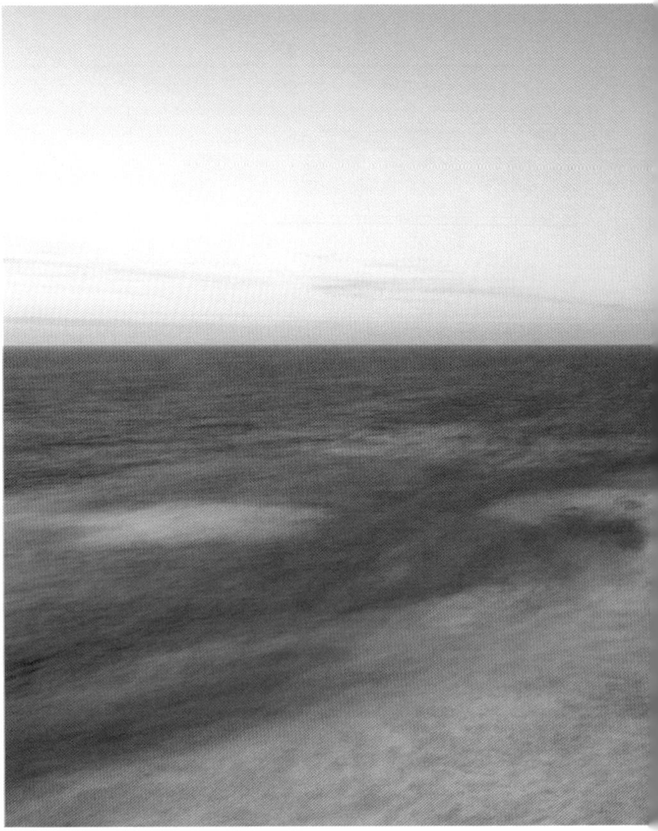

See campsite map page

484

Public Holidays New Year's Day, Good Friday, Easter Sunday, Liberation Day (25 Apr), Labour Day, National Day (10 Jun), Corpus Christi, Assumption, Republic Day (5 Oct), All Saints, Independence Restoration Day (1 Dec), Conception, Christmas Day.

Motoring The standard of roads is very variable, even some of the main roads can be very uneven. Tolls are levied on some motorways (auto-estradas) out of Lisbon, and upon southbound traffic at the Lisbon end of the giant 25th Abril bridge over the Tagus. Parked vehicles must face the same direction as moving traffic.

Environmental Policies Lisbon has implemented a Low Emission Zone in the city centre and outer suburbs which affects all petrol and diesel vehicles. It is monitored through the use of Number Plate Recognition Systems and cameras. Metal, plastic, glass, paper and cardboard are all widely recycled.

View all campsites in Portugal
alanrogers.com/portugal

Portugal

Portugal is the westernmost country of Europe, situated on the Iberian peninsula, bordered by Spain in the north and east, with the Atlantic coast in the south and west. In spite of its relatively small size, the country offers a tremendous variety, both in its way of life and in its history and traditions.

Every year the Algarve is the destination for some ten million sunseekers and watersports enthusiasts who love its sheltered sandy beaches and clear Atlantic sea. In contrast, the lush hills and forests of central Portugal are home to historic buildings and monuments, in particular the capital city of Lisbon, adjacent to the estuary of the River Tagus. Lisbon's history can still be seen in the Alfama quarter, which survived the devastating earthquake of 1755; at night the city comes alive with vibrant cafés, restaurants and discos.

To the south-east of Lisbon, the land becomes rather impoverished, consisting of stretches of vast undulating plains, dominated by cork plantations. Most people head for Evora, a medieval walled town and UNESCO World Heritage Site. The Minho area in the north is said to be the most beautiful part of Portugal, home to the country's only National Park, and vineyards producing the famous Port wine.

Alan Rogers Code: PO8385
40 accommodations
70 pitches
GPS: 41.25920, -7.65280
Post Code: P-5000-037

Vila Real, Porto and The North

www.alanrogers.com/po8385
geral@naturwaterpark.pt
Tel: 259 309 120
www.naturwaterpark.pt

Open (Touring Pitches):
All year.

Naturwaterpark

Naturwaterpark is a purpose-built site located within a large leisure complex with an impressive aqua park. The site is pleasantly situated in the Portuguese countryside, close to Vila Real. This is an important holiday complex with plenty of activities for both young and adult visitors. The waterpark is the main attraction, but the extensive playground, small farm and adventure park will appeal to all. There are 70 touring pitches here, mostly on grass, with some shade and separated by young trees and hedges. A pleasant restaurant and bar make for convivial evenings and an excellent spot for making new friends. Over 40 bungalows/mobile homes are also available to hire.

Modern shower block with access for disabled visitors. Laundry facilities. Kitchen and picnic room. Shop. Bar. Restaurant and snack bar/takeaway. Very impressive swimming pool complex. TV/games room. Tennis. Playground. Free WiFi. Mobile homes to rent.

Key Features

- Open All Year
- Disabled Facilities
- Swimming Pool
- Play Area
- Bar/Restaurant

Scan me for more information.

Alan Rogers Code: PO8030
75 accommodations
620 pitches
GPS: 41.46280, -8.77361
Post Code: 4570-275

Porto, Porto And The North

Orbitur Rio Alto

www.alanrogers.com/po8030
inforioalto@orbitur.pt
Tel: 252 615 699
orbitur.com/en/destinations/region-north/orbitur-rio-alto

Open (Touring Pitches):
All Year.

The first campsite in the world to be certified by the SGS ICS for the quality of its services is to be found in Rio Alto, Estela, close to the town of Póvoa de Varzim. It has excellent facilities, which include a mini-market, restaurant, bar, self-service, social halls, free swimming pool for users, four shower blocks with continuous hot water, nearly 600 electricity points and ten dishwashing blocks. It also has an area of plots for caravans and mobile homes. Make the most of your stay and get to know the area and visit Ofir and Esposende. This site also makes an excellent base for visiting Porto, which is some 35 km. South of Estela. It has pitches on sandy terrain and is next to what is virtually a private beach. The beach is accessed via a novel double tunnel in two lengths of 40 m. beneath the dunes (open 09.00-19.00). The beach shelves steeply at some tidal stages (lifeguard 15/6-15/9).

Four well-equipped toilet blocks have hot water. Laundry facilities. Facilities for disabled visitors. Gas supplies. Motorhome service point. Shop (1/6-15/9). Restaurant (1/6-15/9). Bar, snack bar (all year). Swimming pool (1/6-30/9). Tennis. Playground. Games room. Surfing. TV. First-aid post. Car wash. Evening entertainment twice weekly in season. Bicycle hire can be arranged by reception. WiFi.

Key Features

- Open All Year
- Pets Accepted
- Disabled Facilities
- Beach Access
- Swimming Pool
- Play Area
- Bar/Restaurant

Scan me for more information.

Alan Rogers Code: PO8460
155 accommodations
98 pitches
GPS: 39.62028, -9.05639
Post Code: P-2450-138

Leiria, Lisbon and Vale do Tejo

Vale Paraiso Natur Park

www.alanrogers.com/po8460
info@valeparaiso-naturpark.com
Tel: 351 262 561 800
www.valeparaiso-naturpark.com

Open (Touring Pitches):
21 February - 31 December

A pleasant, well-managed site, Vale Paraiso continues to improve. Its reception and amenities buildings create a good impression and a warm welcome is offered. Occupying eight hectares of undulating pine woods, the site has over 250 shady pitches, mainly in the valley and on terraces either side. Many are occupied by seasonal units, but there are around 100 marked pitches of varying size with 6/10A electricity available. Others on sandy ground are suitable for tents and there are areas occupied by chalets, canvas bungalows and teepees for rent. Many of the pitches have electricity, water and wastewater/chemical disposal.

Four sanitary blocks are equipped with showers and private washing cubicles. Washing machines and dryers. Restaurant. Heated outdoor pool, slide swimming pool, spa, kids playground, gym and sports areas (padel court, volleyball). Activity and entertainment programmes (during school holidays). Surf lessons, bike-rent, free WiFi throughout.

Key Features

- Open All Year
- Pets Accepted
- Disabled Facilities
- Swimming Pool
- Play Area
- Bar/Restaurant
- Bike Hire

Scan me for more information.

Alan Rogers Code: PO8077
750 pitches
GPS: 40.18802, -8.39890
Post Code: P-3030-011

Coimbra, Beiras and The Centre

www.alanrogers.com/po8077
coimbra@cacampings.com
Tel: 239 086 902
www.coimbracamping.com

Open (Touring Pitches):
All year.

Coimbra Camping

This all-year site is an excellent base for exploring Coimbra, an important university city and former capital of Portugal. Pitches are terraced, generally unshaded, of a reasonable size and most have electrical connections. Several fully equipped chalets are available to rent. Leisure facilities are impressive and include a swimming pool, paddling pool, beach volleyball, gym and an all-weather sports terrain. There is also a good restaurant here. The city centre can be easily accessed, thanks to the bus stop close to the site entrance. Coimbra has a spectacular hilltop setting, on a bend in the Mondego River, and has a history dating back to Roman times. Its heyday was during the 12th and 13th centuries when it was Portugal's capital. The entire town centre features on UNESCO's world heritage list and boasts a remarkable array of civic buildings, many linked with its ancient university. There are also many delightful shady parks, including one of the world's oldest botanical gardens, founded in 1772.

Swimming pool. Paddling pool. Beach volleyball. Gym. Children's play area. All-weather sports terrain. Restaurant. Tourist information. Chalets and mobile homes to rent.

Key Features

OPEN 365 Open All Year

Scan me for more information.

Alan Rogers Code: PO8090
150 accommodations
303 pitches
GPS: 40.11860, -8.85639
Post Code: 3090-458

Figueira da Foz, Beiras and The Centre

Orbitur Camping Gala

www.alanrogers.com/po8090
infogala@orbitur.pt
Tel: 233 431 492
orbitur.com/en/destinations/region-center/orbitur-gala

Open (Touring Pitches):
All Year.

On sandy terrain under a canopy of pine trees and close to a dune-lined beach, Gala has around 450 pitches with space for about 300 touring units and is well cared for, with plants and shrubs to welcome you. Chalets occupy the area closest to the road and seasonal units the next; beyond that are some level marked pitches and a large pine-clad area on sloping ground nearest the sea where you choose your own spot between the trees. A short walk from there takes you to a private beach, though you should swim with caution when it is windy. Electrical connections (6/10A) are available throughout. Located in the midst of the Mata de Lavos, the campsite is 400 m from a magnificent beach. It has three shower blocks as well as a swimming pool and bungalows. The wide beach of Figueira da Foz and the city of Coimbra, packed with monuments and history are both worth a visit. The Serra da Boa Viagem is a nature reserve and paradise for nature-lovers. Conímbriga also offers you the chance to visit the beautiful 1st century AD Roman remains.

Key Features

- Open All Year
- Pets Accepted
- Disabled Facilities
- Swimming Pool
- Play Area
- Bar/Restaurant

The three toilet blocks have British and Turkish style toilets, washbasins (some with hot water, a few in cabins) and free hot showers. Facilities for babies, children and disabled campers. Laundry. Motorhome services. Gas supplies. Supermarket and bar (all year). Restaurant with terrace and takeaway (seasonal). Lounge. Open-air pool (June-Sept). Playground. Tennis. TV. Car wash area. WiFi throughout (free).

Scan me for more information.

Alan Rogers Code: PO8115
51 accommodations
492 pitches
GPS: 41.26720, -8.71972
Post Code: 7425-017

Portalegre, Alentejo

Orbitur Montargil

www.alanrogers.com/po8115
infomontargil@orbitur.pt
Tel: 242 90 12 07
orbitur.com/en/destinations/alentejo/orbitur-montargil

Open (Touring Pitches):
All Year

Enjoy the peace and quiet of the Alentejo, but near Lisbon. This is what this campsite, located opposite the Montargil reservoir with its fresh-water beach and pier, can offer you. You can take part in water sports, such as jet-ski, windsurfing or water-skiing on the reservoir, or, simply, go for a sail. If you prefer peace and quiet, you can enjoy unique moments of relaxation while fishing in beautiful surroundings. Montargil campsite has modern facilities and is in a truly wonderful landscape. It has accommodation and commercial services, as well as a fine restaurant with outstanding dishes such as sirloin steak with asparagus crumbs.

Three toilet blocks washbasins (some with hot water, a few in cabins) and free hot shower. Facilities for babies, children and disabled campers. Laundry. Motorhome services. Gas supplies. supermarket and bar (all year). Restaurant with terrace and takeaway (seasonal). Lounge. Open-air pool (June-Sept). Playground. Tennis. TV. Car wash area. WiFi throughout (free).

Key Features

- Open All Year
- Pets Accepted
- Disabled Facilities
- Swimming Pool
- Play Area
- Bar/Restaurant
- Bike Hire

Scan me for more information.

Alan Rogers Code: PO8180
42 accommodations
540 pitches
GPS: 37.73190, -8.78301
Post Code: P-7645-300

Beja, Alentejo

Camping Milfontes

www.alanrogers.com/po8180
geral@campingmilfontes.com
Tel: 283 996 140
www.campingmilfontes.com

Open (Touring Pitches):
All year.

This popular site, with good facilities, has the advantage of being open all year and is within walking distance of the town and beach. As such, it makes a perfect base for those visiting out of main season, or for long winter stays when fees are heavily discounted. Well lit and fenced, it has around 500 shady pitches for touring units on sandy terrain, many marked out and divided by hedges. There is an area, mainly for motorhomes, where you just park under the trees. Some pitches are small and cars may have to be parked in an internal car park. Electricity (6A) is available throughout.

Four clean and well maintained toilet blocks. Two have en-suite units for disabled visitors with ramped entrances. Mainly British style WCs, bidets, washbasins (some with hot water), controllable showers and limited facilities for children. Laundry. Motorhome services. Supermarket, bar, snacks and takeaway (all 15/4-30/9). Outdoor pool (15/6-30/9). TV room. Playground. Car wash. Gas supplies. WiFi throughout (free).

Key Features

- Open All Year
- Pets Accepted
- Disabled Facilities
- Swimming Pool
- Play Area
- Bar/Restaurant

Scan me for more information.

Alan Rogers Code: PO8175
132 pitches
GPS: 37.60422, -8.73142
Post Code: P-7630-011

Beja, Alentejo

www.alanrogers.com/po8175
reservas@zmar.eu
Tel: 283 690 010
www.zmar.eu

Open (Touring Pitches):
All year (facilities all closed in January).

Zmar Eco Campo

Zmar Eco Campo is located near Zambujeira do Mar, on the Alentejo coast. It is a highly ambitious initiative developed along very strict environmental lines. Renewable resources such as locally harvested timber and recycled plastic are used wherever possible and the main complex of buildings is clean cut and impressive. A terrace overlooks an open-air pool that seems to go on forever. The 132 pitches are 90 sq.m. and some, mainly for tents or smaller caravans and motorhomes, benefit from artificial shade. All have 16A electricity. Caravans and wood-clad mobile homes are also available to rent.

Eight toilet blocks provide comprehensive facilities, including for children and disabled visitors. Washing machine. Large supermarket. Bar. Restaurant. Crêperie. Takeaway. Outdoor swimming pool (April-Oct). Covered pool and wellness centre (Feb-Dec). Sports field. Games room. Play area, farm and play house. Tennis. Bicycle hire. Activity and entertainment programme. Mobile homes and caravans to rent. Caravan repair and servicing. The site's own debit card system is used for payment at all facilities. WiFi around central complex (free),

Key Features

- Pets Accepted
- Disabled Facilities
- Swimming Pool
- Play Area
- Bar/Restaurant
- Bike Hire

Scan me for more information.

Alan Rogers Code: PO8202
108 accommodations
240 pitches
GPS: 37.10111, -8.73278
Post Code: P-8600-109

Faro, Algarve

www.alanrogers.com/po8202
info@turiscampo.com
Tel: 282 789 265
www.turiscampo.com/en

Open (Touring Pitches):
All Year

Turiscampo Algarve

Yelloh! Village Turiscampo is an outstanding site which has been thoughtfully refurbished and updated since it was purchased by the friendly Coll family in 2003. The site provides 240 pitches for touring units, mainly in rows of terraces, 197 of which have 6/10A electricity, some with shade. There are 43 deluxe pitches with water and drain. The upper terraces are occupied by 132 bungalows for rent. Just down the road is the fashionable resort of Praia de Luz with a beach, shops, bars and restaurants. Head west and the road takes you to Sagres and the western tip of the Algarve. Portugal's 'Land's End' remains unspoilt and there are numerous rocky coves and little sandy beaches to explore. A member of Leading Campings group.

Two heated toilet blocks provide outstanding facilities. There is a third facility beneath the pool. Spacious controllable showers, hot water throughout. Children & baby room. Facilities for disabled visitors. Dog shower. Laundry facilities. Shop. Gas supplies. Modern restaurant/bar with buffet & some theme party dinners. Pizza bar & takeaway. Swimming pools (all year) with extensive terrace & Jacuzzi. Aquagym. Wellness facility. Bicycle hire. Entertainment on the bar terrace. Miniclub. Two playgrounds. Boules. Archery. Multisports court, WiFi (partial coverage) on payment.

Key Features

- Open All Year
- Pets Accepted
- Disabled Facilities
- Swimming Pool
- Play Area
- Bar/Restaurant
- Bike Hire

Scan me for more information.

Alan Rogers Code: PO8440
51 accommodations
500 pitches
GPS: 37.07543, -8.83134
Post Code: P-8650-196

Faro, Algarve

www.alanrogers.com/po8440
info@salemaecocamp.com
Tel: 282 695 201
www.salemaecocamp.com

Open (Touring Pitches):
1 January - 31 September.

Salema EcoCamp

Salema EcoCamp is an attractive and peaceful valley site. The campsite was formerly known as Parque de Campismo Quinta dos Carriços. On arrival, a traditional tiled Portuguese-style entrance leads you down a steep incline into this excellent, well-maintained site, which has a village atmosphere. Much of the site has been recently redeveloped, along with the introduction of environmental elements such as solar heating for the water, using locally sourced, organic produce in the restaurant and selling eco-products in the shop. The campsite is spread over two valleys (which are real sun traps), with many of the 500 partially terraced pitches marked and divided by trees and shrubs (oleanders and roses). Others are less well defined among trees. There are 6/16A electricity connections to over 300 pitches. A small stream (sometimes dry) meanders through the site.

Three sanitary blocks are equipped with showers, private washing cubicles. Washing machines and dryers. Bar/ Restaurant and a shop where you can find a variety of organic and bioproducts. 1.5km to Salema Beach where kayaking, surfing are available. Indoor badminton. Activity and entertainment programmes (during school holidays). Riding centre. Bicycle hire. Canoe trips. Fishing. Segways. Zip wire. Internet access and WiFi (charged). Shuttle service to the beaches. Booking service for island trips.

Key Features

- Pets Accepted
- Disabled Facilities
- Play Area
- Bar/Restaurant
- Bike Hire

Scan me for more information.

Alan Rogers Code: PO8410
25 accommodations
1200 pitches
GPS: 37.10947, -8.35329
Post Code: P-8365

Faro, Algarve

Armação de Pêra

www.alanrogers.com/po8410
geral@camping-armacao-pera.com
Tel: 282 312 260
camping-armacao-pera.com

Open (Touring Pitches):
All year.

A wide attractive entrance leads to this basic, spacious park with a capacity of 1,200 units. You pitch on level, grassy sand beneath tall trees that provide some shade, accessed from tarmac and gravel roads. Electricity (6/10A) is available for most pitches. As there are no marked pitches, the site can cater for very large units. The beach is a brisk walk away, as are the shops, bars and restaurants of the small town, and for the less energetic a bus runs from close to the entrance. There is a wide choice of beaches and resorts along this stretch of coast. Albufeira is a busy little resort just a short drive to the east, and bustling Faro and Portimão are also within easy reach.

Three traditional sanitary blocks provide British and Turkish style WCs and showers with hot water (on payment). Facilities for disabled campers. Long-stay visitors reported that they are kept clean. Laundry. Supermarket. Self-service restaurant. Three bars (one all year). Swimming and paddling pools (May-Nov; charged July/Aug; no lifeguard). Games and TV rooms. Tennis. Well maintained play area. ATM. Internet access. WiFi on part of site (free).

Key Features

- Open All Year
- Pets Accepted
- Disabled Facilities
- Swimming Pool
- Play Area
- Bar/Restaurant

Scan me for more information.

Alan Rogers Code: PO8230
35 accommodations
800 pitches
GPS: 37.03528, -7.82250
Post Code: P-8700

Faro, Algarve

Camping Olhão

www.alanrogers.com/po8230
parque.campismo@sbsi.pt
Tel: 289 700 300
www.sbsi.pt/atividadesindical/Servicos/ParquedeCampismo

Open (Touring Pitches):
All Year

The large, sandy beaches in this area are on offshore islands reached by ferry and are, as a result, relatively quiet. This site, on the edge of town, has around 800 pitches, all with 6A electrical connections available. Its many mature trees provide good shade. The pitches are marked in rows divided by shrubs, although levelling will be necessary in places and the trees make access tricky on some. There is a separate area for tents and places for very large motorhomes. Seasonal units take up one fifth of the pitches, the touring pitches filling up quickly in July and August, so arrive early. The site has a relaxed, casual atmosphere, though there is some subdued noise in the lower area from an adjacent railway.

Eleven sanitary blocks are adequate, kept clean even when busy and are well sited so that any pitch is close to one. Two blocks have facilities for disabled visitors. Laundry. Excellent supermarket. Kiosk. Restaurant/bar. Café and general room with cable TV. Playgrounds. Swimming pools (all year, charged in season). Tennis courts. Bicycle hire. Internet at reception and Free WI-FI

Key Features

- Open All Year
- Pets Accepted
- Disabled Facilities
- Swimming Pool
- Play Area
- Bar/Restaurant
- Bike Hire

Scan me for more information.

The Church Of St Primoz, Sevnica >

Capital Ljubljana
Currency Euro (€)
Language Slovene
Time Zone CET (GMT+1)
Telephone Code 00 386

Tourist Website
slovenia.info

Climate Cold, sometimes snowy winters and warm summers with highs of 21°C. Coastal areas enjoy a submediterranean climate.

Shops Varied. In high-season 8am to 7pm weekdays, to 1pm Saturdays.

Banks 8.30am to 12.30pm and 2pm to 5pm weekdays.

Accessible Travel Generally well equipped. Many pedestrian crossings are fitted with beepers, public buildings have ramps and car parks have reserved spaces.

Travelling with children Great during the summer months. Most regions have castles that children will love exploring. Most attractions are free for under 7s and those under 15 will pay a discounted fee. Most restaurants cater for children.

See campsite map page

474

Public Holidays New Year's Day, New Year Holiday (2 Jan), Prešeren Day (8 Feb), Easter Sunday, Easter Monday, Resistance Day (27 Apr), May Day, Whit Sunday, National Day (25 Jun), Assumption, Reformation Day (31 Oct), All Saints, Christmas Day, Independence Day (26 Dec).

Motoring A small but expanding network of motorways. Winter driving equipment is mandatory between Nov and Mar. Headlights must be on at all times. You are required to carry a reflective jacket, warning triangle and first aid kit in the vehicle.

Environmental Policies There are no Low Emission Zones in Slovenia however there is a vignette system for motorway travel. The cost is around €35 for a six-month vignette, they can be purchased at petrol stations and DARS offices. Six different coloured containers are used to separate waste: organic, mixed waste, packaging, paper, plastic and glass. Up to 98% of the waste produced in Slovenia is recycled.

View all campsites in Slovenia
alanrogers.com/slovenia

Slovenia

What Slovenia lacks in size it makes up for in exceptional beauty. Situated between Italy, Austria, Hungary and Croatia, it has a diverse landscape; mountains, rivers, forests and the warm Adriatic coast.

Mount Triglav is at the heart of the snow-capped Julian Alps, a paradise for lovers of the great outdoors, with opportunities for hiking, rafting and mountaineering. From the Alps down to the Adriatic coast, the Karst region is home to the famous Lipizzaner horses, vineyards and myriad underground caves, including the Postojna and Skocjan Caves.

The tiny Adriatic coast has several bustling beach towns including Koper, Slovenia's only commercial port, whose 500 years of Venetian rule is evident in its Italianate style. Ljubljana, one of Europe's smallest capitals with beautiful baroque buildings, lies on the Ljubljanica river, spanned by numerous bridges, including Jože Plečnik's triple bridge.

The old city and castle sit alongside a thriving commercial centre. Heading eastwards, the hilly landscape is dotted with monasteries, churches and castles, including the 13th century Zuzemberk castle, one of Slovenia's most picturesque. The Posavje region produces cviček, a famous blend of white and red wines.

Alan Rogers Code: SV4270
8 accommodations
100 pitches
GPS: 46.25100, 13.58680
Post Code: SI-5222

Kobarid

www.alanrogers.com/sv4270
info@kamp-koren.si
Tel: +386 53 891 311
www.campingslovenia.com

Open (Touring Pitches):
All Year

Kamp Koren

Kamp Koren is situated in picturesque valley by the Soča river, 500 m from historical town Kobarid. A unique campsite and sole holder of the eco certificates: EU Ecolabel and Ecocamping. Its policy is to keep the environment clean and have minimum effect on nature. Slovenia's first ecological site is in a quiet location above the emarald coloured river, within easy walking distance of Kobarid. The site has slightly sloping pitches, all with 6/16A electricity and ample tree shade. It is deservedly very popular with those interested in outdoor sports, be it on the water, in the mountains or in the air. At the same time, its peaceful location makes it an ideal choice for those seeking a relaxing break. At the top of the site there are also a number of well equipped chalets and a shady area, mainly for tents and glamping.

Three attractive and well maintained log-built toilet blocks, two recently renovated. Facilities for disabled visitors. Laundry facilities. Motorhome services. Shop (March-Nov). Café/Bar serves light meals, snacks and drinks (flexible closing hours). TV. Multi-purpose hall. Play area. Volleyball. Table tennis. Boules. Gym. Fishing. Bicycle hire. Canoe hire. Climbing walls. Adventure park. Communal barbecue. Sauna. Grocery shop with eco products and electric vehicle charging station. WiFi.

Key Features

- Open All Year
- Pets Accepted
- Disabled Facilities
- Play Area
- Bar/Restaurant
- Skiing
- Bike Hire
- Fishing

Scan me for more information.

Alan Rogers Code: SV4440
23 accommodations
120 pitches
GPS: 46.42268, 15.85495
Post Code: SLO-2251

Ptuj

www.alanrogers.com/sv4440
info@terme-ptuj.si
Tel: 027 494 100
www.sava-camping.com

Open (Touring Pitches):
All year.

Camping Terme Ptuj

Camping Terme Ptuj is close to the river, just outside the interesting town of Ptuj. It is a small site with around 120 level pitches, all for tourers and all with 10A electricity. In two areas, the pitches to the left are on part grass and part gravel hardstanding and are mainly used for motorhomes. The pitches on the right-hand side are on grass under mature trees, off a circular, gravel access road. The main attraction of this site is clearly the adjacent thermal spa and fun pool complex that also attracts many local visitors. It has several slides and fun pools, as well as a sauna, solarium and spa bath. The swimming pools and saunas are free for campsite guests. This site would also be a useful stopover en route to Croatia and the beautiful historic towns of Ptuj and Maribor are well worth a visit. There is some road noise.

Modern toilet block with British style toilets, open washbasins and controllable, hot showers (free). En-suite facilities for disabled visitors with toilet and basin. Two washing machines. Football field. Torch useful.

Key Features

- Open All Year
- Pets Accepted
- Disabled Facilities
- Play Area

Scan me for more information.

Alan Rogers Code: SV4220
20 pitches
GPS: 46.32611, 14.23402
Post Code: SLO-4243

Brezje

www.alanrogers.com/sv4220
breda.policar@gmail.com
Tel: 040 260 414
www.turisticna-kmetija-hribar.si

Open (Touring Pitches):
1 May - 31 September.

Hribar Farm Camping

This is a very small, quiet, peaceful campsite of only 20 level, grassy pitches, 16 with electricity (16A), laid out in a farmyard orchard. It is near the small village of Brezje which is situated in the Alpine area of north-west Slovenia, not far from the Austrian and Italian borders and only 30 minutes' drive from the large town of Ljubljana. Brezje has a large Basilica, which is a major centre for pilgrimage and there is a hop-on tourist bus, in July and August, that tours the area and visits Lake Bled. The site entrance is not suitable for larger units. The campsite makes a good base for exploring the nearby Alpine resorts and the beautiful mountains are within easy reach. They offer a wide range of pursuits for the more active. The region is also well known for its many walking and cycle routes ranging from easy to very difficult.

A new central sanitary building with four showers, four basins and one urinal. In a separate block there are four new toilets and two basins with hot water. Facilities for the disabled. Washing machine. Table and chairs for campers. Waste disposal for motorhomes. Camp fires. Free WiFi throughout.

Key Features

- Pets Accepted
- Disabled Facilities
- Play Area
- Skiing

Scan me for more information.

Alan Rogers Code: SV4325
2 accommodations
60 pitches
GPS: 45.94179, 13.71748
Post Code: SLO-5261

Sempas

Camp Park Lijak

www.alanrogers.com/sv4325
info@parklijak.com
Tel: 053 088 557
parklijak.com

Open (Touring Pitches):
All year.

Camp Lijak is a small campsite with well-maintained facilities and enthusiastic and friendly owners. They are continuously working on projects to improve the site and aim to provide the ultimate holiday experience for campers. There are 60 level pitches spread over one hectare, all with electricity (6A), water, sewerage and WiFi access. There are also two bungalows and partially underground hobbit style huts. Camp Lijak is a good base for active outdoor pursuits such as hiking, cycling and paragliding which are actively promoted by the owners. The site has its own landing strip for paragliding and offers a minibus service to suitable launch sites. A different event is organised each day during the season and varies depending on the prevailing weather conditions. These can include trips to the Postonja and Skocjan caves, to Lake Bled and the Triglav National Park. Other more local trips are available for wine tasting at vineyards, rafting and even donkey rides. The Croatian coast, for a day at the beach, is within reach by car. Equally accessible, and in complete contrast, are the Austrian Alps.

One large toilet block with showers and open style vanity basins. Laundry facilities. Motorhome services. Fresh bread to order (daily). Freezer box hire. Organised cooking competitions and picnics. Communal barbecue. Transport for outdoor pursuits. Paragliding landing strip. WiFi throughout (charged).

Key Features

- Open All Year
- Pets Accepted
- Swimming Pool
- Play Area
- Skiing
- Bike Hire

Scan me for more information.

Alan Rogers Code: SV4230
40 accommodations
200 pitches
GPS: 46.33824, 13.64833
Post Code: SLO-5232

Soca

Camp Soca

www.alanrogers.com/sv4230
info@kamp-soca.si
Tel: 065 893 18
kamp-soca.si

Open (Touring Pitches):
1 April - 31 October.

Camp Soca is just off the main road on a shelving bluff formed by a wide curve of the Soca River. The site, with around 200 touring pitches, is literally theatrical as its two upper terraces and its large lower platform form a natural amphitheatre from which the mountains at the head of the Lepena valley can be readily admired. From Kranjska Gora an amazing road runs southwest to the upper Soca valley. This road was built by Russian prisoners of war during WW1 in order to allow Austria to move troops and supplies towards the Italian frontier. Those with large motorhomes or towed caravans should note that it is tough going with over 50 hairpin bends! Those in need of a good restaurant or bar, a game of tennis or a ride on a Lipizzaner can cross the Soca on a wobbly wire and plank bridge which leads directly from the camp, through the woods on the opposite bank, to a small, tasteful holiday resort.

Small but well equipped toilet block. Laundry facilities. Small reception office/shop. Fresh bread available. Bar and snack bar. Small play area. River fishing. WiFi.

Key Features

- Pets Accepted
- Play Area
- Bar/Restaurant
- Fishing

Scan me for more information.

Alan Rogers Code: SV4200
8 accommodations
280 pitches
GPS: 46.36155, 14.08075
Post Code: SLO-4260

Bled

www.alanrogers.com/sv4200
info@camping-bled.com
Tel: 045 752 000
www.camping-bled.com

Open (Touring Pitches):
25 March - 15 October, 20 December - 6 January.

Camping Bled

Camping Bled is situated on the western tip of Lake Bled. The waterfront here has a small public beach, immediately behind which runs a gently sloping narrow wooded valley. There are wonderful views across the lake towards its famous island. Pitches at the front, used mainly for overnighters, are now marked, separated by trees and enlarged, bringing the total number to 280. All are on gravel/grass with 16A electricity. A railway line passes close by but it is only a local line with few trains and they do not disturb the peacefulness of the site. Prominently perched, high above the lake, is an imposing castle which is open to the public. A tour around the lake is possible either on foot, by boat, by horse-drawn carriage or the road train which passes the site every half an hour. The town of Bled is just 2 km. away with all the usual facilities. Being on the edge of the Triglav National Park with its magnificent mountain scenery, Bled is a paradise for walking and mountain biking.

Toilet facilities in five blocks are of a high standard (with free hot showers). Three blocks are heated. Private bathrooms for rent. Solar energy used. Washing machines and dryers. Motorhome services. Gas supplies. Fridge hire. Supermarket. Restaurant. Play area and children's zoo. Games area. Trampolines. Organised activities in July/Aug including children's club, excursions and sporting activities. Mountain bike tours. Live entertainment. Fishing. Bicycle hire. Free WiFi over site.

Key Features

- Pets Accepted
- Disabled Facilities
- Play Area
- Bar/Restaurant
- Bike Hire
- Fishing

Scan me for more information.

La Giralda, Seville >

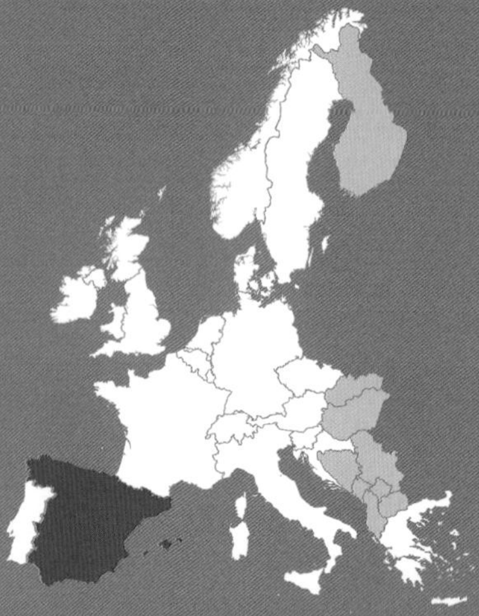

Capital Madrid
Currency Euro (€)
Language Spanish and some regional variants
Time Zone CET (GMT+1)
Telephone Code 00 34

Tourist Website
spain.info

Climate Temperate in the North with most of the rainfall; dry and hot in the centre; sub-tropical along the Mediterranean.

Shops Varied. In high season 10am to 2pm and 4.30 to 7.30pm or 5am to 8pm weekdays.

Banks 8.30am to 2pm weekdays, some also open late on Thurs and Sat mornings.

Accessible Travel Overall, access isn't great, but there is an effort to improve the situation. Buildings and transport in major cities are adapting.

Travelling with children Spain is very family-friendly and has a good range of attractions for all ages. Many restaurants cater well for kids and beaches are safe. Extremely hot during the summer, weather remains warm well into October.

See campsite map pages

478 484 485

Public Holidays New Year's Day, Epiphany, Good Friday, Labour Day, Assumption, Fiesta Nacionak de España (12 Oct), All Saints, Constitution Day (6 Dec), Conception, Christmas Day. There are also many regional public holidays that may affect opening hours and services.

Motoring The surface of the main roads is generally good, although secondary roads in some rural areas can be rough and winding. Tolls are payable on certain roads and for the Cadi Tunnel, Vallvidrera Tunnel and the Tunnel de Garraf on the A16.

Environmental Policies There is a Low Emission Zone in place in Barcelona and a Zero Emissions Zone in Madrid which affects both driving and parking in the municipal area of the city. All vehicles are affected and must meet certain requirements to enter the zone. Metal, plastic, glass, paper and cardboard are all widely recycled through collections and recycling centres.

View all campsites in Spain
alanrogers.com/spain

Spain

One of the largest countries in Europe with glorious beaches, a fantastic sunshine record, vibrant towns and laid back sleepy villages, plus a diversity of landscape, culture and artistic traditions, Spain has all the ingredients for a great holiday.

Spain's vast and diverse coastline is a magnet for visitors; glitzy, hedonistic resorts packed with bars and clubs are a foil to secluded coves backed by wooded cliffs.

Yet Spain has much more to offer – the verdant north with its ancient pilgrimage routes where the Picos de Europa sweep down to the Atlantic gems of Santander and Bilbao. Vibrant Madrid in the heart of the country boasts the Prado with works by Velázquez and Goya, the beautiful cobbled Plaza Major, plus all the attractions of a capital city.

Passionate Andalucía in the sun-soaked south dazzles with the symbolic art of flamenco. It offers the cosmopolitan cities of Córdoba, Cádiz and Málaga, alongside magnificent examples of the past such as the Alhambra at Granada and the awe-inspiring Alcázar, a magical Moorish palace with scents of orange and Jasmine wafting through the air, a must-see in dreamy Seville. On the Mediterranean east coast, Valencia has a wealth of monuments and cultural sites, including the magnificent City of Arts and Science.

Alan Rogers Code: ES91130
66 pitches
GPS: 42.57216, 1.09796
Post Code: E-25597

Lleida, Cataluña-Catalunya

www.alanrogers.com/es91130
camping@solineu.com
Tel: 973 624 001
www.solineu.com

Open (Touring Pitches):
1 July - 31 August

Camping Sol I Neu

Sol I Neu can be found at the entrance to the Sant Maurici National Park at Aigüestortes. It is a paradise for nature lovers, with alpine meadows, lakes and forest, home to chamois, black woodpecker and capercaillie. Families are welcome at this traditional site (no bungalows or mobile homes) set against the stunning backdrop of the Pyrenees. Mature trees shade the 66 grass touring pitches (80-120 sq.m) It is a no-frills holiday destination without the usual entertainment and sports facilities, but there are two small pools on-site and older children will enjoy amusing themselves in the shallow river that runs through it.

Sanitary block with hot showers and facilities for disabled visitors. Laundry. Motorhome services. Small, well-stocked shop in reception. TV room. Playing field. Fishing. Bicycle hire. WiFi (free).

Key Features

- Pets Accepted
- Disabled Facilities
- Swimming Pool
- Play Area
- Bike Hire
- Fishing

Scan me for more information.

Alan Rogers Code: ES81020
252 accommodations
376 pitches
GPS: 41.95680, 3.15730
Post Code: E-17256

Girona, Cataluña-Catalunya

Mas Patoxas

www.alanrogers.com/es81020
info@campingmaspatoxas.com
Tel: 972 636 928
www.campingmaspatoxas.com

Open (Touring Pitches):
Early March - Mid November

This is a mature, friendly and well laid out site for those who prefer to be apart from, but within easy travelling distance of, the beaches (5 km) and town (1 km). It has very easy access and is set on a slight slope with wide avenues on level terraces providing 376 grassy pitches (minimum 72 sq.m). All have shared 6A electricity and water points. There are a variety of mature trees throughout the site providing welcome shade. On-site amenities include an attractive swimming pool complex with a large terrace, an air-conditioned restaurant, an ice cream parlour and a children's play area.

Three modern sanitary blocks provide controllable hot showers, some washbasins with hot water. Baby bath and three cabins for children. Facilities for disabled campers. Laundry facilities. Fridges to rent. Gas supplies. Supermarket, restaurant/bar, ice cream parlour, pizzeria and takeaway (19/3-25/9,limited opening in low season). Swimming pool with bar (1/5-25/9). Tennis. Entertainment and children's club (high season). Fitness area. Games areas. Massage. Disco. Bicycle hire. Small farm with goats, donkeys and ponies etc. Internet access. WiFi over site (charged). Torches useful in some areas.

Key Features

- Pets Accepted
- Disabled Facilities
- Swimming Pool
- Play Area
- Bar/Restaurant
- Bike Hire

Scan me for more information.

Alan Rogers Code: ES80300
32 accommodations
1100 pitches
GPS: 42.20608, 3.10389
Post Code: E-17486

Girona, Cataluña-Catalunya

www.alanrogers.com/es80300
info@almata.com
Tel: 0034 972 454 477
www.almata.com

Open (Touring Pitches):
17 May - 15 September

Camping Nautic Almata

In the Bay of Roses, south of Empuriabrava and beside the Parc Natural dels Aiguamolls de l'Empordà, this is a high quality site of particular interest to nature lovers (especially birdwatchers) and families. A large site, there are 1,110 well kept, large, numbered pitches, all with electricity and on flat, sandy ground. Beautifully laid out, it is arranged around the river and waterways, so will suit those who like to be close to water or who enjoy watersports and boating. It is also a superb beachside site.

Sanitary blocks of a very high standard include some en-suite showers with washbasins. Good facilities for disabled visitors. Washing machines. Gas supplies. Excellent supermarket. Restaurants, pizzeria and bar. Two separate bars and snack bar by beach where discos are held in main season. Sailing, diving and windsurfing schools. 300 sq.m. swimming pool. Tennis courts. Badminton. Paddle tennis. Minigolf. Games room. Children's play park and miniclub. Fishing (licence required). Car, motorcycle and bicycle hire. Hairdresser. Internet access and WiFi over site (charged). ATM. Torches are useful near beach.

Key Features

- Pets Accepted
- Disabled Facilities
- Beach Access
- Swimming Pool
- Play Area
- Bar/Restaurant
- Bike Hire
- Fishing

Scan me for more information.

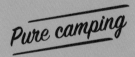

Alan Rogers Code: ES80220
125 accommodations
200 pitches
GPS: 41.66202, 2.78043
Post Code: E-17300

Girona, Cataluña-Catalunya

Camping Solmar

www.alanrogers.com/es80220
campingsolmar@campingsolmar.com
Tel: 972 348 034
www.campingsolmar.com

Open (Touring Pitches):
19 March - 12 October.

Camping Solmar has been run by the Ribas family for over 40 years and a warm welcome awaits you. The site is located 150 m. from a sandy beach in the busy urban resort of Blanes. The accessible, shaded pitches are 65-85 sq.m. and all have 6A electricity connections. On-site amenities include an attractive restaurant, bar and terrace area, as well as a central swimming pool complex with islands and bridges. A children's club operates in peak season (4-12 years) and an outdoor complex of sports facilities is available. A range of fully equipped mobile homes and wooden chalets are available for rent.

Four toilet blocks are clean and have open style washbasins, controllable showers in cabins and baby baths. Facilities for disabled visitors. Washing machines. Motorhome services. Supermarket. Restaurant. Bar. Swimming pool and terrace complex. Outdoor sports complex. Play areas. Miniclub (June onwards). Evening entertainment (high season). Tourist information and excursions. WiFi over site (charged). Mobile homes and chalets for rent.

Key Features

- Pets Accepted
- Swimming Pool
- Play Area
- Bar/Restaurant

Scan me for more information.

Alan Rogers Code: ES80350
138 accommodations
692 pitches
GPS: 42.18147, 3.10405
Post Code: E-17470

Girona, Cataluña-Catalunya

www.alanrogers.com/es80350
info@campingamfora.com
Tel: 972 520 540
www.campingamfora.com

Open (Touring Pitches):
23 April 2018 - 28 September 2018

Camping l'Amfora

This spacious, friendly site is run by Michelle, Josep and their daughter. It is spotlessly clean and well maintained and the owners operate the site in an environmentally friendly way. There are 830 level, grass pitches (692 for touring units) laid out in a grid system, all with 10A electricity. Attractive trees and shrubs have been planted around each pitch. There is good shade in the more mature areas, which include 64 large pitches (180 sq.m), each with an individual sanitary unit (toilet, shower and washbasin). The newer area is more open with less shade and you can choose which you would prefer.

Three excellent sanitary blocks, one heated, provide washbasins in cabins and roomy free showers. Baby rooms. Laundry facilities and service. Motorhome services. Supermarket. Terraced bar, self-service and waiter-service restaurants. Pizzeria/takeaway. Restaurant and bar on the beach with limited menu (high season). Disco bar. Swimming pools with 2 new long waterslides for the 2017 season (1/5-27/9) as also SPA area. Pétanque. Tennis. Minigolf. Play area. Miniclub. Entertainment and activities. Windsurfing. Kite surfing (low season).Sailing, kayak, fishing. Games rooms. Bicycle hire. Internet room and WiFi over site (charged). Car wash. Torches required in most areas.

Key Features

- Pets Accepted
- Disabled Facilities
- Beach Access
- Swimming Pool
- Play Area
- Bar/Restaurant
- Bike Hire
- Fishing

Scan me for more information.

Alan Rogers Code: ES80400
100 accommodations
1500 pitches
GPS: 42.16098, 3.10777
Post Code: E-17470

Girona, Cataluña-Catalunya

www.alanrogers.com/es80400
info@campinglasdunas.com
Tel: 972 521 717
www.campinglasdunas.com

Open (Touring Pitches):
20 May - 15 September.

Camping Las Dunas

Las Dunas is an extremely large, impressive and well organised resort-style site with many on-site activities and an ongoing programme of improvements. It has direct access to a superb sandy beach that stretches along the site for nearly a kilometre with a windsurfing school and beach bar. There is also a much used, huge swimming pool, plus a large double pool for children which opened in 2015. Las Dunas has 1,700 individual hedged pitches (1,500 for touring units) of around 100 sq.m. laid out on flat ground in long, regular parallel rows. All have electricity (6/10A) and 400 have water and drainage.

Five excellent large toilet blocks with electronic sliding glass doors. Toilets without seats, controllable hot showers and washbasins in cabins. Excellent facilities for children, babies and disabled campers. Laundry facilities. Motorhome services. Supermarket, boutique and other shops. Large bar with terrace. Large restaurant & takeaway. Ice cream parlour. Beach bar (seasonal). Disco club. Swimming pools. Adventure crazy golf. Playgrounds. Tennis. Minigolf. Sailing/windsurfing school and other watersports. Programme of sports, games, excursions and entertainment, partly in English. Exchange facilities. ATM. Safety deposit. Internet café. WiFi over site (charged). Dogs taken in one section. Torches required in some areas.

Key Features

- Pets Accepted
- Disabled Facilities
- Beach Access
- Swimming Pool
- Play Area
- Bar/Restaurant
- Bike Hire
- Fishing

Scan me for more information.

CAMPING LAS DUNAS

COSTA BRAVA
SPAIN

CAMPING BUNGALOWPARK

anwb ERKENDE CAMPING TOP 2019

Seaside holiday paradise for the whole family!

Camping & Bungalow Park located right at one of the most beautiful beaches in the Bay of Rosas. Offers a large variety of entertainment and activities for all ages, state-of-the-art sanitary facilities and a large shopping centre. Newly inaugurated AQUAPARK with slides guarantees fun and relax for the whole family.

Your UK Agent: Derek & Jessica Callaway
Tel. 01205 366856 - callaway@campinglasdunas.com

Camping Las Dunas
17130 L'Escala (Girona)
Tel. +34 972 521 717
info@campinglasdunas.com

www.campinglasdunas.com

alan rogers Winner 2015 Awards
alan rogers Winner 2010 Awards

Alan Rogers Code: ES80720
12 accommodations
170 pitches
GPS: 42.04800, 3.18810
Post Code: E-17258

Girona, Cataluña-Catalunya

www.alanrogers.com/es80720
info@campinglesmedes.com
Tel: 972 751 805
www.campinglesmedes.com

Open (Touring Pitches):
All year.

Camping les Medes

Les Medes is different from some of the 'all singing, all dancing' sites so popular along this coast. The friendly family of Pla-Coll are rightly proud of their innovative and award-winning site, which they have owned for almost 30 years. With just 170 pitches, the site is small enough for the owners and their staff to know their visitors, some of whom have been coming for many years. The top class facilities, along with the personal attention and activities available, make this a year-round home in the sun. The level, grassy pitches range in size from 70-80 sq.m. and are shaded. All have electricity (5/10A) and 155 also have water and drainage.

Two modern spacious sanitary blocks can be heated and are extremely well maintained. Washbasins in cabins, top class facilities for disabled visitors. Baby baths. Washing machines and dryer. Dog bathing room. Motorhome services. Shop. Bar with snacks and pizza (all year). Good value restaurant (1/4-31/10). Swimming and paddling pools (1/5-15/9). Indoor pool with sauna, solarium and massage (15/9-15/6). Play area. TV room. Entertainment, activities and excursions (July/Aug). Diving activities. Multisports area. Boules. Bicycle hire and self-repair shop. Internet access and WiFi. Torches are useful. Dogs are not accepted in July/Aug.

Key Features

- OPEN 365 Open All Year
- Pets Accepted
- Disabled Facilities
- Swimming Pool
- Play Area
- Bar/Restaurant
- Skiing
- Bike Hire

Scan me for more information.

Alan Rogers Code: ES81010
105 accommodations
650 pitches
GPS: 42.00113, 3.19380
Post Code: E-17256

Girona, Cataluña-Catalunya

www.alanrogers.com/es81010
info@playabrava.com
Tel: 972 636 894
www.playabrava.com

Open (Touring Pitches):
16 May - 13 September

Camping Playa Brava

This is an attractive and efficiently run site with an open feel, having direct access to an excellent soft sand beach and a freshwater lagoon. The ground is level and grassy with shade provided for many of the 650 spacious touring pitches by a mixture of conifer and broadleaf trees. All the pitches have 10A electricity and 238 have water and drainage. The large swimming pool has an extensive grass sunbathing area and is overlooked by the terrace of the restaurant and bar. This is a clean, secure and pleasant family site, suitable for sightseeing and for those who enjoy beach and water activities.

Five modern, fully equipped toilet blocks include facilities for disabled visitors. Washing machines and dryers. Motorhome services. Supermarket. Bar/restaurant. Takeaway. Swimming pool. Pétanque. Tennis. Minigolf. Beach volleyball. Play area. Bicycle hire. Watersports on beach. Stage show. Internet. WiFi over site (charged). Satellite TV. Gas supplies. Dogs are not accepted.

Key Features

- Disabled Facilities
- Beach Access
- Swimming Pool
- Play Area
- Bar/Restaurant
- Bike Hire
- Golf

Scan me for
more information.

Alan Rogers Code: ES81300
103 accommodations
466 pitches
GPS: 41.83333, 3.08417
Post Code: E-17251

Girona, Cataluña-Catalunya

Camping de Calonge

www.alanrogers.com/es81300
info@intercalonge.com
Tel: 972 651 233
www.intercalonge.com

Open (Touring Pitches):
All year.

This spacious, well laid out site has access to a fine beach via a footbridge over the coast road. Calonge is a family site with two attractive pools on different levels, a paddling pool and large sunbathing areas. A restaurant, bar and snack bar with great views are by the pool. The 466 touring pitches are on terraces and all have electricity (5A), with 84 being fully serviced. There is good shade from the tall pine trees, and there are some spectacular coastal views. Some access roads and steps are steep, but a road train operates in high season. There are wonderful views from the upper levels where there are some larger comfort pitches. The pools are overlooked by the restaurant terraces which have great views over the mountains.

Generous sanitary provision. One block is heated in winter. Laundry facilities. Motorhome services. Gas supplies. Shop (25/3-30/10). Restaurant (1/2-31/12). Bar, patio bar with pizzas and takeaway (25/3-30/9, weekends for the rest of the year). Swimming pools (25/3-12/10). Playground. Electronic games. Disco two nights a week (but not late) in high season. Bicycle hire. Tennis. Hairdresser. ATM. WiFi (free in hotspots). Torches necessary in some areas. Road train from the bottom of the site to the top in high season.

Key Features

- Open All Year
- Pets Accepted
- Disabled Facilities
- Swimming Pool
- Play Area
- Bar/Restaurant
- Bike Hire

Scan me for more information.

Alan Rogers Code: ES80090
50 accommodations
233 pitches
GPS: 42.26588, 3.15762
Post Code: E-17480

Girona, Cataluña-Catalunya

Camping Salatà

www.alanrogers.com/es80090
info@campingsalata.com
Tel: 972 256 086
www.campingsalata.com

Open (Touring Pitches):
1 March - 30 November.

Situated in the heart of Roses, in one of the most attractive areas of the Costa Brava, Salatà is a short walk from the magnificent seafront promenade with its bars, restaurants and shops. There are 233 grass touring pitches, all with 16A electricity and some shade (80-110 sq.m). Buildings and amenities are very well maintained. The campsite is part of a complex that includes apartments and the Hotel Terraza where a spa centre, indoor pool and other amenities can be enjoyed by campers in low season (extra charge). Within the site, there is a very large garden with an attractive pond, fountain and picnic tables. A small pool with a pizzeria and an attractive bar serving snacks is co-located with a supermarket and entertainment area. Camping Salata is ideally situated to explore beautiful local beaches, historic sites such as Empuries, nearby National Parks, the wonderful Dalí museum in Figueres and the Dalí house at Cadaques.

Very clean toilet blocks have British style toilets and very good showers. Facilities for disabled visitors. Facilities for babies and children. Washing machines. Gas supplies. Bar with snacks. Swimming pool. Playground. Entertainment programme for adults and children (15/6-15/9). Internet. WiFi. Barbecue area. Bicycle hire. Minigolf. No dogs from 29/6-23/08.

Key Features

- Pets Accepted
- Disabled Facilities
- Swimming Pool
- Play Area
- Bar/Restaurant

Scan me for more information.

Alan Rogers Code: ES81400
165 accommodations
371 pitches
GPS: 41.83631, 3.08711
Post Code: E-17250

Girona, Cataluña-Catalunya

www.alanrogers.com/es81400
info@campingtreumal.com
Tel: 972 651 095
www.campingtreumal.com/en

Open (Touring Pitches):
23 March - 30 September

Camping Treumal

This very attractive terraced site has been developed on a hillside around the beautiful gardens of a large, spectacular estate house which is close to the sea. The house is the focus of the site's excellent facilities, including a superb restaurant with terraces overlooking two tranquil beaches, protected in pretty coves. The site has 542 pitches on well shaded terraces. Of these, 371 are accessible to touring units and there are some 50 pitches on flat ground alongside the sea – the views are stunning and you wake to the sound of the waves. Electricity (6/10/16A) is available in all parts. Cars must be left on car parks or the site roads.

Four well maintained sanitary blocks have free hot water in the washbasins (with some private cabins) and controllable showers, and a tap to draw from for the sinks. No facilities for disabled visitors. New beach block. Washing machines. Motorhome services. Gas supplies. Supermarket, bar and takeaway (all season). Restaurant (15/6-15/9). Beach bar. Fishing. Play area. Sports area. Games room. Bicycle hire. Satellite TV. Internet access and WiFi (charged). ATM. Safes. Dogs are not accepted.

Key Features

- Beach Access
- Swimming Pool
- Play Area
- Bar/Restaurant
- Bike Hire
- Fishing
- Sailing

Scan me for more information.

Càmping
TREUMAL
Costa Brava
YOU WILL FIND US ON THE BEACH ...
Apdo. Correos nº 348 17250 PLATJA D'ARO (GIRONA)
TLF. (0034) 972 65 10 95 FAX. (0034) 972 65 16 71 E mail: Info@campingtreumal.com
www.campingtreumal.com

Alan Rogers Code: ES81750
127 accommodations
481 pitches
GPS: 41.81117, 3.01822
Post Code: E-17246

Girona, Cataluña-Catalunya

www.alanrogers.com/es81750
info@campingmassantjosep.com
Tel: 972 835 108
www.campingmassantjosep.com

Open (Touring Pitches):
9 April - 20 September

Yelloh! Village Mas Sant Josep

This is a very large, well appointed, open site in two parts. There are 1,023 level pitches (100 sq.m) with 481 for touring units in a separate area which has shade from established trees. All have 10A electricity connections. There are wide access roads and long avenues between the zones. The main side of the site is centred around charming historic buildings, including a beautiful, but mysterious, locked and long unused chapel. Nearby is a huge, irregular lagoon-style pool with a bridge to a palm decorated island (lifeguards) and an excellent, safe paddling pool. A large complex including a bar, restaurant, takeaway and entertainment areas overlooks the pool. There are also mobile homes for rent.

Two adequate toilet blocks for touring units (ignore the block for permanent pitches). Very good facilities for disabled visitors and pleasant baby rooms. Washing machines. Dryers. Large supermarket, bars, restaurant, snack bar and takeaway, swimming pools (all open as site). Safe playgrounds. Huge, well equipped games room. Tennis. Squash. Minigolf. 5-a-side football. Spa room and gym. Entertainment programme. Hairdresser. Internet. WiFi over part of site (charged). ATM. Bicycle hire. Torches useful. Dogs only in designated areas.

Key Features

- Pets Accepted
- Disabled Facilities
- Swimming Pool
- Play Area
- Bar/Restaurant
- Bike Hire

Scan me for more information.

Alan Rogers Code: ES80640
64 accommodations
58 pitches
GPS: 42.30654, 2.70933
Post Code: E-17733

Girona, Cataluña-Catalunya

Camping Bassegoda Park

www.alanrogers.com/es80640
info@bassegodapark.com
Tel: 972 542 020
www.bassegodapark.com

Open (Touring Pitches):
Mid March - Early December.

Surrounded by mountains alongside the Muga river, Bassegoda Park is a place to experience Spain in a natural environment but with a touch of luxury. This totally rebuilt site is just beyond Albanyà on the edge of the Alta Garrotxa National Park in an area of great beauty. In their own area, the 58 touring pitches are level and shaded, all on hardstanding and with access to electricity, water and drainage. Tents are dotted informally in the terraced forest areas. Particular care has been taken in the landscaping, layout and design of the attractive pool, bar and restaurant, the hub of the site. Regional wines and dishes are available in the reasonably priced restaurant.

A new spacious and well equipped, main toilet building is centrally located and provides controllable showers and facilities for babies and disabled visitors. Two smaller refurbished blocks. Washing machine and dryer. Gas. Supermarket. Bar, restaurant and takeaway. Swimming pool (seasonal). Playground. Leisure area (5-a-side football, volleyball, basketball). Minigolf. Activities and entertainment for adults and children. Bicycle hire. Fridge hire. Barbecue areas. WiFi (charged). Torches useful. Air-conditioned bungalows to rent.

Key Features

- Pets Accepted
- Disabled Facilities
- Swimming Pool
- Play Area
- Bar/Restaurant
- Skiing
- Bike Hire

Scan me for more information.

Alan Rogers Code: ES84830
156 accommodations
425 pitches
GPS: 41.13160, 1.36100
Post Code: E-43008

Tarragona, Cataluña-Catalunya

www.alanrogers.com/es84830
resort@tamarit.com
Tel: 977 650 128
www.tamarit.com

Open (Touring Pitches):
14 March - 11 October

Tamarit Beach Resort

This is a marvellous, beach-side site, attractively situated at the foot of Tamarit Castle at one end of a superb one-kilometre long beach of fine sand. It is landscaped with lush Mediterranean shrubs, studded with pines and palms, and home to mischievous red squirrels. There are 425 good sized pitches for touring, all with electricity (16A), 340 of which are fully serviced with water, drainage, TV connection and 16A electricity. Fifty very popular pitches are virtually on the beach. On hard sand and grass, some are attractively separated by hedging and shaded by trees. Accommodation in the form of bungalows (156 pitches) is also available to rent. The management and staff here are very keen to please and the standards are very high. The charming restaurant and snack bar both serve typical Spanish dishes whilst enjoying superb views of the sandy beach and castle.

The high quality sanitary blocks (two heated) are modern and tiled. Private bathrooms to rent. Laundry facilities. Motorhome services. Fridge hire. Gas supplies. Supermarket, boutique, bars, restaurant and takeaway. Bakery. Wellness area. Swimming pool. Tennis. Pétanque. Bicycle hire. Minigolf. Playground. Sports zone. Club room with bar. Miniclub. Entertainment programme. Fishing. WiFi throughout (code).

Key Features

- Pets Accepted
- Disabled Facilities
- Beach Access
- Swimming Pool
- Play Area
- Bar/Restaurant
- Bike Hire
- Fishing

Scan me for more information.

Alan Rogers Code: ES84820
84 accommodations
250 pitches
GPS: 41.08850, 1.18233
Post Code: E-43481

Tarragona, Cataluña-Catalunya

www.alanrogers.com/es84820
info@campinglapineda.com
Tel: 977 373 080
www.campinglapineda.com

Open (Touring Pitches):
Mid March - End September.

Camping La Pineda de Salou

La Pineda is a clean, neat site north of Salou, just 1.5 km. from an aquapark and 2.5 km. from Port Aventura, to which there is an hourly bus service from outside the site entrance. There is some noise from the road. The site has two swimming pools; the smaller is heated. A colourful themed paddling pool and outdoor spa are also here, behind tall hedges close to the entrance. A large terrace has sun loungers, and various entertainment aimed at young people is provided in season. The 250 flat pitches for touring units (all with 5A electricity) are shaded by mature trees in attractive gardens. A further 82 are available for tents and 84 are occupied by mobile homes for rent. La Pineda is a cut above other city sites.

Sanitary facilities have been completely refurbished and are excellent. Baby bath. Facilities for disabled visitors. Washing machines. Gas. Shop, restaurant and snacks (July/Aug). Swimming pools, themed paddling pool and outdoor spa (July/Aug). Small wellness centre with spa in private rooms. Bar (all season). New community room with satellite TV. Bicycle and road cart hire. Games room. Playground (3-12 yrs). Entertainment (July/Aug). Torches may be required. No pets in August. WiFi throughout (charged or free with advanced booking).

Key Features

- Pets Accepted
- Swimming Pool
- Play Area
- Bar/Restaurant
- Bike Hire

Scan me for more information.

Alan Rogers Code: ES84800
417 accommodations
976 pitches
GPS: 41.07546, 1.11651
Post Code: E-43840

Tarragona, Cataluña-Catalunya

Camping Resort Sanguli Salou

www.alanrogers.com/es84800
mail@sangulisalou.com
Tel: 977 381 641
www.sangulisalou.com

Open (Touring Pitches):
23 March - 4 November

Camping Resort Sanguli Salou is a superb site boasting excellent pools and entertainment. Owned, developed and managed by a local Spanish family, it has something for all the family with everything open when the site is open. There are 976 pitches of varying sizes (75-120 sq.m) all with electricity (7.5-10A). Mobile homes occupy 58 pitches and there are fully equipped bungalows on 147. A wonderful selection of trees, palms and shrubs provide natural shade and an ideal space for children to play. The good sandy beach is little more than 50 metres across the coast road and a small railway crossing. Although large, Sanguli has a pleasant, open feel and maintains a quality family atmosphere due to the efforts of the very keen and efficient staff.

The six sanitary blocks are constantly cleaned and are always exceptional, including many individual cabins with en-suite facilities. Improvements are made each year. Some blocks have excellent facilities for babies. Launderette with service. Motorhome services. Car wash (charged). Gas supplies. Snack bars. Indoor and outdoor restaurants with takeaway. Swimming pools. Fitness centre. Sports complex. Bicycle hire. Fitness room (charged). Playgrounds including adventure play area. Miniclub. Minigolf. Free WiFi throughout. Security bracelets. Medical centre.

Key Features

- Pets Accepted
- Disabled Facilities
- Beach Access
- Swimming Pool
- Play Area
- Bar/Restaurant
- Skiing
- Bike Hire

Scan me for more information.

Alan Rogers Code: ES85300
263 accommodations
990 pitches
GPS: 41.03345, 0.96921
Post Code: E-43300

Tarragona, Cataluña-Catalunya

Playa Montroig Camping Resort

www.alanrogers.com/es85300
info@playamontroig.com
Tel: 977 810 637
www.playamontroig.com

Open (Touring Pitches):
27 March - 25 October

What a superb site! Playa Montroig is about 30 kilometres beyond Tarragona, set in its own tropical gardens with direct access to a very long, narrow, soft sand beach. The main part of the site lies between the sea, road and railway (as at other sites on this coast, occasional train noise on some pitches) with a huge underpass. The site is divided into spacious, marked pitches with excellent shade provided by a variety of lush vegetation including very impressive palms set in wide avenues. There are 990 pitches, all with electricity (10A) and 661 with water and drainage. Some 47 pitches are directly alongside the beach. A member of Leading Campings group.

Very good quality sanitary buildings with washbasins in private cabins and separate WCs. Facilities for babies and disabled campers. Several launderettes. Motorhome services. Gas. Good shopping centre. Restaurants and bars. Fitness suite. Hairdresser. TV lounges. Beach bar. Playground. Jogging track. Sports area. Tennis. Minigolf. Organised activities including pottery. Pedalo hire. Boat mooring. Bicycle hire. WiFi over site. Dogs are not accepted.

Key Features

- Disabled Facilities
- Beach Access
- Swimming Pool
- Play Area
- Bar/Restaurant
- Bike Hire
- Fishing

Scan me for more information.

PLAYA MONTROIG
CAMPING RESORT
Camping in Style

Alan Rogers Code: ES85400
230 accommodations
700 pitches
GPS: 41.03707, 0.97478
Post Code: E-43300

Tarragona, Cataluña-Catalunya

www.alanrogers.com/es85400
info@latorredelsol.com
Tel: 977 810 486
www.latorredelsol.com

Open (Touring Pitches):
15 March - 31 October

Camping La Torre del Sol

A pleasant tree-lined approach road gives way to avenues of palms as you arrive at Torre del Sol. This large, well designed site occupies a good position in southern Catalunya with direct access to a 800m. long soft sand beach. The site is exceptionally well maintained. There is good shade on a high proportion of the 1,500 individual, numbered pitches, all of which have electricity (700 for touring.) The site boasts three attractive pools with two jacuzzis in the bar and restaurant area. A seawater jacuzzi and Turkish sauna opened in 2012. Occasional train noise on some pitches.

Five very well maintained, fully equipped, toilet blocks include units for disabled visitors, babies & children. Washing machines. Gas supplies. Large supermarket, bakery and souvenir shops at the entrance. Full restaurant. Takeaway. Bar with large terrace with entertainment. Beach bar, coffee bar and ice-cream bar. Pizzeria. Open-roof cinema with permanent seating for 520. 3 TV lounges. Soundproofed disco. Swimming pools (two heated). Solarium. Sauna. Two large jacuzzis. Sports areas. Tennis. Squash. Language school (Spanish). Minigolf. Sub-aqua diving. Bicycle hire. Fishing. Windsurfing school. Sailboards and pedaloes for hire. Playground and crèche. Fridge hire. Library. Hairdresser. Business centre. WiFi. Car repair and car wash. No animals permitted. No jet skis accepted.

Key Features

- Disabled Facilities
- Beach Access
- Swimming Pool
- Play Area
- Bar/Restaurant
- Bike Hire
- Fishing

Scan me for more information.

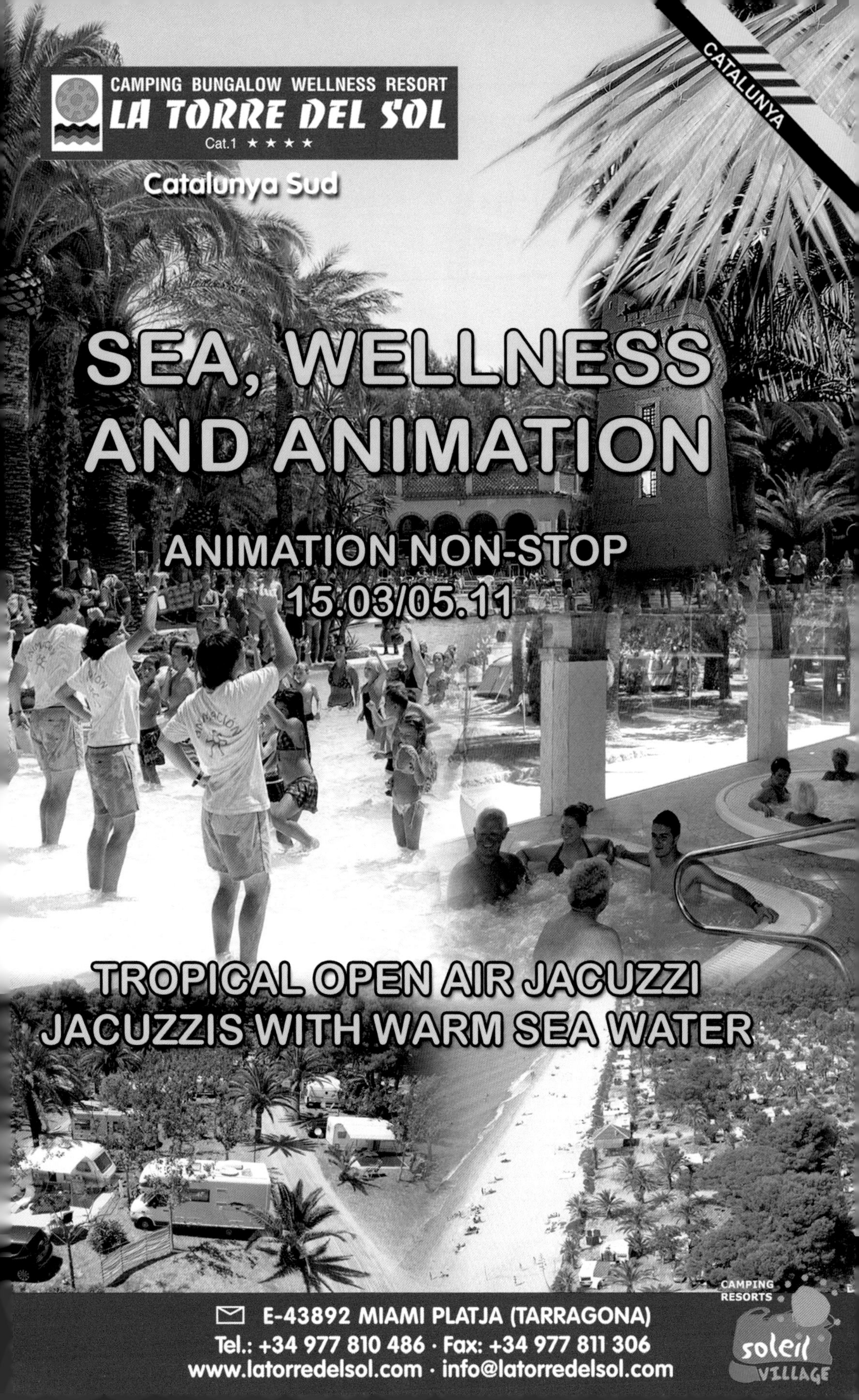
CATALUNYA
CAMPING BUNGALOW WELLNESS RESORT
LA TORRE DEL SOL
Cat.1 ★★★★
Catalunya Sud
SEA, WELLNESS
AND ANIMATION
ANIMATION NON-STOP
15.03/05.11
TROPICAL OPEN AIR JACUZZI
JACUZZIS WITH WARM SEA WATER
E-43892 MIAMI PLATJA (TARRAGONA)
Tel.: +34 977 810 486 · Fax: +34 977 811 306
www.latorredelsol.com · info@latorredelsol.com
CAMPING RESORTS
soleil VILLAGE

Alan Rogers Code: ES85370
132 accommodations
387 pitches
GPS: 40.97723, 0.90093
Post Code: E-43890

Tarragona, Cataluña-Catalunya

www.alanrogers.com/es85370
info@eltemplodelsol.com
Tel: 977 823 434
www.eltemplodelsol.com

Open (Touring Pitches):
15 March - 31 October

Naturista El Templo del Sol

El Templo del Sol is a large, luxurious, terraced naturist site with a distinctly Arabesque feel and superb buildings in Moorish style. The owner has designed the magnificent main turreted building at the entrance with fountains and elaborate Moorish arches. The site has over 387 pitches of two different sizes, some with car parking alongside and 118 with full services. There is shade and the pitches are on terraces giving rewarding views over the sea. Attractive steps give ready access to the sandy beach. There is some daytime rail noise especially in the lower areas of the site where the larger pitches are located.

The sanitary blocks are amongst the best providing everything you could require. Extensive facilities for disabled campers. Washing machines. Well stocked supermarket. Health shop. Souvenir shop. Bars. Restaurant, snack bar, swimming pools (all open all season). Jacuzzi. Cinema. Games area. Boules. Separate children's pool and play area. Miniclub. Library. Entertainment. Hairdresser. Bicycle hire. ATM. Dogs are not accepted. No jet skis. WiFi over site (charged).

Key Features

- Naturist Site
- Disabled Facilities
- Beach Access
- Swimming Pool
- Play Area
- Bar/Restaurant
- Bike Hire
- Fishing

Scan me for more information.

Alan Rogers Code: ES83900
431 accommodations
343 pitches
GPS: 41.23237, 1.69092
Post Code: E-08800

Barcelona, Cataluña-Catalunya

Vilanova Park

www.alanrogers.com/es83900
info@vilanovapark.com
Tel: 938 933 402
www.vilanovapark.com

Open (Touring Pitches):
All year.

Sitting on the terrace in front of the restaurant - a beautifully converted Catalan farmhouse dating from 1908 - it is difficult to believe that in 1982 this was still a farm with few trees and known as Mas Roque (Rock Farm). Since then, imaginative planting has led to there being literally thousands of trees and gloriously colourful shrubs making this large campsite most attractive. It has an impressive range of high quality amenities and facilities open all year. There are 343 marked pitches for touring units in separate areas, all with 6/10A electricity, 168 larger pitches also have water and, in some cases, drainage. They are on hard surfaces, on gently sloping ground and with plenty of shade. A further 1,000 or so pitches are mostly occupied by chalets to rent, and by tour operators.

Excellent toilet blocks can be heated and have controllable showers and many washbasins in cabins. Baby rooms. Units for disabled visitors. Serviced and self-service laundry. Motorhome services. Supermarket. Souvenir shop. Restaurants. Bar with simple meals and tapas. Outdoor pools (1/4-15/10), indoor pool (all year, charged). Wellness centre including sauna, jacuzzi and gym. Play areas. Sports field. Games room. Excursions. Activity and entertainment programme for all ages. Bicycle hire. Tennis. ATM and exchange facilities. WiFi throughout (charged). Caravan storage.

Key Features

- Open All Year
- Pets Accepted
- Disabled Facilities
- Swimming Pool
- Play Area
- Bar/Restaurant
- Bike Hire

Scan me for more information.

Alan Rogers Code: ES91390
6 accommodations
40 pitches
GPS: 42.21642, 1.83692
Post Code: E-08694

Barcelona, Cataluña-Catalunya

www.alanrogers.com/es91390
info@campingbergueda.com
Tel: 938 227 432

Open (Touring Pitches):
Easter - 30 October (and weekends).

Camping El Berguedà

The short scenic drive through the mountains to reach this site is breathtakingly beautiful. This attractively terraced campsite next to the Cadi-Moixer Natural Park, is not far from the majestic Pedraforca mountain, and the area is a favourite for Catalan climbers and walkers. Access on the site is quite easy for large units, although the road from Guardiola de Berguedà is twisting. Of the 73 grass or gravel pitches, there are 40 for touring, all with 6A electricity. The welcoming and helpful campsite owners will do all in their power to make your stay enjoyable.

Two well maintained and well equipped modern toilet blocks are heated and clean. Facilities for disabled visitors. Three private cabins with washbasin, toilet and bidet. Washing machines. Small shop, restaurant, bar and takeaway (w/ends only then 1/7-1/9). Outdoor pools (24/6-31/8). Play areas. WiFi throughout (charged). Communal barbecues on each terrace (individual barbecues not permitted).

Key Features

- Pets Accepted
- Disabled Facilities
- Swimming Pool
- Play Area
- Bar/Restaurant

Scan me for more information.

Alan Rogers Code: ES85610
41 accommodations
66 pitches
GPS: 40.27028, 0.30673
Post Code: E-12579

Castelló, Comunidad Valenciana

www.alanrogers.com/es85610
info@campingribamar.com
Tel: 964 761 601
www.campingribamar.com

Open (Touring Pitches):
All Year

Camping Ribamar

Camping Ribamar is tucked away within the National Park of the Sierra de Irta, to the north of Alcossebre, and with direct access to a rugged beach. All the pitches are classes as Premium (90-100sqm) with electricity (6A/10A) and a water supply. A number of bungalows with air conditioning are available for rent. Leisure facilities here include a large swimming pool plus delightful children's pool and a paddling pool. A main amenities building is adjacent and houses the site's basic bar/restaurant and shop. Twice per week a free shuttle service to the town, available during the winter.

One spotlessly clean toilet block with facilities for babies and campers with disabilities. Laundry facilities. Bar. Restaurant. Shop. Swimming pool. Paddling pool. Multisports terrain. Tennis. Five-a-side football. Boules. Paddle court. Bicycle hire. Play area. Library/ social room. Chalets to rent. Direct access to rocky beach. Fishing. WiFi (charged). Charcoal barbecues are not allowed.

Key Features

- Open All Year
- Pets Accepted
- Disabled Facilities
- Beach Access
- Swimming Pool
- Play Area
- Bar/Restaurant
- Bike Hire

Scan me for more information.

Alan Rogers Code:
15 accommodations
100 pitches
GPS: 40.37680, 0.39257
Post Code: E-12598

Castelló, Comunidad Valenciana

Camping El Cid

www.alanrogers.com/es85645
info@campingelcid.com
Tel: 964 48 03 80
www.campingelcid.com

Open (Touring Pitches):
Open all year.

Camping El Cid is a welcoming family campsite located just North of Peniscola on the Costa del Azahar. A recent change of owners has brought some much-needed renovations to some of the facilities, including the sanitary facilities and further improvements are promised. Delicious woodfired pizza is available in the bar/restaurant. The pool is immaculately kept, with a slide in the children's pool. Entertainments are arranged in the high season including various parties. The Valencian paella party should not be missed. In addition to the touring pitches, the site offers a number of accommodation options, including traditional wooden bungalows and two vintage/retro caravans. The site is ideally located between the sea and the Sierra de Irta natural park. The nearby fortified town of Peñiscola was one of the locations used for the 1960's Anthony Mann film, El Cid (hence the campsite name!) The town is also home to a comedy film festival which usually takes place in early June.

Outdoor pool, soccer field, petanque field, recreational games, bar-restaurant (buffet service). Open all year. Laundry facilities (fee). Bicycle Hire on site. 2x swimming pools. Motorhome service point. Supermarket (small).

Key Features

- Open All Year
- Pets Accepted
- Disabled Facilities
- Swimming Pool
- Play Area
- Bar/Restaurant
- Bike Hire

Scan me for more information.

Alan Rogers Code: ES86240
23 accommodations
87 pitches
GPS: 39.32296, -0.30957
Post Code: E-46012

Valencia, Comunidad Valenciana

Devesa Gardens

www.alanrogers.com/es86240
contacto@devesagardens.com
Tel: 961 611 136
www.devesagardens.com

Open (Touring Pitches):
All year.

This campsite has recently been acquired by the La Marina Group, and the huge investment made is now starting to show as the comprehensive renovation programme gets underway. It is situated between the Albufera lake and the sea, with rice fields on both sides. The 87 level touring pitches are on sand and gravel, all with 16A electricity hook-ups (2-pin sockets). There are no water connections on pitches at the moment. They are separated by fir hedges and young trees, but there is shade from more mature trees. A modern amenities complex is at the heart of the site and includes a swimming pool, extensive play facilities for children and a large auditorium. Bungalows for rent are located in a separate area from the touring pitches.

Three heated sanitary blocks, one modern, two old and requiring updating. Facilities for disabled visitors and families. Washing machine and dryer. Bar. Restaurant and takeaway. Outdoor swimming pool (lifeguard in Apr-Oct, open to public). Riding school. Bullring. Tennis courts. Play area with bouncy castle. Children's club and entertainment. Mini farm. Boat trips. Bicycle hire. WiFi throughout (free).

Key Features

- Open All Year
- Pets Accepted
- Disabled Facilities
- Swimming Pool
- Play Area
- Bar/Restaurant
- Skiing
- Bike Hire

Scan me for more information.

Alan Rogers Code: ES86130
51 accommodations
308 pitches
GPS: 38.89430, -0.05360
Post Code: E-46780

Valencia, Comunidad Valenciana

www.alanrogers.com/es86130
campingole@hotmail.com
Tel: 962 857 517
www.camping-ole.com

Open (Touring Pitches):
All year.

Camping Olé

Olé is a large, flat, seaside holiday site south of Valencia and close to the modern resort of Oliva. Its entrance is only 250 m. from the pleasant sandy beach. For those who do not want to share the busy beach, a large swimming pool is opened in July and August. There are 308 small pitches of compressed gravel, all with 6/10A electricity. Many are separated by hedges with pruned trees giving good shade to those away from the beach. A bar and a restaurant stand on the dunes overlooking the sea, together with a few unmarked pitches that are ideal for larger units. There are small groups of chalets and a few apartments to rent, all within their own areas.

Three clean, well maintained sanitary blocks provide very reasonable facilities. The central one serves most of the touring pitches. Laundry facilities. Fridge rental. Well stocked supermarket (1/3-30/9). Various vending machines. Bar with TV and restaurant with daily menu, drinks and snacks (1/3-15/12). Takeaway. Swimming pool (1/7-1/9). Playground. Entertainment (July/Aug). Fishing off the beach. WiFi (charged).

Key Features

- Open All Year
- Pets Accepted
- Disabled Facilities
- Beach Access
- Swimming Pool
- Play Area
- Bar/Restaurant
- Fishing

Scan me for more information.

Alan Rogers Code: ES86150
180 pitches
GPS: 38.93160, -0.09680
Post Code: E-46780

Valencia, Comunidad Valenciana

Kiko Park Oliva

www.alanrogers.com/es86150
kikopark@kikopark.com
Tel: 962 850 905
www.kikopark.com

Open (Touring Pitches):
All Year

Kiko Park is a smart site nestling behind protective sand dunes alongside a Blue Flag beach. There are sets of attractively tiled steps over the dunes or a long boardwalk near the beach bar (good for prams and wheelchairs) to take you to the fine white sandy beach and the sea. From the central reception point (where good English is spoken), flat, fine gravel pitches and access roads are divided to the left and right. Backing onto one another, the 180 large pitches all have electricity and the aim is to progressively upgrade all these with full services. There are plenty of flowers, hedging and trees adding shade, privacy and colour.

Four heated shower and toilet blocks, including facilities for babies and for disabled visitors (who will find this site flat and convenient). Outdoor swimming pools. ATM. Laundry. Restaurant, bar and beach-side bar. Supermarket. Motorhome services. Gas supplies. Playground. Watersports facilities. Diving school in high season. Paddle Sup. Entertainment for children. Pétanque. WiFi. Car rental. Bicycle hire.

Key Features

- Open All Year
- Pets Accepted
- Disabled Facilities
- Beach Access
- Swimming Pool
- Play Area
- Bar/Restaurant
- Bike Hire

Scan me for more information.

Alan Rogers Code: ES87420
36 accommodations
465 pitches
GPS: 38.12965, -0.64958
Post Code: E-03194

Alacant, Comunidad Valenciana

Camping La Marina

www.alanrogers.com/es87420
info@campinglamarina.com
Tel: 965 419 200
www.lamarinaresort.com

Open (Touring Pitches):
All year.

Very efficiently run by a friendly Belgian family, Camping Internacional La Marina has 465 touring pitches of three different types and sizes ranging from 50 sq.m. to 150 sq.m. with electricity (10/16A), TV, water and drainage. Artificial shade is provided and the pitches are well maintained on level, well drained ground with a special area allocated for tents in a small orchard. The lagoon swimming pool complex is fabulous and has something for everyone (with lifeguards). William Le Metayer, the owner, is passionate about La Marina and it shows in his search for perfection. A magnificent new, modern building which uses the latest architectural technology, houses many superb extra amenities. A member of Leading Campings group.

The sanitary blocks offer modern facilities and are regularly cleaned. Heated in winter, they include private cabins and facilities for disabled visitors & babies. Laundry facilities. Motorhome services. Gas. Supermarket. Bars. Restaurant and café. Ice cream kiosk. Swimming pools (seasonal). Indoor pool. Fitness centre. Sauna. Solarium. Jacuzzi. Play rooms. Extensive activity and entertainment programme including barbecues and swimming nights. Sports area. Tennis. Huge playgrounds. Hairdresser. Bicycle hire. Road train to beach. Exclusive area for dogs. Internet café (charged) and free WiFi.

Key Features

- Open All Year
- Pets Accepted
- Disabled Facilities
- Swimming Pool
- Play Area
- Bar/Restaurant
- Skiing
- Bike Hire

Scan me for more information.

Alan Rogers Code: ES87435
56 accommodations
1200 pitches
GPS: 38.17790, -0.80950
Post Code: E-03330

Alacant, Comunidad Valenciana

www.alanrogers.com/es87435
reservas@marjalresorts.com
Tel: 965 484 945
www.marjalresorts.com

Open (Touring Pitches):
All Year

Alannia Costa Blanca

Alannia Costa Blanca (formerly Marjal) is a fully equipped site situated 15 km. inland on the southern Alicante coast, close to the towns of Crevillente and Catral, and the Parque Natural de El Hondo. The 1,200 hardstanding pitches range in size from 90-95 sq.m, and all have electricity (16A), water, drainage, TV and high-speed internet connections (charged). On-site amenities include a tropical-themed swimming pool complex and a state-of-the-art wellness centre. There is full disabled access, including at the swimming pool and staffed gym. There is accommodation to rent, including 46 Balinese-style bungalows adapted for disabled visitors. The site is ideal for both family holidays in summer and for winter sun-seekers.

Six modern, spotlessly clean toilet blocks have washbasins and free showers in cabins. Facilities for children, babies & disabled visitors. Well equipped shop. Bar, restaurant and takeaway (all year). Swimming pool complex with outdoor pool (Mar-Sept), heated indoor pool (all year), sauna and Hammam. Fully equipped gym. Wellness centre. Hairdresser. Play areas. Games rooms. Library. Multisports courts. Minigolf. Tennis. Football. Entertainment and activity programme (inc Spanish lessons). Kids club. Bicycle hire. Car hire service. Doctor and vet. Free WiFi areas. Mobile homes and chalets to rent.

Key Features

- Open All Year
- Pets Accepted
- Disabled Facilities
- Swimming Pool
- Play Area
- Bar/Restaurant
- Bike Hire

Scan me for more information.

Alan Rogers Code: ES87520
35 accommodations
300 pitches
GPS: 37.58500, -1.06717
Post Code: E-30394

Cartagena, Murcia

Camping El Portus

www.alanrogers.com/es87520
elportus@elportus.com
Tel: 968 553 052
www.elportus.com

Open (Touring Pitches):
All year.

Set in a secluded south-facing bay fringed by mountains, El Portus is a fairly large naturist site enjoying magnificent views and with direct access to a small sand and pebble beach. This part of Spain enjoys almost all-year-round sunshine. There are some 400 pitches, 300 for touring units, ranging from 60-100 sq.m, all but a few having electricity (6A). They are mostly on fairly level, if somewhat stony and barren ground. El Portus has a reasonable amount of shade from established trees and nearly every pitch has a view. Residential units are situated on the hillside above the site.

Five acceptable toilet blocks, all unisex, are of varying styles and fully equipped with hot showers. Opened as required, they are clean and bright. Unit for disabled visitors, key from reception. Washing machines. Motorhome services. Well stocked shop. Bar with TV and library. Restaurants. The beach restaurant is closed in low season. Swimming pools (June-Sept). Wellness centre. Play area. Tennis. Pétanque. Yoga. Scuba-diving club (high season). Windsurfing. Fishing. Small boat moorings. Spanish lessons. Entertainment programme all season. WiFi over site (charged).

Key Features

- Naturist Site
- Open All Year
- Pets Accepted
- Disabled Facilities
- Beach Access
- Swimming Pool
- Play Area
- Bar/Restaurant

Scan me for more information.

Alan Rogers Code: ES87530
50 accommodations
800 pitches
GPS: 37.62445, -0.74442
Post Code: E-30386

La Manga del Mar Menor, Murcia

Caravaning La Manga

www.alanrogers.com/es87530
lamanga@caravaning.es
Tel: 968 563 014
www.caravaning.es

Open (Touring Pitches):
All year.

This is a very large, well equipped, holiday-style site with its own beach and both indoor and outdoor pools. With a good number of typical Spanish long stay units, the length of the site is impressive (1 km) and a bicycle is very helpful for getting about. The 800 regularly laid out, gravel touring pitches (84 or 110 sq.m) are generally separated by hedges which provide some privacy but very little shade. Each has a 10A electricity supply, water and the possibility of satellite TV reception. This site's excellent facilities are ideally suited for holidays in the winter when the weather is very pleasantly warm. Daytime temperatures in November usually exceed 20 degrees.

Nine clean toilet blocks of standard design, well spaced around the site, include washbasins (all with hot water). Laundry. Gas supplies. Large well stocked supermarket. Restaurant. Bar. Snack bar. Swimming pool complex (April-Sept). Indoor pool, gymnasium (Oct-Apr), sauna, jacuzzi and massage service. Outdoor fitness course for adults. Open-air family cinema (July/Aug). Tennis. Pétanque. Minigolf. Play area. Watersports school. Internet café (also WiFi). Winter activities including Spanish classes. Pet washing area.

Key Features

- Open All Year
- Pets Accepted
- Disabled Facilities
- Beach Access
- Swimming Pool
- Play Area
- Bar/Restaurant
- Fishing

Alan Rogers Code: ES87905
22 accommodations
86 pitches
GPS: 37.10809, -4.68712
Post Code: E-29531

Málaga, Andalucia

www.alanrogers.com/es87905
campinglasierrecilla@gmail.com
Tel: 951 199 090
www.campinglasierrecilla.com

Open (Touring Pitches):
All year.

Camping la Sierrecilla

La Sierrecilla is a fairly new site situated in the heart of Andalucia on the edge of a pine-covered Natural Park. It is one of the areas where eagles, falcons and vultures can still be seen. The 86 good sized touring pitches are on level ground and all have electricity. There is little shade from the young trees, and being on a plain the pitches could become extremely hot during summer. There is a beautiful pool with access for visitors with disabilities, and a good value restaurant with magnificent views of the surrounding countryside. Paths lead through the site to a viewpoint and picnic area, which are extremely popular at weekends. It is an ideal site for those wishing to explore Andalucia; it is just 40 minutes from the beaches at Malaga and one hour from Seville, Granada and Cordoba.

Two modern sanitary units have some British and some Turkish style toilets, open style washbasins and free hot showers. En-suite unit for disabled visitors. Washing machine. Dishwashing facilities. Swimming pool (seasonal). Excellent bar (all year) and charming restaurant (seasonal). Takeaway. Play area. Tennis. Climbing wall. Aerial runway. Caravan storage. WiFi. Barbecues are not permitted in summer. Mobile homes and bungalows to rent.

Key Features

- Open All Year
- Pets Accepted
- Disabled Facilities
- Swimming Pool
- Play Area
- Bar/Restaurant

Scan me for more information.

Alan Rogers Code: ES87810
192 accommodations
290 pitches
GPS: 36.73925, -3.94971
Post Code: E-29793

Málaga, Andalucia

Camping El Pino

www.alanrogers.com/es87810
info@campingelpino.com
Tel: 952 530 006
www.campingelpino.com

Open (Touring Pitches):
All year.

El Pino is in the Axarquia region of the Costa del Sol, east of Malaga and is surrounded by avocado groves. The old but well-maintained site enjoys some fine views of the surrounding countryside. There are now 290 pitches here, mostly well shaded, and a further 57 mobile homes and chalets to rent. Most pitches have electrical connections and vary in size from 60-100 sq.m. The site is open all year and has some good facilities including a swimming pool, supermarket and bar/restaurant. The nearest beach is 800 m. distant - a bus service runs there from the site.

Four toilet blocks with hot showers and individual cabins. Facilities for disabled visitors. Laundry facilities. Bar, restaurant and shop (all year). Takeaway. Swimming pool with new children's pool (1/6-15/9). Play area. Games room. Pétanque. Children's club. WiFi throughout (free). Mobile homes and chalets to rent. Communal barbecue - only gas or electric barbecues permitted on pitches.

Key Features

- Open All Year
- Pets Accepted
- Disabled Facilities
- Swimming Pool
- Play Area
- Bar/Restaurant

Scan me for more information.

Alan Rogers Code: ES88030
11 accommodations
250 pitches
GPS: 36.50230, -4.80400
Post Code: E-29600

Málaga, Andalucia

www.alanrogers.com/es88030
info@campingbuganvilla.com
Tel: 952 831 973
www.campingbuganvilla.com

Open (Touring Pitches):
All year.

Camping la Buganvilla

La Buganvilla is a large, uncomplicated site with mature trees providing a little shade to some of the 250 touring pitches. However, increasingly static caravans, seasonal pitches and bungalows are taking over many pitches. They all have 16A electricity and are mostly on terraces, so there are some views across to the mountains and hinterland of this coastal area. The terrain is a little rugged in places all three sanitary blocks are well maintained and clean. A pool complex near the bar and restaurant is ideal for cooling off after a day's sightseeing. This is a pleasant base from which to explore areas of the Costa del Sol and it is an easy drive to the picturesque Ronda Valley.

Three sanitary blocks of varying ages are clean and adequate. Laundry facilities (not all sinks have hot water). Motorhome services. Bar/restaurant with basic food. Well stocked small supermarket. Outdoor pool (all year). Play area. Tennis (high season). WiFi (charged). Dogs are not accepted in July/Aug.

Key Features

- Open All Year
- Pets Accepted
- Disabled Facilities
- Swimming Pool
- Bar/Restaurant

Scan me for more information.

Alan Rogers Code: ES88570
32 accommodations
152 pitches
GPS: 36.19998, -6.03463
Post Code: E-11159

Cádiz, Andalucia

www.alanrogers.com/es88570
info@campingpinarsanjose.com
Tel: 956 437 030
www.campingpinarsanjose.com

Open (Touring Pitches):
All year.

Camping Pinar San José

Pinar San José first opened in 2008. The site is located in the La Breña Nature Park and has been developed to reflect the natural beauty that surrounds it. The nearest beaches on the Costa de la Luz are around 1 km. distant. On-site amenities are modern and well designed and include two swimming pools, tennis and a sports court. Pitches are grassy, and all have electrical connections. There is good provision of water points, and many pitches also have drainage and internet connections. Several brick-built chalets are available for rent. Cabo de Trafalgar (Cape Trafalgar) is nearby and, of course, gave its name to the famous battle several kilometres to the west. The nearest village to the site is Zahora and the great cities of Cádiz and Jerez, as well as Gibraltar, are all accessible in less than an hour. La Breña Nature Park was formerly a massive sand dune and is now a large, forested area crisscrossed by cycle tracks and footpaths. Riding is also possible in the park.

Shop. Bar. Restaurant. Two swimming pools. Tennis. Sports court. Play area. Games room. Chalets for rent. Dogs are not accepted in high season.

Key Features

- Open All Year
- Pets Accepted
- Disabled Facilities
- Swimming Pool
- Bar/Restaurant
- Bike Hire

Scan me for more information.

Alan Rogers Code: ES90950
30 accommodations
106 pitches
GPS: 40.41655, -1.43332
Post Code: E-44100

Teruel, Aragon

www.alanrogers.com/es90950
campingalbarracin5@hotmail.com
Tel: 978 710 197
www.campingalbarracin.com

Open (Touring Pitches):
6 March - 15 November.

Ciudad de Albarracin

Albarracin, in southern Aragón, is set in the Reserva Nacional de los Montes Universales and is a much frequented, fascinating town with a Moorish castle. The old city walls towering above date from the days when it attempted to become a separate country within Spain. This neat and clean family site is set on three levels on a hillside behind the town, with a walk of 1 km. to the centre. It is very modern and has high quality facilities including a superb building for barbecuing (all materials provided). There are 130 pitches (106 for touring units), all with 10A electricity (2-pin sockets) and separated by trees. Some require cars to be parked separately.

The two spotless, modern sanitary buildings provide British style WCs, quite large showers and hot water throughout. Baby bath. Facilities for disabled visitors. Washing machines. Well stocked shop (seasonal). Bar/restaurant with TV (all season). Special room for barbecues with fire and wood provided. Play area. Torches required in some areas. WiFi (free in reception).

Key Features

- Pets Accepted
- Disabled Facilities
- Swimming Pool
- Play Area
- Bar/Restaurant

Scan me for more information.

Alan Rogers Code: ES90600
130 accommodations
330 pitches
GPS: 42.43520, 0.13618
Post Code: E-22360

Huesca, Aragon

www.alanrogers.com/es90600
info@penamontanesa.com
Tel: 974 500 032
www.penamontanesa.com

Open (Touring Pitches):
All year.

Camping Peña Montañesa

A large site situated in the Pyrenees near the Ordesa National Park, Peña Montañesa is easily accessible from Ainsa or from France via the Bielsa Tunnel (steep sections on the French side). The site is essentially divided into three sections opening progressively throughout the season and all have shade. The 330 pitches on fairly level grass are of about 75 sq.m. and 6/10A electricity is available on virtually all (no charge is made for upgrade). Grouped near the entrance are the facilities that make the site so attractive, including an outdoor pool and a heated (out of season), glass covered indoor pool with jacuzzi and sauna. Here too is an attractive bar/restaurant with an open fire and a terrace; a supermarket and takeaway are opposite.

A newer toilet block, heated when necessary, has free hot showers but cold water to open plan washbasins. Facilities for disabled visitors. Small baby room. An older block in the original area has similar provision. Washing machine and dryer. Bar, restaurant, takeaway and supermarket (all 1/1-31/12). Outdoor swimming pool (1/4-31/10). Indoor pool, sauna and jacuzzi (all year). Outdoor social area with large TV screen and stage. Multisports court. Tennis. Playground. Boules. Only gas barbecues are permitted. WiFi in bar area (free).

Key Features

- Open All Year
- Pets Accepted
- Disabled Facilities
- Swimming Pool
- Play Area
- Bar/Restaurant
- Skiing
- Fishing

Scan me for more information.

Alan Rogers Code: ES90970
29 accommodations
272 pitches
GPS: 38.93717, -2.84744
Post Code: E-02611

Albacete, Castilla-La-Mancha

www.alanrogers.com/es90970
camping@losbatanes.com
Tel: 926 699 076
www.losbatanes.com

Open (Touring Pitches):
All year.

Camping Los Batanes

This large campsite is in a lovely setting at the side of one of the many lakes in this area. The route to get here is beautiful and it is well worth the trip, but careful driving was necessary in parts with our large motorhome. A smaller, older part of the campsite houses reception, a small shop and a bar/restaurant. Here are medium sized pitches, shaded by pine trees with a small river running through. By the entrance are 18 new, fully serviced, hardstanding pitches. Over a wooden bridge is the main, newer part of the site with over 200 level, gravel and sand pitches of mixed sizes, shaded again by pine trees. Electricity is 6A on most pitches.

Three modern toilet blocks have hot showers, washbasins in cabins and facilities for disabled visitors. Small shop. Simple restaurant, snacks and bar. Swimming and paddling pools (15/6-10/9). Play area. Children's activities (4-12 yrs, July/Aug).

Key Features

- Open All Year
- Pets Accepted
- Disabled Facilities
- Swimming Pool
- Bar/Restaurant

Scan me for more information.

Alan Rogers Code: ES90960
18 accommodations
44 pitches
GPS: 39.32190, -4.64950
Post Code: E-13110

Ciudad Real, Castilla-La-Mancha

El Mirador de Cabañeros

www.alanrogers.com/es90960
info@campingcabaneros.com
Tel: 926 775 439
www.campingcabaneros.com

Open (Touring Pitches):
All year.

With panoramic views all around of the Sierra de Valdefuertes mountains, Camping El Mirador de Cabañeros is set in the Cabañeros National Park. This is a well cared for, landscaped site with 44 terraced pitches on gravel, all with 6A electricity. Although pitches are level once sited, the approach is via a steep slope which may cause difficulties for larger units. Run by a very helpful and friendly family, this site is in a very peaceful location where you can just sit and relax or visit the many attractions that the National Park has to offer. It is an ideal base for walking and birdwatching.

One spotlessly clean central toilet block with solar heating includes open washbasins and cubicle showers. Facilities for disabled visitors and babies. Laundry. Motorhome services. No shop but basics from reception. Bar and restaurant (15/6-15/9, w/ends in low season). Covered swimming pool (all year). Games room. Play areas. Outside fitness area.

Key Features

- Open All Year
- Pets Accepted
- Disabled Facilities
- Swimming Pool
- Play Area
- Bar/Restaurant

Scan me for more information.

Alan Rogers Code: ES92000
107 accommodations
470 pitches
GPS: 40.62400, -4.09900
Post Code: E-28280

El Escorial, Madrid

www.alanrogers.com/es92000
info@campingelescorial.com
Tel: 902 014 900
www.campingelescorial.com

Open (Touring Pitches):
All year.

Caravanning El Escorial

El Escorial is very large and everything on site is on a grand scale – indeed a bicycle is very useful for getting around. There are 1,358 individual pitches of which 470 are for touring units, with the remainder used for permanent or seasonal units, but situated to one side of the site. The pitches are shaded (ask for a pitch without a low tree canopy if you have a 3 m. high motorhome). An attractive area of five hectares is set aside for 'wild camping' in tents on open fields with good shade from mature trees (long cables may be necessary for electricity). The general amenities are comprehensive and good, and include three swimming pools (unheated), plus a paddling pool.

One large toilet block for the touring pitches, plus small blocks for the 'wild' camping area, are all fully equipped with some washbasins in cabins. Facilities for babies and disabled campers. The blocks can be heated. Large supermarket (all year). Restaurant/bar and snack bar with takeaway (w/ends and B.Hs only in low season). Meeting rooms. Disco-bar. Swimming pools (15/5-15/9). Multisports areas. Family activities (high season, weekends in low season). Two well equipped playgrounds on sand. Bicycle hire. ATM. Car wash. WiFi in some areas (free).

Key Features

- Open All Year
- Pets Accepted
- Disabled Facilities
- Swimming Pool
- Play Area
- Bar/Restaurant
- Skiing
- Bike Hire

Scan me for more information.

Alan Rogers Code: ES90910
23 accommodations
162 pitches
GPS: 40.04218, -3.59947
Post Code: E-28300

Aranjuez, Madrid

www.alanrogers.com/es90910
info@campingaranjuez.com
Tel: 918 911 395
www.campingaranjuez.com

Open (Touring Pitches):
All year.

Camping Aranjuez

Aranjuez, supposedly Spain's version of Versailles, is worthy of a visit with its beautiful palaces, leafy squares, avenues and gardens. This useful, popular and unusually well equipped site is therefore excellent for enjoying the unusual attractions or for an en route stop. It is 47 km. south of Madrid and 46 km. from Toledo. The site is alongside the River Tajo in a park-like situation with mature trees. There are 162 touring pitches, all with electricity (16A), set on flat grass amid tall trees. The site is owned by the owners of la Marina (ES87420) who have worked hard to improve the pitches and the site in general.

Two of the three modern sanitary blocks are heated and all are well equipped with some washbasins in cabins. Laundry facilities. Gas supplies. Shop, bar and restaurant (all year) with attractive riverside patio (also open to the public). Takeaway. TV in bar. Swimming and paddling pools, (1/5-15/10). Tennis courts. Central play area. Pétanque. Bicycle hire. Canoe hire. Activities for children (high season). WiFi over site (charged).

Key Features

- Open All Year
- Pets Accepted
- Disabled Facilities
- Swimming Pool
- Play Area
- Bar/Restaurant
- Bike Hire
- Fishing

Scan me for more information.

Alan Rogers Code: ES90430
17 accommodations
90 pitches
GPS: 42.62423, -1.84259
Post Code: E-31150

Mendigorria, Navarra

www.alanrogers.com/es90430
info@campingelmolino.com
Tel: 948 340 604
www.campingelmolino.com

Open (Touring Pitches):
21 January - 10 December

El Molino de Mendigorria

This is an extensive site set by an attractive weir near the town of Mendigorria, alongside the River Arga. It takes its name from an old disused water mill (molino) close by. The site is split into separate permanent and touring sections. The touring area is a new development with 90 good sized flat pitches with electricity and water for touring units, and a separate area for tents. Many trees have been planted around the site but there is still only minimal shade. The friendly owner, Anna Beriain, will give you a warm welcome.

The well equipped toilet block is very clean and well maintained, with cold water to washbasins. Facilities for children and disabled visitors. Washing machine. Large restaurant, pleasant bar. Supermarket. 2 swimming pools for adults and children (1/6-15/9) including a new indoor pool with spa, and another outside with slide. Bicycle hire. Riverside bar. Weekly entertainment programme (July/Aug) and many sporting activities. Squash courts. River walk. Torches useful. Gas barbecues only. WiFi on part of site (charged).

Key Features

- Pets Accepted
- Disabled Facilities
- Swimming Pool
- Play Area
- Bar/Restaurant
- Bike Hire
- Fishing

Scan me for more information.

Alan Rogers Code: ES90240
12 accommodations
113 pitches
GPS: 42.88939, -8.52418
Post Code: E-15704

A Coruña, Galicia

www.alanrogers.com/es90240
info@campingascancelas.com
Tel: 981 580 476
www.campingascancelas.com

Open (Touring Pitches):
All year.

Camping As Cancelas

The beautiful city of Santiago has been the destination for European Christian pilgrims for centuries and they now follow ancient routes to this unique city, the whole of which is a national monument. The As Cancelas campsite is excellent for sharing the experiences of these pilgrims in the city and around the magnificent cathedral. It has 113 marked pitches (60-90 sq.m), arranged in terraces and divided by trees and shrubs. On a hillside overlooking the city, the views are very pleasant. The site has a steep approach road.

Two modern toilet blocks are fully equipped, with ramped access for disabled visitors. The quality and cleanliness of the fittings and tiling is good. Laundry with service wash for a small fee. Small shop. Restaurant. Bar with TV. Well kept, unsupervised swimming pool and children's pool. Small playground. Internet access. WiFi throughout.

Key Features

- OPEN 365 Open All Year
- Pets Accepted
- Disabled Facilities
- Swimming Pool
- Play Area
- Bar/Restaurant
- Bike Hire

Scan me for more information.

Alan Rogers Code: ES89570
156 pitches
GPS: 43.39161, -4.57571
Post Code: E-33590

Ribadedeva, Asturias

www.alanrogers.com/es89570
info@campinglashortensias.com
Tel: 985 412 442
www.campinglashortensias.com

Open (Touring Pitches):
1 June - 21 September.

Camping Las Hortensias

Open for just four months from June to September, Las Hortensias is a friendly site located on the Cantabrian coast of northern Spain. The site enjoys a fine setting on a sheltered sandy beach, adjacent to the Mirador Hotel. There are 156 pitches connected by well lit tarmac roads. Each pitch has 6-10A electricity and there are water points throughout. After a day on the beach or exploring the nearby rock pools, the bar terrace is a great spot to enjoy the sunset. Many pitches are well shaded by pine trees, in pleasant, peaceful locations.

Two adequate sanitary blocks, one with WCs only, the other with open plan washbasins and showers. Washing machine and dryer. Basic motorhome services. Small supermarket. Bar with terrace overlooking beach. Basic restaurant (campers can use the hotel restaurant with 10% discount), snack bar and takeaway. TV in bar. Play area. Gas and charcoal barbecues only. WiFi.

Key Features

- Pets Accepted
- Beach Access
- Play Area
- Bar/Restaurant

Scan me for more information.

Alan Rogers Code: ES89600
434 pitches
GPS: 43.39957, -4.65149
Post Code: E-33597

Vidiago-Llanes, Asturias

Camping la Paz

www.alanrogers.com/es89600
delfin@campinglapaz.com
Tel: 985 411 235
www.campinglapaz.com

Open (Touring Pitches):
Easter - 15 October.

This unusual site occupies a spectacular mountain location. The small reception building is opposite a solid rock face and many hundreds of feet below the site. The ascent to the upper part of the site is quite daunting, but staff will place your caravan for you if required, although motorhome drivers will have an exciting drive to the top, especially to the loftier pitches. Once there, the views are absolutely outstanding, both along the coast and inland to the Picos de Europa mountains. There are 434 pitches, all with 10/15A electricity. There is also a lower section in a shaded valley to which access is easier, if rather tight in places.

Four good, modern toilet blocks are well equipped with hot showers and open plan washbasins. They are kept very clean even at peak times. Baby bath. Full laundry facilities. Motorhome services. Restaurant and bar/snack bar with small shop (all season). Watersports. Games room. Fishing. Torches useful in some areas. Gas and charcoal barbecues only. WiFi in the restaurant.

Key Features

- Pets Accepted
- Beach Access
- Bar/Restaurant
- Fishing

Scan me for more information.

Alan Rogers Code: ES90000
315 accommodations
800 pitches
GPS: 43.48948, -3.53700
Post Code: E-39180

Noja, Cantabria

www.alanrogers.com/es90000
info@playajoyel.com
Tel: 942 630 081
www.playajoyel.com

Open (Touring Pitches):
27 March - 27 September.

Playa Joyel

This very attractive holiday and touring site is some 40 kilometres from Santander and 80 kilometres from Bilbao. It is a busy, high quality, comprehensively equipped site by a superb beach providing 800 well shaded, marked and numbered pitches with 6A electricity available. These include 80 large pitches of 100 sq.m. Some 250 pitches are occupied by tour operators and seasonal units. This well-managed site has a lot to offer for family holidays with much going on in the high season when it gets crowded. The swimming pool complex (with lifeguard) is free to campers and the superb beaches are cleaned daily mid-June to mid-September. Two beach exits lead to the main beach where there are some undertows, or if you turn left you will find a reasonably placid estuary. An unusual feature here is the nature park within the site boundary which has a selection of animals to see. This overlooks a protected area of marsh where European birds spend the winter.

Six excellent, spacious and fully equipped toilet blocks include baby baths. Large laundry. Motorhome services. Gas supplies. Freezer service. Supermarket. General shop. Kiosk. Restaurant and bar. Takeaway (July/Aug). Swimming pools, bathing caps compulsory (20/5-15/9). Entertainment organised with a soundproofed pub/disco (July/Aug). Gym park. Tennis. Playground. Riding. Fishing. Nature animal park. Hairdresser (July/Aug). Medical centre. Torches necessary in some areas. Animals are not accepted. WiFi on part of site (charged).

Key Features

- Disabled Facilities
- Beach Access
- Swimming Pool
- Play Area
- Bar/Restaurant
- Bike Hire
- Fishing

Scan me for more information.

Alan Rogers Code: ES89710
50 accommodations
120 pitches
GPS: 43.38527, -4.33814
Post Code: E-39547

San Vicente de la Barquera, Cantabria

www.alanrogers.com/es89710
camping@oyambre.com
Tel: 942 711 461
www.oyambre.com

Open (Touring Pitches):
6 March - 31 October.

Camping Oyambre

This exceptionally well managed site is ideally positioned to use as a base to visit the spectacular Picos de Europa or one of the many sandy beaches along this northern coast. Despite its name, it is a kilometre from the beach on foot. The 120 touring pitches all have 10A electricity (long leads needed in places), ten are fully serviced. The fairly flat central area is allocated to tents while caravans are mainly sited on wide terraces (access to some could be a little tight for larger units) and there is some shade. There may be some traffic noise on the lower terraces.

Good, clean sanitary facilities are in one well kept block. Facilities for babies and disabled visitors. Washing machines. Motorhome services. Shop in bar. Restaurant. Takeaway. Swimming pools with lifeguard. Playground. Bicycle hire. Free WiFi over site.

Key Features

- Pets Accepted
- Disabled Facilities
- Swimming Pool
- Play Area
- Bar/Restaurant
- Bike Hire

Scan me for more information.

Alan Rogers Code: ES90300
55 accommodations
261 pitches
GPS: 43.30458, -2.04589
Post Code: E-20008

Gipuzkoa, Pais Vasco-Euskadi

www.alanrogers.com/es90300
info@campingigueldo.com
Tel: 943 214 502
campingigueldo.com

Open (Touring Pitches):
All year.

Camping Igueldo

A five-kilometre drive from the city takes you to this terraced campsite, high above San Sebastián, between the mountains and the sea. It offers mostly level, shaded, small (max. 70 sq.m) grass pitches with electricity (5/10A) and drainage. Pitches are separated by neat, low hedging and some have excellent views. The restaurant and bar are open all year and a sun terrace looks toward the mountains. Excellent bus service to and from San Sebastián runs every 30 minutes (all year). There are 25 attractive chalets to rent at the entrance to the site. These are often occupied by groups of younger visitors and can become lively at the weekends. English is spoken in reception. Nearby in San Sebastián, you will find numerous shops with the work of artists crafted in wood, ceramics, textiles, iron and glass. Not to be missed is a visit to the aquarium complete with 360º walk-through tunnel and the museum with 700 years of naval history. San Telmo Museum is the oldest in Spain's Basque country, housed in a former Dominican convent and reopened in 2011 with a state-of-the-art architectural extension.

Three traditional toilet blocks are clean and bright with open style washbasins and controllable showers. Facilities for disabled visitors, children and babies (key). Laundry facilities. Motorhome services. Shop for basics (all year). Bar/restaurant (all year, closed Wednesdays in low season). Fenced play area. Plans for a communal barbecue area. WiFi throughout.

Key Features

- Open All Year
- Pets Accepted
- Disabled Facilities
- Play Area
- Bar/Restaurant

Scan me for more information.

Alan Rogers Code: ES90390
100 accommodations
440 pitches
GPS: 43.28958, -2.14603
Post Code: E-20800

Gipuzkoa, Pais Vasco-Euskadi

www.alanrogers.com/es90390
info@grancampingzarautz.com
Tel: 943 831 238
www.grancampingzarautz.com

Open (Touring Pitches):
All year.

Gran Camping Zarautz

This friendly site sits high in the hills to the east of the Basque town of Zarautz and has commanding views over the bay and the island of Getaria. Of the 540 pitches, 440 are for touring units, with 6A electricity; ten also have water and drainage. The remaining pitches are for tents and seasonal caravans. The grass pitches are of average size, shaded by mature trees and those on the perimeter have superb sea views. A new footpath leads down to the ruins of a once busy iron ore works and a small exhibition. This path continues along the coastline for 1.5 km. into Zarautz, but does involve a lot of steep steps. The town of Zarautz offers a cultural programme in summer and the pedestrian promenade with modern sculptures is a good vantage point to enjoy the beach and watch the surfers.

Three well-equipped toilet blocks, one of which is new (plans to build a sauna, gym and spa area above this block). Separate facilities for children and four large toilet/shower rooms for disabled visitors. Laundry facilities. New motorhome service point. Well stocked shop. Restaurant with 'menu del día' and à la carte meals. Bar/snack bar with TV plus terrace. Communal barbecue area with picnic tables. Play area. WiFi (80% coverage).

Key Features

- Open All Year
- Pets Accepted
- Disabled Facilities
- Play Area
- Bar/Restaurant

Scan me for more information.

Smögen, Sotenäs Municipality >

Capital Stockholm
Currency Swedish Krona (SEK)
Language Swedish
Time Zone CET (GMT+1)
Telephone Code 00 46

Tourist Website
visitsweden.com

Climate Temperate climate but very varied. Extremely cold above the Arctic Circle, mild across much of the rest of the country. Cold, short winters and summers similar to those in UK.

Shops Varied. In high-season 9am to 6pm weekdays, to 1pm Saturday.

Banks 9.30am to 3pm weekdays, larger branches may be open until 6pm.

Accessible Travel One of the best equipped European countries for disabled visitors. Most transport, public spaces/ buildings offer adapted facilities

Travelling with children Sweden is great for children of all ages with good transport links and accommodating locals. Most museums are free for children under 18. Restaurants often offer a kids menu.

See campsite map page

486

Public Holidays New Year's Day, Epiphany, Good Friday, Easter Sunday, Easter Monday, May Day, Ascension, Whit Sunday, National Day (6 Jun), Midsummer (20 Jun), All Saints, Christmas Day, Boxing Day (2nd Day of Christmas).

Motoring Roads are generally much quieter than in the UK. Dipped headlights are obligatory. Away from large towns, petrol stations rarely open 24 hours but most have self-serve pumps (with credit card payment). Buy diesel during working hours, it may not always be available at self-service pumps.

Environmental Policies There are Low Emission Zones enforced in many of the major cities, most (with the exception of Stockholm) only apply to heavy-duty vehicles. Metal, plastic, glass, paper and cardboard are all widely recycled. Nearly 100% of waste in Sweden is recycled. In Helsingborg, public recycling bins play music to make recycling a more pleasant experience!

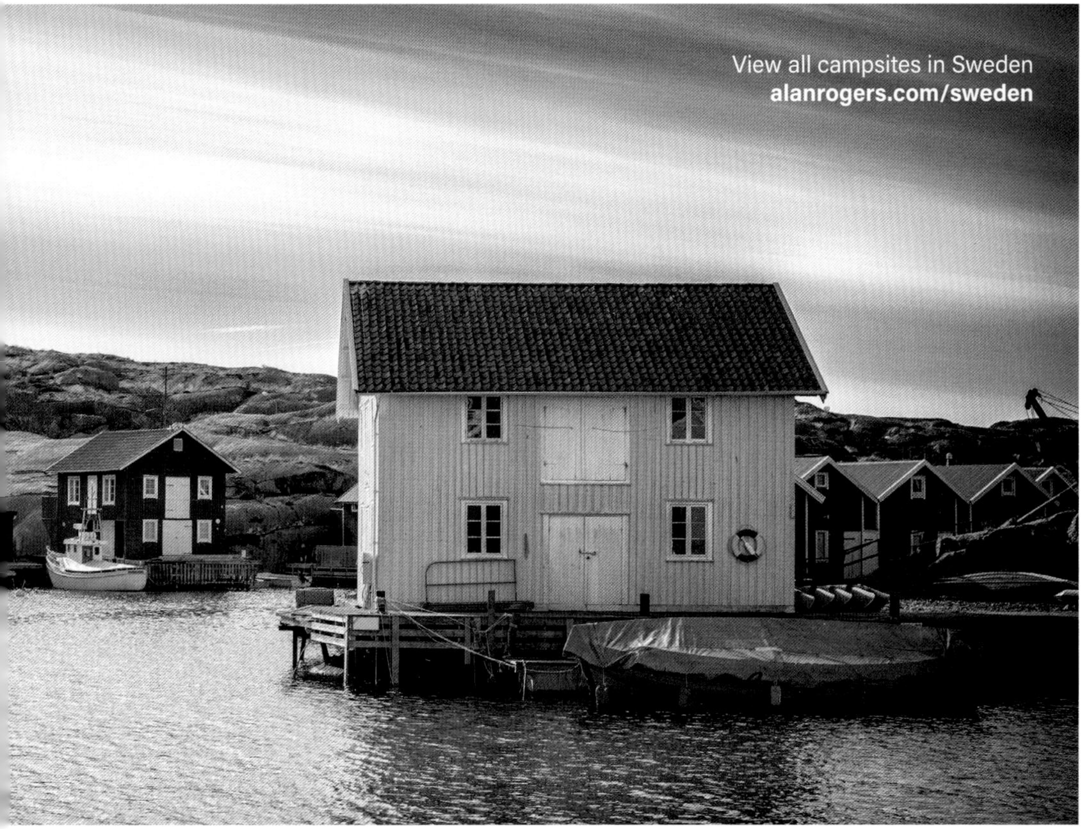
View all campsites in Sweden
alanrogers.com/sweden

Sweden

With giant lakes and waterways, rich forests, majestic mountains and glaciers, and vast, wide-open countryside, Sweden is almost twice the size of the UK but with a fraction of the population.

Southern Sweden's unspoiled islands with their beautiful sandy beaches offer endless opportunities for boating and island hopping. The coastal cities of Gothenburg and Malmö, once centres of industry, now have an abundance of restaurants, cultural venues and attractions.

With the Oresund Bridge, Malmö is just a short ride from Copenhagen. Stockholm, the capital, is a delightful place built on fourteen small islands on the eastern coast. It is an attractive, vibrant city with magnificent architecture, fine museums and historic squares. Sparsely populated northern Sweden is a land of forests, rivers and wilderness inhabited by moose and reindeer.

Östersund, located at the shores of a lake in the heart of the country, is well known for winter sports, while Frösö Zoo is a popular attraction. Today Sweden is one of the world's most developed societies and enjoys an enviable standard of living.

Alan Rogers Code: SW2650
4 accommodations
120 pitches
GPS: 55.96033, 13.53808
Post Code: S-243 93

Skåne Län, South

www.alanrogers.com/sw2650
info@grottbyn.se
Tel: +46 732 45 15 12
www.grottbyn.se

Open (Touring Pitches):
2 June - 30 September

Grottbyns Camping

This site is probably one of the most unusual we feature. It is next to the Skånes Djurpark, a zoo park with Scandinavian species. The site is located in a sheltered valley and has 120 large, level grassy pitches for caravans and motorhomes all with 10A electricity (2-pin) and a separate area for about 40 tents. The most unusual feature of the site is one of the sanitary blocks – it is underground! The air-conditioned building houses a kitchen and dining area and sanitary facilities for families and disabled visitors. Apart from these particular facilities, the rest of the site remains more traditional rather than modern. Well placed for the Copenhagen - Malmo bridge or the ferries, this is also a site for discerning campers who want something distinctly different.

The sanitary facilities (one underground) include roomy showers and sauna. Facilities for disabled visitors. Family room and baby changing. Laundry and separate drying room. Two fully equipped kitchens. Enormous dining/TV room. Motorhome services. Small shop and café. Small swimming pool (15/6-15/8). Playground. Small football pitch. Free WiFi at reception.

Key Features

- Open All Year
- Pets Accepted
- Disabled Facilities
- Swimming Pool
- Play Area
- Bike Hire

Scan me for more information.

Alan Rogers Code: SW2590
45 accommodations
93 pitches
GPS: 57.01185, 16.50497
Post Code: S-38392

Blekinge-Kalmar Län, South

Oknö Mönsterås

www.alanrogers.com/sw2590
moensteras@regenbogen.ag
Tel: 049 944 902
firstcamp.se/destination/okno-monsteras

Open (Touring Pitches):
1 April - 31 October.

Camping Oknö lies between the Swedish mainland and the island of Öland on an archipelago approximately 5 km. from the town of Mönsterås. A single road leads to the site, which is surrounded by coves, forest trails and meadows. The campsite and nearby beaches are sheltered from the winds and waves, making the area well suited for boating, fishing and bathing. There are 155 slightly sloping, patchy grass pitches, randomly arranged with 93 for touring, all with electricity (10-16A), some with their own sanitary facility and all with varying amounts of shade from tall trees. Some have good views over the coastal area. This area of Sweden has the least rainfall and most sunshine and there is 150 km. of coastline and over 300 islands providing perfect environments for birds and fish, including pike, perch and salmon. In the surrounding area, there is a wide choice of local shops, small boutiques, museums, abbey ruins, art and handicraft exhibitions, canoeing and hiking trails. In summer, there is a blues festival, music on the main street and church concerts.

Traditional style toilet blocks. Facilities for disabled visitors and children, hob and microwave. Washing machine and dryer. Excellent licensed restaurant with a wide ranging menu. Spacious wellness area with spas, sauna, solarium, steam bath, whirlpool, massage and beauty treatment. Playground. Bicycle hire. Motorboat and rowing boat hire. Minigolf. Tennis.

Key Features

- Pets Accepted
- Disabled Facilities
- Beach Access
- Play Area
- Bar/Restaurant
- Bike Hire
- Sailing

Scan me for more information.

Alan Rogers Code: SW2800
35 accommodations
109 pitches
GPS: 58.42135, 15.56152
Post Code: S-584 37

Östergötlands Län, South

Glyttinge Linköping

www.alanrogers.com/sw2800
glyttinge@nordiccamping.se
Tel: 013 174 928
firstcamp.se/destination/glyttinge-linkoping

Open (Touring Pitches):
All year.

Glyttinge Camping is situated in a wooded area on the outskirts of Linköping and only five minutes by car from the IKEA shopping mall. It is a site with varied terrain - some flat, some sloping and some woodland. It has enthusiastic and friendly management, is maintained to a good standard, and trees and shrubs throughout create a cosy, garden-like atmosphere. There are 109 pitches of varying sizes, some are very large, all with 10/16A electricity. A number of unmarked pitches are provided for tents and 30 chalets are available for hire. Children are well catered for - the manager has laid out a fenced and very safe children's play area. The site is also a good stopover place halfway between Kolmården and Astrid Lindgren's World.

The main, central toilet block with key access (supplemented by additional smaller facilities at reception) is well equipped and maintained. It has showers in cubicles, washbasins and WC suites and hand dryers. Separate facilities for disabled visitors. Baby rooms. Laundry. Kitchen and dining/TV room, fully equipped. Motorhome services. Small shop (20/6-31/8). Playground. Minigolf. Badminton. WiFi (charged).

Key Features

- Open All Year
- Pets Accepted
- Disabled Facilities
- Play Area

Scan me for more information.

Alan Rogers Code: SW2840
55 accommodations
58 pitches
GPS: 59.23043, 17.88818
Post Code: S-141 32

Stockholms Län, South

SweCamp Flottsbro

www.alanrogers.com/sw2840
info@flottsbro.se
Tel: 085 353 2700
www.flottsbro.se

Open (Touring Pitches):
All year (full services 15/6-15/8).

Stockholm SweCamp Flottsbro is located at the south entrance to Stockholm, just 20 minutes from Stockholm city centre. The site offers 58 large numbered pitches for touring, arranged on level terraces; all have electricity (10A) and 53 also have TV connections. The site itself slopes down to Lake Alby and there is a good restaurant at the bottom. Flottsbro is within a large recreation area with hiking and mountain bike trails, beaches and other activities during the summer and downhill and cross-country skiing during the winter. The ski lift is next to the site and guests are entitled to a discounted lift pass and equipment hire. Although the site is set in the countryside it is just a 25 km. drive into the city but a congestion charge does apply. There are plenty of 'park and ride' locations to choose from. The other option is to take the train from nearby Flemingsberg or Huddinge. The friendly and helpful staff in reception will give excellent local advice and information.

Key Features

- Open All Year
- Pets Accepted
- Disabled Facilities
- Play Area
- Bar/Restaurant
- Skiing
- Sailing

Two modern sanitary facilities include free showers, a suite for disabled visitors, baby facilities and a family bathroom. Motorhome services. Excellent campers' kitchen (inside and outside) with electric cookers, microwaves and sinks with hot water. Washing machine, dryer (charged) and sink. Shop (1/7-1/8). Restaurant. Minigolf. Frisbee. Jogging tracks. Canoe hire. Playground. Beach volley and sauna raft. Barbecue huts.

Scan me for more information.

Svegs Camping

On the 'Inlandsvägen' route through Sweden, the town centre is only a short walk from this neat, friendly site. Two supermarkets, a café and tourist information office are adjacent. The 91 pitches are in rows, on level grass, divided into bays by tall hedges, and with electricity (10/16A) available to 70. The site has boats, canoes and bicycles for hire, and the river frontage has a barbecue area with covered seating and fishing platforms. Alongside the river with its fountain, and running through the site is a pleasant well lit riverside walk. Places to visit include the town with its lovely church and adjacent gardens, some interesting old churches in the surrounding villages, and 16th-Century Remsgården, 14 km. to the west.

In the older style, sanitary facilities are functional rather than luxurious, providing stainless steel washing troughs, controllable hot showers with communal changing areas, and a unit for disabled visitors. Although a little short on numbers, facilities will probably suffice at most times as the site is rarely full. Kitchen and dining room with TV, four full cookers and sinks. Laundry facilities. TV room. Minigolf. Canoe, boat and bicycle hire. Fishing.

Alan Rogers Code: SW2845
25 accommodations
91 pitches
GPS: 62.03367, 14.37250
Post Code: S-842 32

Jämtlands Län, North

www.alanrogers.com/sw2845
info@svegscamping.se
Tel: 068 013 025
www.svegscamping.se

Open (Touring Pitches):
All year.

Key Features

- Open All Year
- Pets Accepted
- Disabled Facilities
- Bike Hire
- Fishing

Scan me for more information.

Alan Rogers Code: SW2855
16 accommodations
32 pitches
GPS: 62.92562, 17.75642
Post Code: S-872 80

Västernorrlands Län, North

www.alanrogers.com/sw2855
flogstacamping@telia.com
Tel: 061 210 005
www.flogstacamping.n.nu

Open (Touring Pitches):
1 May - 30 September.

Flogsta Camping

Kramfors lies just to the west of the E4, and travellers may well pass by over the Höga Kusten bridge, and miss this friendly little site. This area of Ådalen and the High Coast, reaches as far as Örnsköldsvik. The attractive garden-like campsite has 32 pitches, 21 with electricity connections (10A), which are arranged on level grassy terraces, separated by shrubs and trees into bays of two to four units. All overlook the heated outdoor public swimming pool complex and an attractive minigolf course. The non-electric pitches are on an open terrace nearer reception. The town centre is a 20-minute walk through a housing estate, where a covered and elevated walkway crosses the main road and railway to the pedestrian shopping precinct with its floral arrangements and fountain. The site also has ten cabins to rent. Good mobile phone reception.

Sanitary facilities comprise nine bathrooms, each with British style WCs, basin with hand dryer, shower. Laundry facilities. More WCs and showers are in the reception building with free sauna. A further sanitary block with a sauna and outside hot tub. Separate building housing a kitchen, with hot plates, fridge/freezer and TV/ dining room (all free). The reception building has a small shop and snack bar. Heated outdoor swimming pools. Playground. Snow mobile hire.

Key Features

- Pets Accepted
- Swimming Pool
- Play Area
- Bike Hire

Scan me for more information.

Alan Rogers Code: SW2857
31 accommodations
150 pitches
GPS: 63.84652, 15.53441
Post Code: S-833 24

Jämtlands Län, North

www.alanrogers.com/sw2857
turism@stromsund.se
Tel: 067 016 410
www.stromsund.se/stromsundscamping

Open (Touring Pitches):
All year.

Strömsunds Camping

A quiet waterside town on the north-south route 45, known as the Inlandsvägen, Strömsund is a good place to begin a journey on the Wilderness Way. This is route 342 which heads northwest towards the mountains at Gäddede and the Norwegian border. Being on the confluence of many waterways, there is a wonderful feeling of space and freedom in Strömsund. This eight-hectare site with its 150 touring pitches (94 with 10A electricity) is set on a gentle grassy slope backed by forest. Another part of the site, across the road, overlooks the lake. Cabins are set in circular groups of either six or seven. The site is owned by the town council. Besides the main bridge is an excellent open-air museum with a collection of buildings dating back several centuries, in the forests there are well-marked trails. Walk here alone at midnight on Midsummer's Eve in an intense blue light – nothing moves as the path ahead leads deeper into the dense forest – it is a memorable experience.

Excellent facilities include two toilet blocks, one on each side of the road. Both contain showers, toilets, washbasins with dividers and underfloor heating. Facilities for disabled visitors. Laundry. Large campers' kitchen with cooking rings, microwave and sinks. Motorhome services. Café (seasonal). Fishing. Golf. Bicycle, canoe, pedalo and boat hire. Play area. WiFi throughout (charged).

Key Features

- Open All Year
- Pets Accepted
- Disabled Facilities
- Swimming Pool
- Play Area
- Bike Hire
- Fishing
- Golf

Scan me for more information.

Alan Rogers Code: SW2870
58 accommodations
170 pitches
GPS: 66.59497, 19.89270
Post Code: S-962 22

Norrbottens Län, North

Jokkmokks Camping Center

www.alanrogers.com/sw2870
campingcenter@jokkmokk.com
Tel: 097 112 370
www.arcticcampjokkmokk.se

Open (Touring Pitches):
15 May - 15 September.

This attractive site is just 8 km. from the Arctic Circle. Large and well organised, it is bordered on one side by the river and by woodland on the other, and is just 3 km. from the town centre. It has 170 level, grassy touring pitches, with an area for tents, plus 58 cabins to rent. Electricity (10A) is available to 159 pitches. The site has a heated, open-air pool complex open in summer (no lifeguard). There are opportunities for snowmobiling, cross-country skiing in spring and ice fishing in winter. Try visiting for the famous Jokkmokk Winter Market (first Thursday to Saturday in February) or the less chilly Autumn Market (end of August).

Heated sanitary buildings provide mostly open washbasins and controllable showers - some are curtained with a communal changing area, a few are in cubicles with divider and seat. A unit by reception has a baby bathroom, a fully equipped suite for disabled visitors, games room, plus a very well appointed kitchen and launderette. A further unit with WCs, washbasins, showers plus a steam sauna, is by the pool. Shop, restaurant and bar (in summer). Takeaway (10/6-10/8). Swimming pools (25x10 m. main pool with water slide, two smaller pools and paddling pool, 20/6-8/8). Sauna. Bicycle hire. Playground and adventure playground. Minigolf. Football field. Games machines. Free fishing.

Key Features

- Pets Accepted
- Disabled Facilities
- Swimming Pool
- Play Area
- Bar/Restaurant
- Bike Hire
- Fishing

Scan me for more information.

Thun, Canton of Bern >

Capital Bern
Currency Swiss Franc (CHf)
Language German in central and eastern areas, French in the west, Italian in the south, Raeto-Romansch in the southeast.
Time Zone CET (GMT+1)
Telephone Code 00 41

Tourist Website
myswitzerland.com

Climate Mild and refreshing in the north. South of the Alps it is warmer, influenced by the Mediterranean. The Valais is noted for its dryness.

Shops Varied. In high-season 10am to 6pm weekdays, to 4pm Saturday.

Banks 8.30am to 4.30pm weekdays.

Accessible Travel Like Sweden, Switzerland ranks highly when it comes to ease of access for the less abled. Transport and public spaces offer adapted facilities.

Travelling with children
Switzerland is a great destination for families. Most restaurants offer a kids menu. Children aged 6 or under travel free on trains.

See campsite map page

487

Public Holidays New Year's Day, Good Friday, Easter Monday, Ascension, Whit Monday, Corpus Christi, National Day (1 Aug), All Saints, Christmas Day, Boxing Day. Some cantons observe regional public holidays.

Motoring The road network is comprehensive and well planned. An annual road tax is levied on all cars using Swiss motorways and the 'Vignette' windscreen sticker must be purchased at the border, or in advance from the Swiss National Tourist Office, plus a separate one for a towed caravan or trailer.

Environmental Policies There are no Low Emission Zones currently in force in Switzerland although many mountain resorts are vehicle-free. In these areas you are encouraged to use Park and Ride schemes and access the resorts using cable cars. Metal, plastic, glass, paper and cardboard are all widely recycled.

Switzerland

A small, wealthy country best known for its outstanding mountainous scenery, fine cheeses, delicious chocolates, Swiss bank accounts and enviable lifestyles. Centrally situated in Europe, it shares its borders with four countries: France, Austria, Germany and Italy, each one having its own cultural influence on Switzerland. Switzerland boasts a picture postcard landscape of mountains, valleys, waterfalls and glaciers.

The Bernese Oberland with its snowy peaks and rolling hills is the most popular area, Gstaad is a favourite haunt of wealthy skiers, while the mild climate and breezy conditions around Lake Thun are perfect for watersports and other outdoor activities. German-speaking Zurich is a multicultural metropolis with over 50 museums, sophisticated shops and colourful festivals set against a breathtaking backdrop of lakes and mountains. The south-east of Switzerland has densely forested mountain slopes and the wealthy and glamorous resort of Saint Moritz.

Geneva, Montreux and Lausanne on the northern shores of Lake Geneva make up the bulk of French Switzerland, with vineyards that border the lakes and medieval towns. The southernmost canton, Ticino, is home to the Italian-speaking Swiss, with the Mediterranean style lakeside resorts of Lugano and Locarno.

Alan Rogers Code: CH9800
180 pitches
GPS: 46.45165, 9.78164
Post Code: CH-7513

Graubünden, East

Camping Silvaplana

www.alanrogers.com/ch9800
reception@campingsilvaplana.ch
Tel: 081 828 8492
www.campingsilvaplana.ch

Open (Touring Pitches):
Mid May - Mid October.

Silvaplana is situated at the junction of the road from Italy over the Malojapass, the road from northern Switzerland via the Julierpass, and the road that continues through Saint Moritz to Austria. Camping Silvaplana, therefore, might be useful for a night stop if travelling this way. The site is mainly level and the 180 pitches for touring units are numbered and marked by posts or tapes, with 120 electrical connections (16A). Although the surrounding scenery across the lake is very pleasant, there is nothing remarkable about the site, except that most afternoons a wind blows along the lake, which is used by windsurfing enthusiasts. However, it is probably the best campsite in the area, with good walking and climbing opportunities. A fenced river runs through it, but the lake shore is unprotected (giving boats access to the water).

The heated toilet block has hot showers and a baby room, but no facilities for disabled visitors. Washing machines. Motorhome services. Gas supplies. Shop for basics (seasonal). Bar. TV room. Small play area. WiFi (free).

Key Features

- Pets Accepted
- Play Area
- Bar/Restaurant
- Fishing
- Sailing

Scan me for more information.

Alan Rogers Code: CH9840
130 accommodations
60 pitches
GPS: 46.69800, 9.55900
Post Code: CH-7083

Graubünden, East

www.alanrogers.com/ch9840
info@st-cassian.ch
Tel: 081 384 2472
camping-lenzerheide.ch

Open (Touring Pitches):
All year.

Camping Saint Cassian

Saint Cassian, owned and managed by three generations of the Nadig family, caters mainly for static holiday caravans, but has some room for touring units and is suitable for a night stop when travelling to or from Saint Moritz. The site is on a fairly steep slope but the 60 touring pitches (out of 190) are terraced between the statics under a cover of tall pines. Forty have 10A electricity. Being 1,415 m. above sea level in a north-south valley, this is a peaceful location surrounded by scenic views and abundant sunshine; 140 signed walking paths of various degrees of difficulty start from the site. Although there is no organised entertainment on the site, there are many opportunities at the holiday resort of Lenzerheide Valbella 3 km. away including tennis, an 18-hole golf course, bars and discos, and a heated swimming pool. The owners are keen supporters of mountain biking and several important competitions are held in the area, but winter sports are the principal attraction to the site. The drive from Chur to St Moritz is challenging but exhilarating.

Small, heated, good quality toilet block with free hot water in washing troughs and sinks and on payment in showers. WCs and showers (on payment) below the reception office. Washing machine and dryer. Dishwasher. Motorhome services. Gas supplies. Excellent restaurant. Torches and long leads useful. WiFi (charged).

Key Features

- Open All Year
- Pets Accepted
- Disabled Facilities
- Swimming Pool
- Bar/Restaurant
- Skiing

Scan me for more information.

Alan Rogers Code: CH9313
25 accommodations
39 pitches
GPS: 47.10915, 7.22026
Post Code: CH-2572

Bern, Central

www.alanrogers.com/ch9313
mail@camping-sutz.ch
Tel: +41 (0)32 397 13 45
camping-sutz.ch

Open (Touring Pitches):
01 January - 31 December

Hotel Camping Sutz

Hotel Camping Sutz am Bielersee has a variety of pitches suitable for caravans and motorhomes and idyllic meadows which are just right for camping. Over twenty of the pitches are more than10m long, making it a perfect choice for owners of longer motorhomes. The pitches drain well, so if there is a downpour, you'll be sure to stay dry. Electricity, water and sewerage hookups are available. A small playground for younger campers can be found in the touring meadow; this also features a chessboard for older guests. There is also a large playing field and barefoot nature trail on-site. The touring meadow is about a three-minute walk to the lakeshore. The large lakeside lawn is the perfect sunbathing spot, but if you prefer to be a little more active there is also a playground and beach volleyball court available. Cold drinks and ice cream are available from the campsite shop/restaurant which is located next to the sunbathing lawn. Bike hire is available on site and fishing and boat launching facilities can both be found nearby.

Bar. Restaurant. Well stocked shop. Play Area. Lake Beach. BBQ Area. Laundry Room. Rental Bikes. Baby Room. Tent Fields. Free WiFi.

Key Features

- Pets Accepted
- Disabled Facilities
- Play Area
- Bar/Restaurant
- Bike Hire

Scan me for more information.

Alan Rogers Code: CH9496
37 accommodations
54 pitches
GPS: 46.73421, 8.17115
Post Code: CH-3860

Bern, Central

www.alanrogers.com/ch9496
info@alpencamping.ch
Tel: 033 971 3676
alpencamping.ch

Open (Touring Pitches):
All year excl. November.

AlpenCamping

AlpenCamping is a small family site located just west of Meiringen, an important winter sports resort and hiking centre in the summer with good road and rail links. Opened in 2007, the enthusiastic owners have developed this into a good all-year site (closed November) and continue to make steady improvements. There are 54 touring pitches, some occupied by seasonal caravans, which are flat and grassy and all have electrical connections and many have water. A further 32 pitches are occupied by well maintained residential units. This is a simple site with few amenities but there is an excellent centrally located toilet block and a small shop for essentials.

Heated toilet block with good showers includes facilities for disabled visitors and a baby changing unit. Washing machine and dryer. Drying area for ski kit. Small shop for essentials with coffee machine. Undercover area with tables, chairs and a microwave for open-air catering. Inflatable pool (in summer). Communal barbecue. Community room with tables, easy chairs, games, TV and books. Winter sauna room. Play area. Dogs accepted (max. 2). WiFi throughout.

Key Features

- Pets Accepted
- Disabled Facilities
- Swimming Pool
- Play Area
- Skiing

Scan me for more information.

Alan Rogers Code: CH9570
68 pitches
GPS: 46.80940, 8.42367
Post Code: CH-6390

Unterwalden, Central

Camping Eienwäldli

www.alanrogers.com/ch9570
info@eienwaeldli.ch
Tel: 041 637 1949
www.eienwaeldli.ch

Open (Touring Pitches):
All year.

Idyllically situated near the beautiful village of Engelberg, surrounded by mountains, 3,500 feet above sea level, this all-year site must be one of the very best in Switzerland. The comprehensive range of facilities would be hard to beat. Nearly half of the site is taken up by static caravans which are grouped together at one side. The touring area is in two parts, there are 68 hardstandings for caravans and motorhomes, 11 are comfortplatze, and 12 are prestigeplatze, but all have electricity. Over the small bridge is a flat meadow for about 70 tents. Reception can be found in the very modern foyer of the Eienwäldli Hotel which also houses the indoor pool, spa complex, excellent shop and café/bar.

The main toilet block, heated in cool weather, is situated at the rear of the hotel and has free hot water in washbasins (in cabins) and charged for showers (CHF 1.00). A small second toilet and shower block has been added at the top of the site. Washing machines and dryers. Shop. Café/bar. New restaurant. Small lounge with kitchen, TV/DVD and library. Indoor pool complex with spa facilities. Physiotherapy suite. Ski facilities including a drying room. Large refurbished play area with a rafting pool fed by freshwater from the mountain stream. Dog bath. Free shuttle bus. Torches useful. WiFi (charged).

Key Features

- Open All Year
- Pets Accepted
- Disabled Facilities
- Swimming Pool
- Play Area
- Bar/Restaurant
- Skiing

Scan me for more information.

Alan Rogers Code: CH9120
28 accommodations
150 pitches
GPS: 47.04960, 8.34158
Post Code: CH-6006

Luzern, Central

Camping Lido Luzern

www.alanrogers.com/ch9120
luzern@camping-international.ch
Tel: 041 370 2146
www.camping-international.ch

Open (Touring Pitches):
All year.

Luzern is a traditional holiday resort of the British, and this site has many British visitors. It lies near the shore of Lake Luzern, just 1 mile outside the town itself. This good but expensive site (£42 in low season per night) is divided into separate sections for caravans, motorhomes and tents; the first two have hardstandings which, in effect, provide rather formal and small individual pitches with shade in parts. There are 150 marked touring pitches all with 16A electricity connections. Quiet in the early season, from late June to late August it can become full and feel rather crowded, especially in the tent section. Good English is spoken. Next to the site (but not associated with it, so you have to pay for entrance) is the Lido proper, which has a large sandy beach, bathing in the lake and sports fields. The town of Luzern, which you can reach by bus or ferry, has excellent shopping and sightseeing.

The heated sanitary facilities are in three sections, two close to reception, and all fully equipped. A large, fully equipped modern block includes a restroom and cooking area with gas rings (free). Some washbasins in cabins. Free hot water for showers and sinks. Facilities for disabled visitors. The third block is the other side of the site with good facilities. Motorhome services. Shop. Bar. Restaurant. Takeaway. Community room. Play area. Bicycle hire. Internet access and WiFi (charged). Organised excursions.

Key Features

- Open All Year
- Pets Accepted
- Disabled Facilities
- Play Area
- Bar/Restaurant
- Bike Hire

Scan me for more information.

Alan Rogers Code: CH9040
4 accommodations
160 pitches
GPS: 47.05253, 7.07001
Post Code: CH-2525

Neuchâtel, West

Camping des Pêches

www.alanrogers.com/ch9040
info@camping-lelanderon.ch
Tel: 032 751 2900
www.camping-lelanderon.ch

Open (Touring Pitches):
1 April - 15 October.

This relatively recently constructed, touring campsite is on the side of Lake Biel and the river Thielle, close to the old town of Le Landeron. The site is divided into two sections, on the lake side of the road are residential seasonal caravans, and on the other is the modern campsite for tourers. The 160 touring pitches are all on level grass, numbered but not separated; a few have shade, all have 13A electricity and many conveniently placed water points. All the facilities are well maintained and in good condition. A short walk brings you to the historic old town.

The spacious, modern sanitary block contains all the usual facilities including a food preparation area with six cooking rings, a large freezer and refrigerator. Payment for showers is by card (1 CHF/min). Baby room. Facilities for disabled visitors. Laundry. Motorhome services. Community room and small café in reception building. Shop, restaurant and takeaway (all season). Playground. Bicycle hire. TV and general room. WiFi throughout.

Key Features

- Pets Accepted
- Disabled Facilities
- Swimming Pool
- Play Area
- Bar/Restaurant
- Bike Hire

Scan me for more information.

Alan Rogers Code: CH9775
3 accommodations
160 pitches
GPS: 46.29808, 7.87271
Post Code: CH-3930

Valais, South

Camping Mühleye

www.alanrogers.com/ch9775
info@camping-visp.ch
Tel: 027 946 2084
www.camping-visp.ch

Open (Touring Pitches):
25 March - 31 October.

Camping Schwimmbad Mühleye is a popular family site located in the Valais near the busy centre of Visp. The site has 199 grassy pitches, 160 for touring units with 18A electricity, ranging in size from 80-150 sq.m, including 20 very large (150 sq.m) pitches (with electricity, water and drainage). Although the pitches are marked and numbered, the site has a relaxed informal appearance with plenty of space between units. The valley and mountain views are typically Swiss. The town of Visp is a 15 minute walk away, from where it is easy to explore the area by bus and train. Saas Fee, Zermatt and the Matterhorn are all within reach.

New central sanitary block is modern and spacious. Facilities for disabled visitors. Washing machines and dryers. Free use of fridges and freezers. Motorhome services. Two children's play areas and an indoor play room if wet. Large covered sitting area with tables and chairs. Extensive information for walking, hiking and mountain biking. Internet access. WiFi throughout (free).

Key Features

- Pets Accepted
- Disabled Facilities
- Swimming Pool
- Play Area
- Bar/Restaurant
- Skiing

Scan me for more information.

Austria & Czech Republic Map

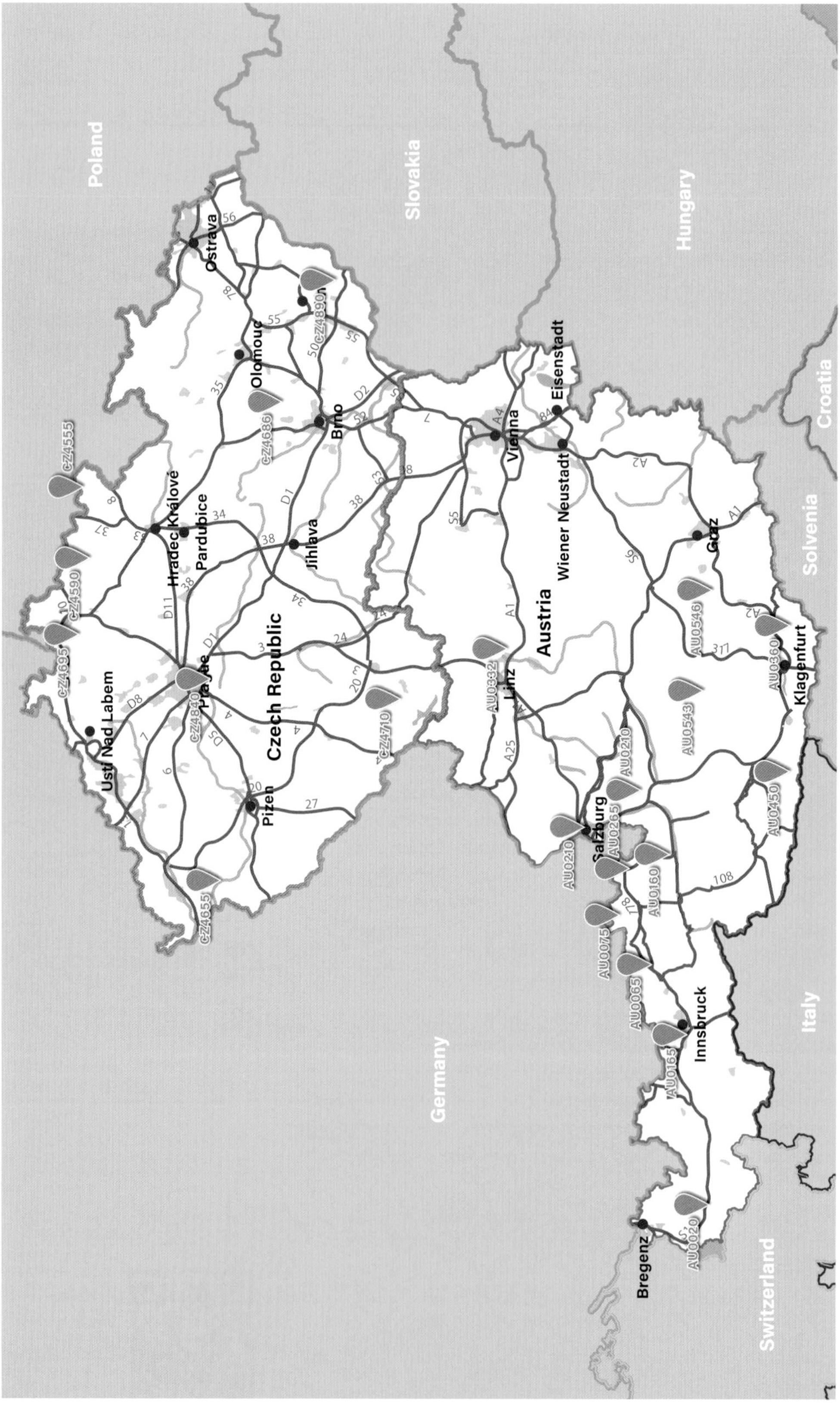

Belgium & Luxembourg Map

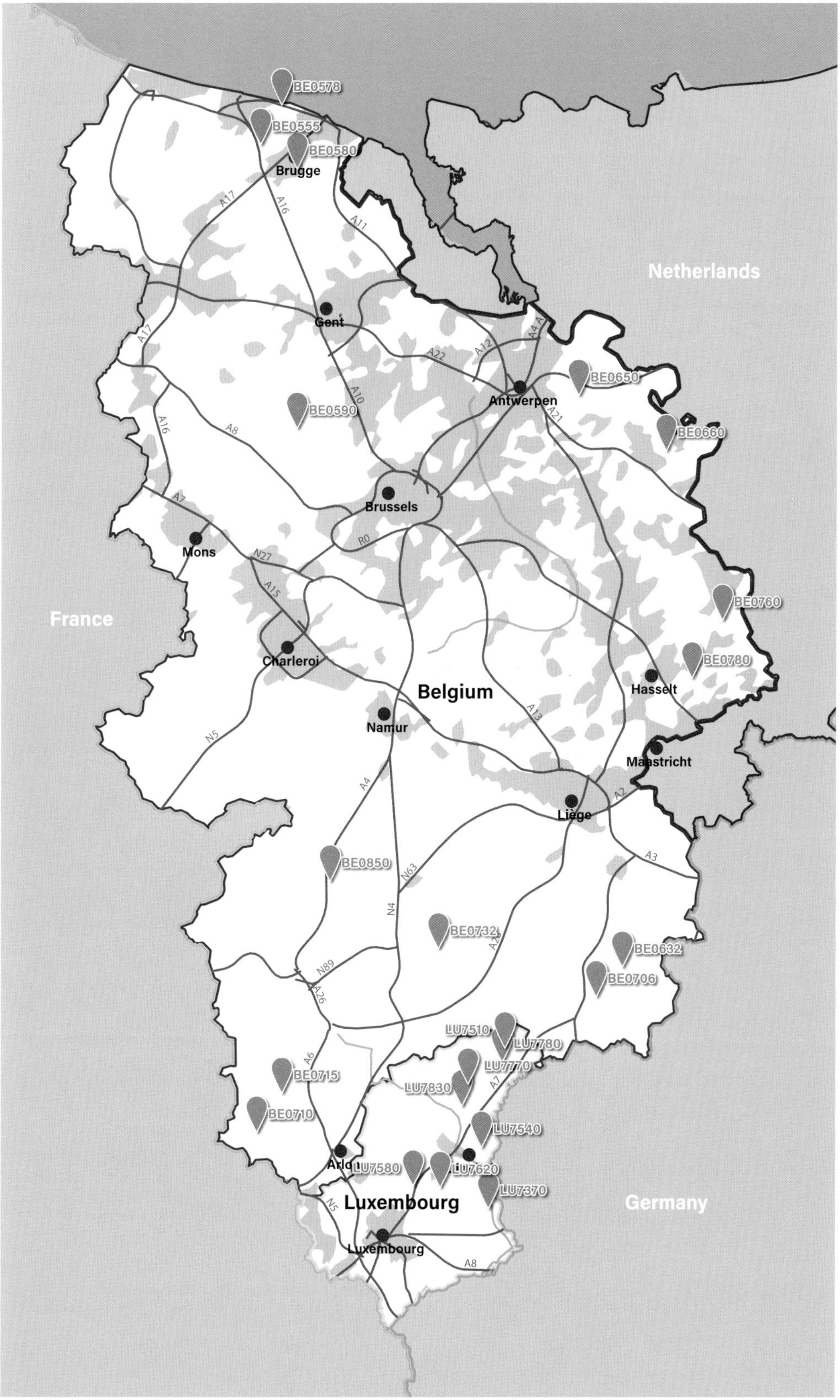

Croatia & Solvenia Map

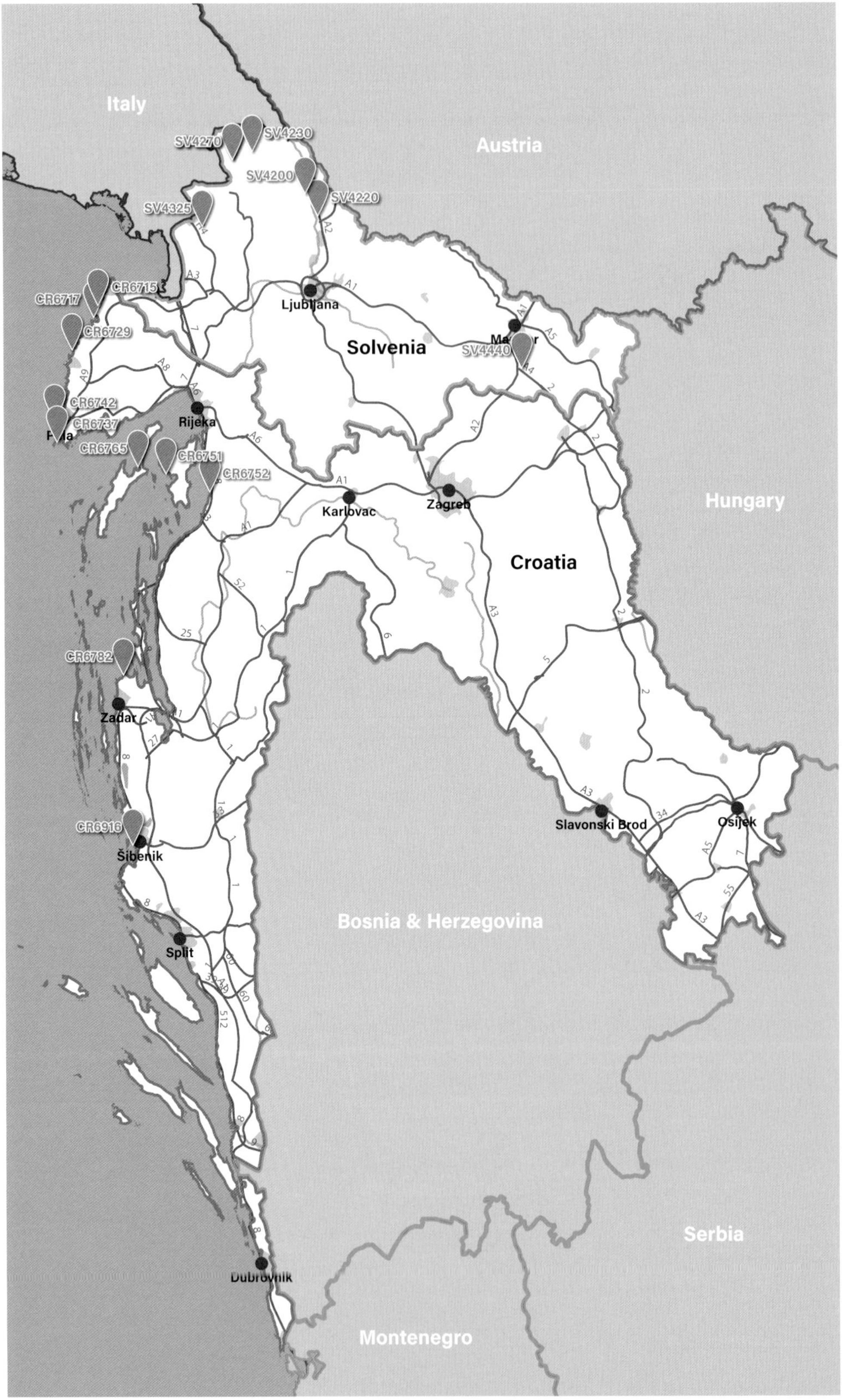

Denmark Map

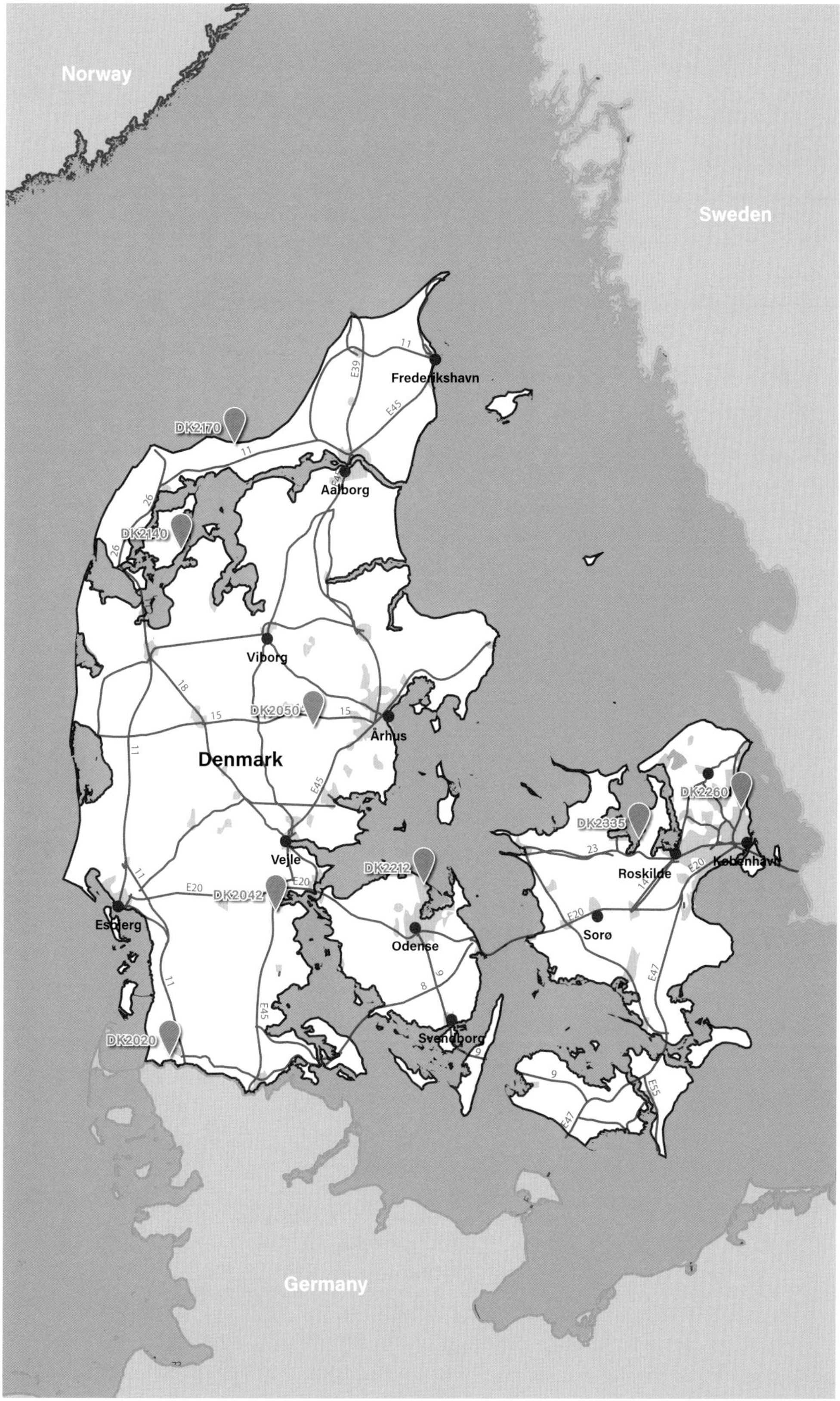
Norway
Sweden
Germany
Denmark
Frederikshavn
Aalborg
Viborg
Århus
Vejle
Esbjerg
Odense
Svendborg
Sorø
Roskilde
København
DK2170
DK2140
DK2050
DK2335
DK2260
DK2212
DK2042
DK2020
E39
E45
E20
E47
E55
11
26
18
15
23
14
9
8

West France Map

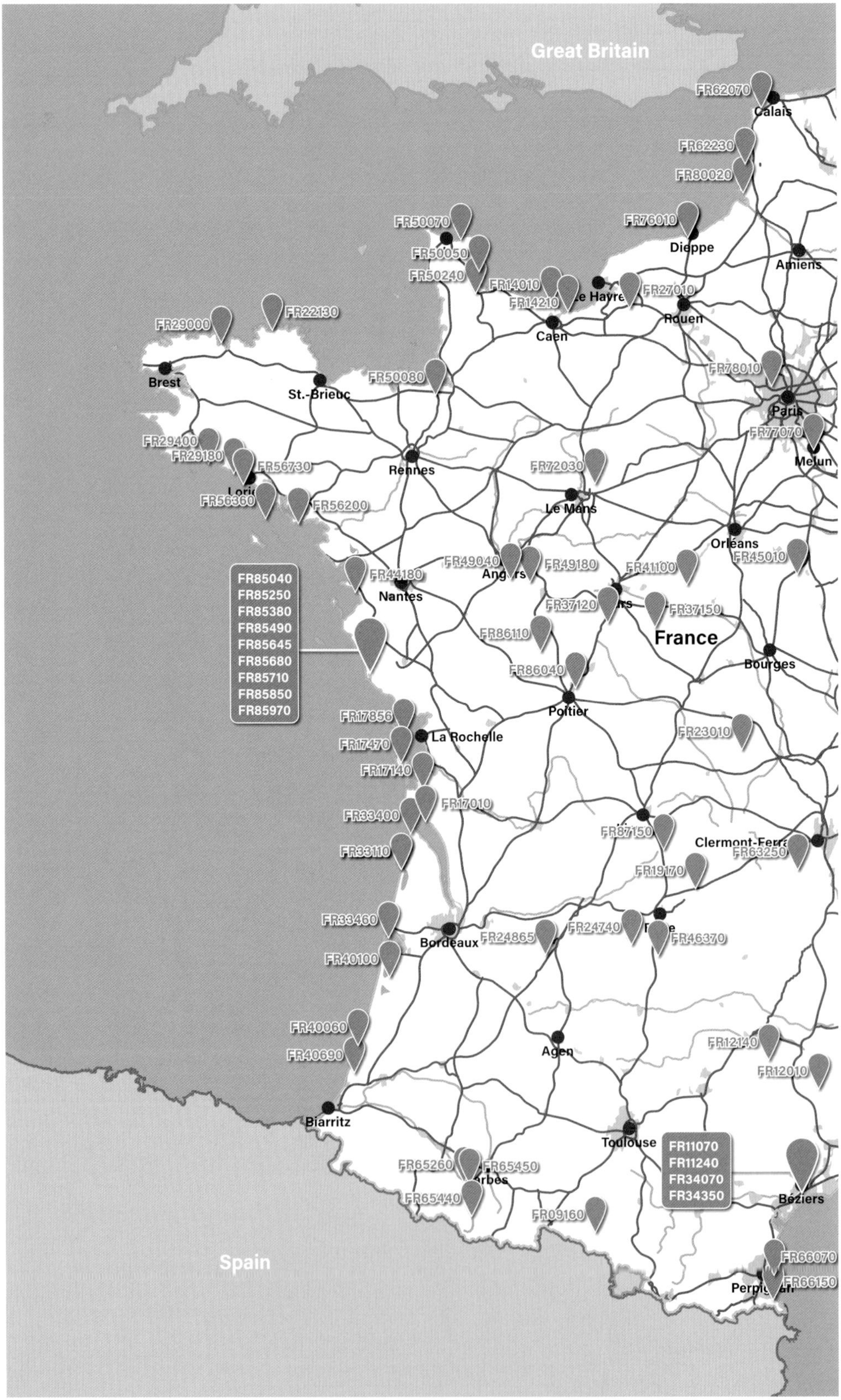

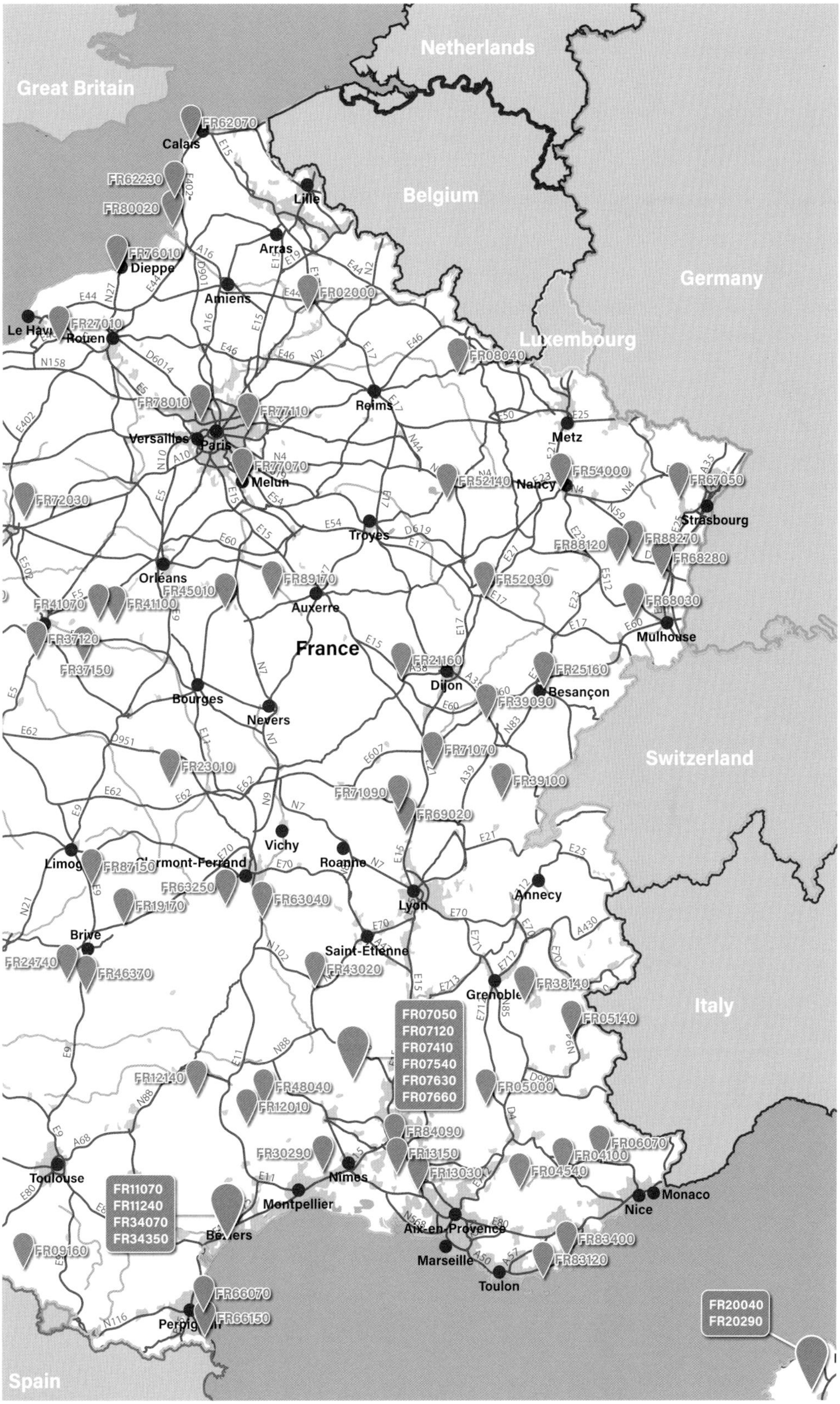
Netherlands
Great Britain
Belgium
Germany
Luxembourg
France
Switzerland
Italy
Spain
Monaco
Calais
Lille
Arras
Dieppe
Amiens
Rouen
Reims
Metz
Versailles
Paris
Melun
Nancy
Strasbourg
Troyes
Orléans
Auxerre
Mulhouse
Dijon
Besançon
Bourges
Nevers
Vichy
Roanne
Lyon
Annecy
Brive
Saint-Etienne
Grenoble
Toulouse
Montpellier
Nîmes
Aix-en-Provence
Marseille
Toulon
Nice
FR62070
FR62230
FR80020
FR76010
FR02000
FR27010
FR08040
FR78010
FR77110
FR77070
FR52140
FR54000
FR67050
FR72030
FR88120
FR88270
FR68280
FR52030
FR89170
FR45010
FR41070
FR41100
FR68030
FR37120
FR37150
FR21160
FR25160
FR39090
FR71070
FR23010
FR39100
FR71090
FR69020
FR87150
FR63250
FR63040
FR19170
FR24740
FR46370
FR43020
FR38140
FR05140
FR07050
FR07120
FR07410
FR07540
FR07630
FR07660
FR12140
FR48040
FR12010
FR05000
FR84090
FR06070
FR30290
FR13150
FR04100
FR13030
FR04540
FR11070
FR11240
FR34070
FR34350
FR83400
FR09160
FR83120
FR66070
FR66150
FR20040
FR20290

France Languedoc & Spain Catalunya Map

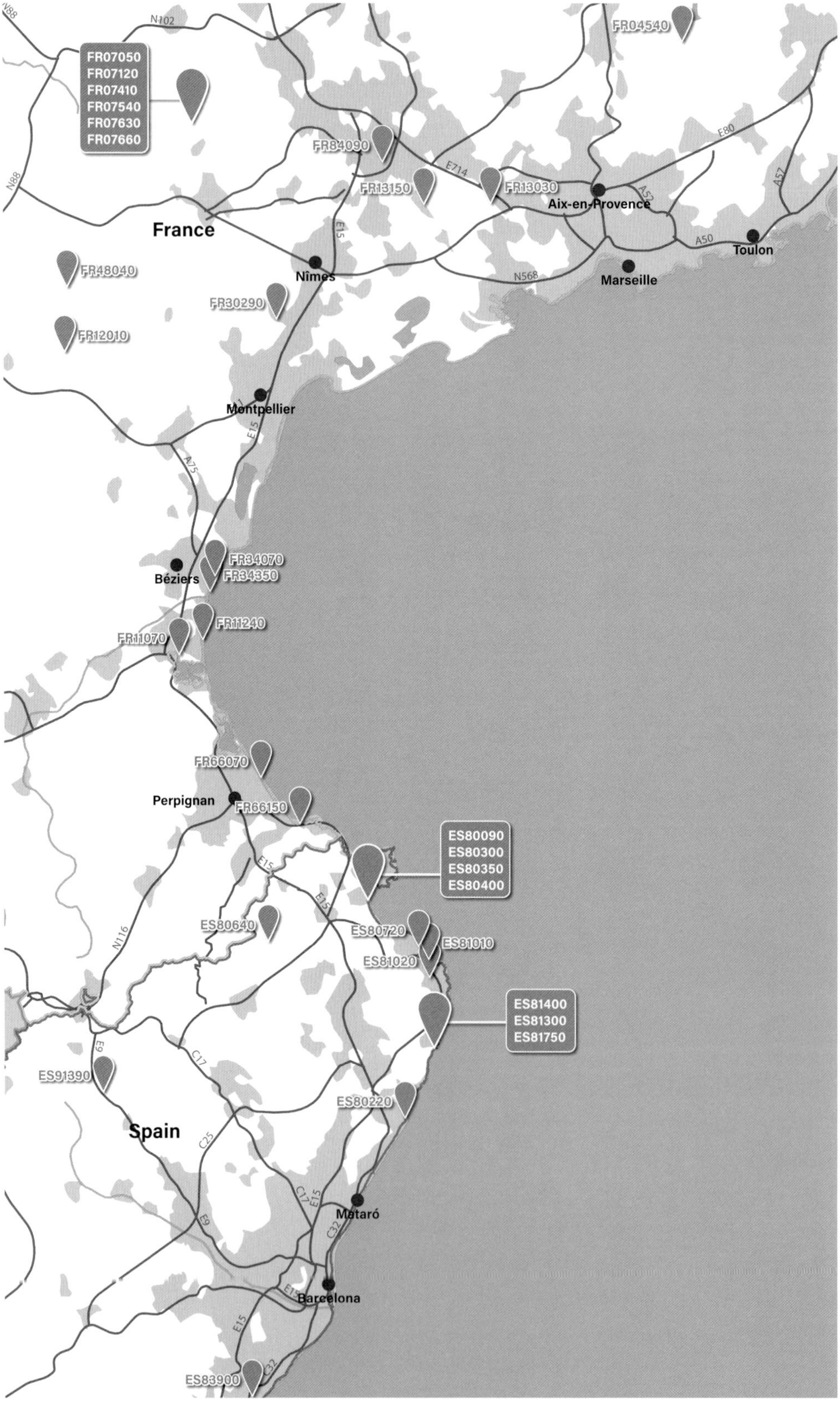

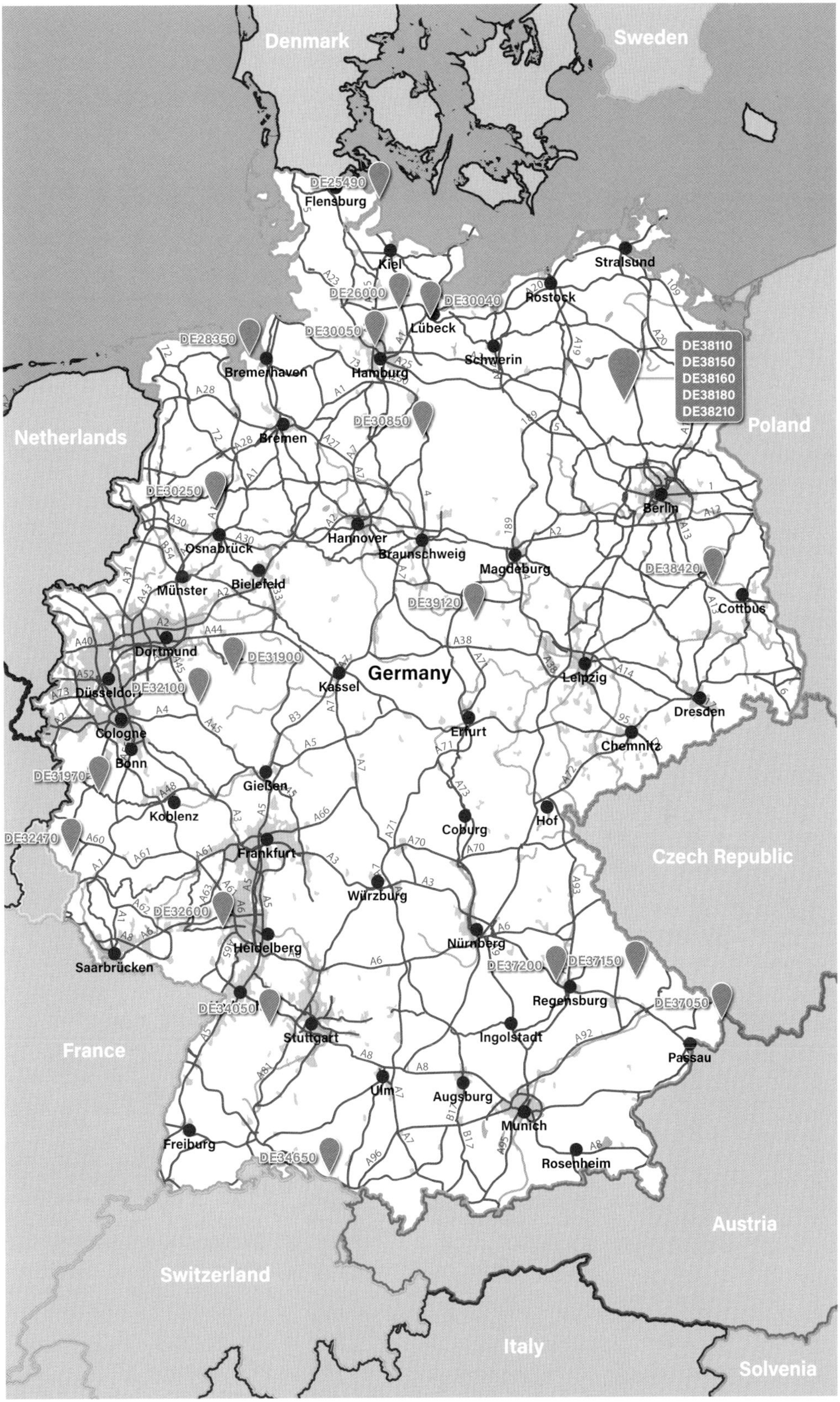
Denmark
Sweden
DE25490
Flensburg
Kiel
Stralsund
DE26000
DE30040
Rostock
Lübeck
DE30050
DE28350
DE38110
DE38150
DE38160
DE38180
DE38210
Schwerin
Bremerhaven
Hamburg
DE30850
Netherlands
Bremen
Poland
DE30250
Berlin
Osnabrück
Hannover
Braunschweig
Magdeburg
DE38420
Münster
Bielefeld
DE39120
Cottbus
Dortmund
DE31900
Germany
Düsseldorf
DE32100
Kassel
Leipzig
Dresden
Cologne
Erfurt
Chemnitz
Bonn
DE31970
Gießen
Koblenz
Coburg
Hof
DE32470
Frankfurt
Czech Republic
Würzburg
DE32600
Nürnberg
Heidelberg
DE37200
DE37150
Saarbrücken
Regensburg
DE37050
DE34050
Stuttgart
Ingolstadt
Passau
France
Ulm
Augsburg
Munich
Freiburg
DE34650
Rosenheim
Austria
Switzerland
Italy
Solvenia

Great Britain & Ireland Map

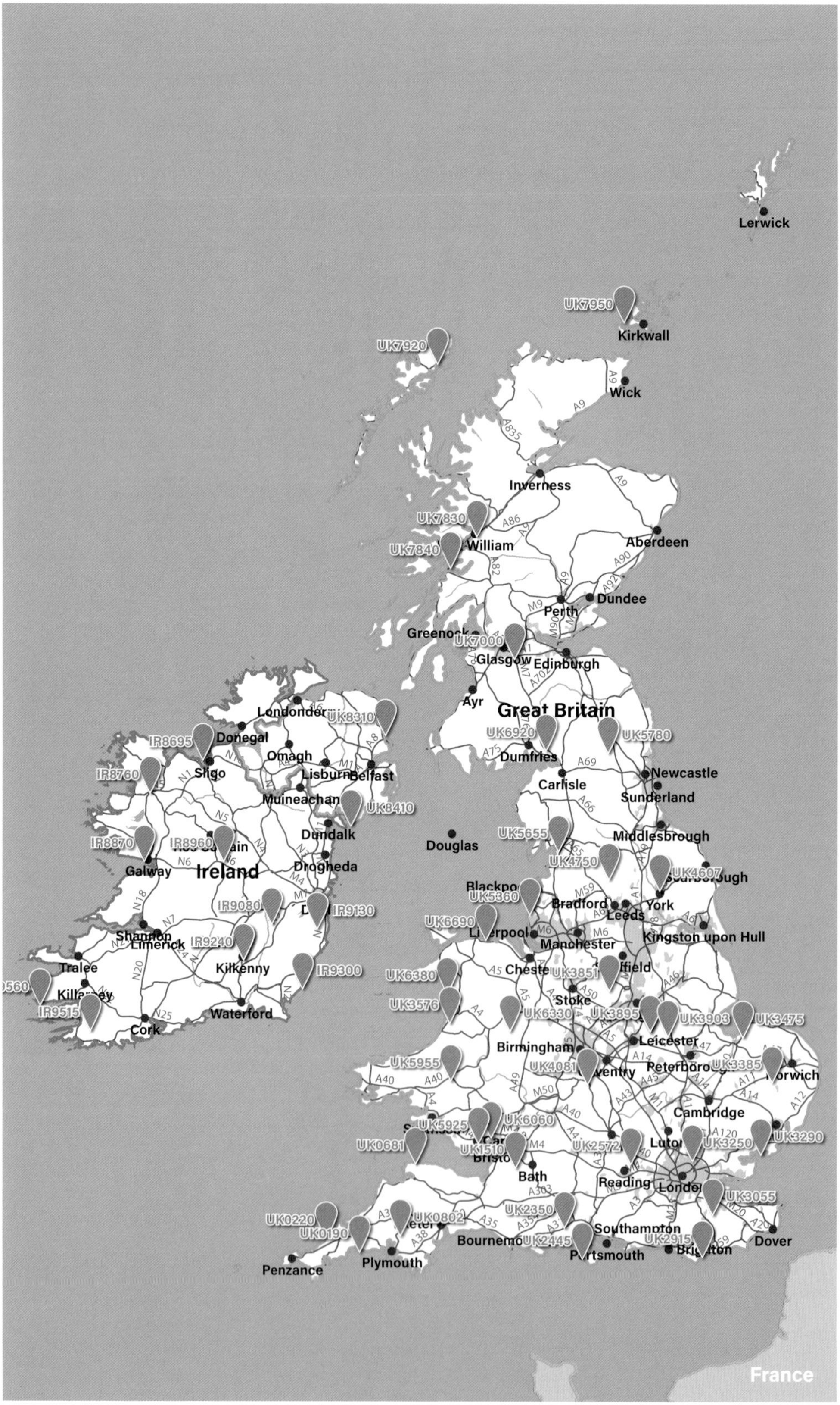

Greece Map

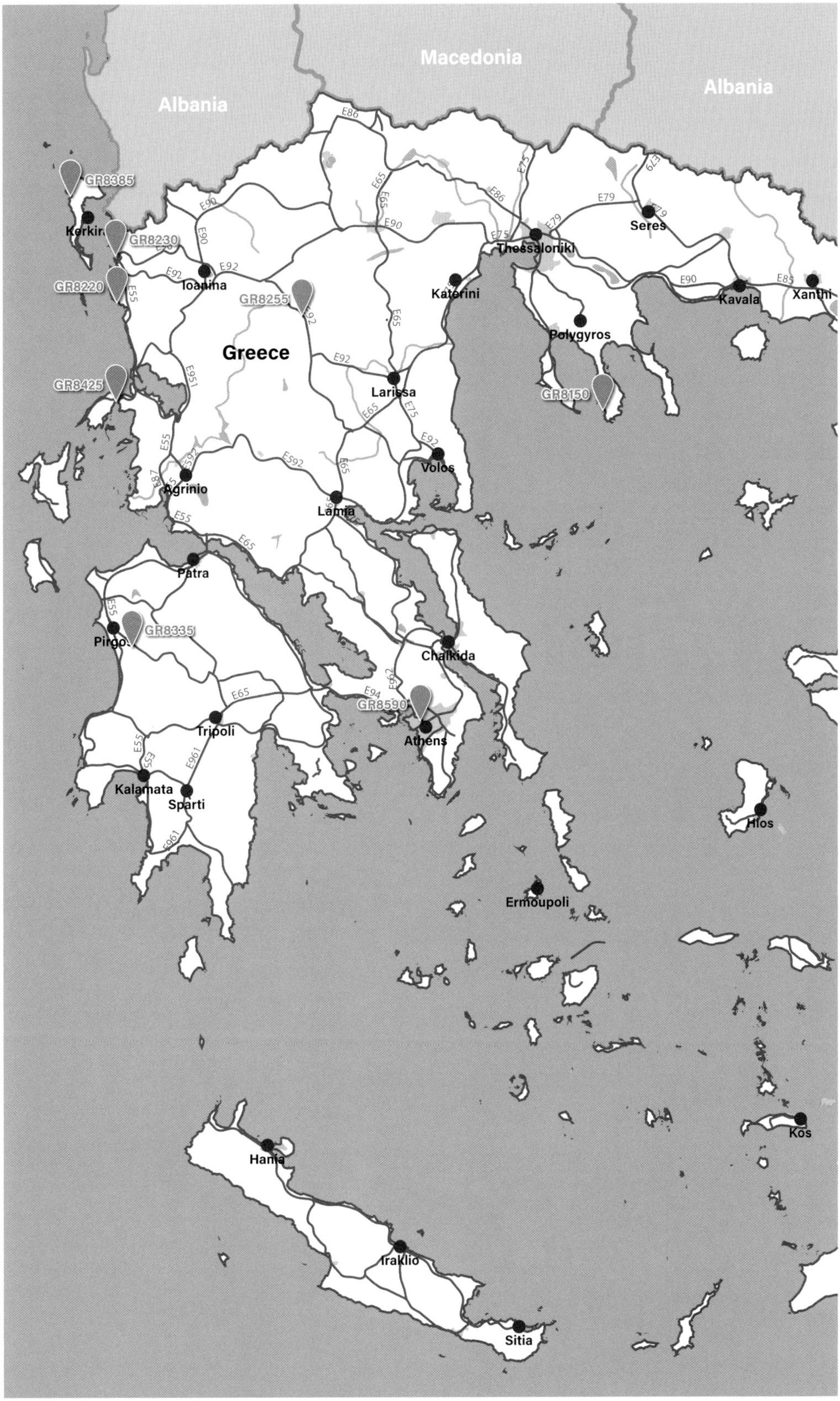
Macedonia
Albania
Albania
GR8385
Kerkira
GR8230
GR8220
Ioanina
GR8255
Greece
GR8425
Katerini
Thessaloniki
Seres
Kavala
Xanthi
Polygyros
GR8150
Larissa
Volos
Agrinio
Lamia
Patra
Pirgos
GR8335
Chalkida
GR8590
Athens
Tripoli
Kalamata
Sparti
Hios
Ermoupoli
Kos
Hania
Iraklio
Sitia
E86
E65
E75
E79
E90
E92
E55
E951
E592
E94
E961
E87
E85

Italy Map

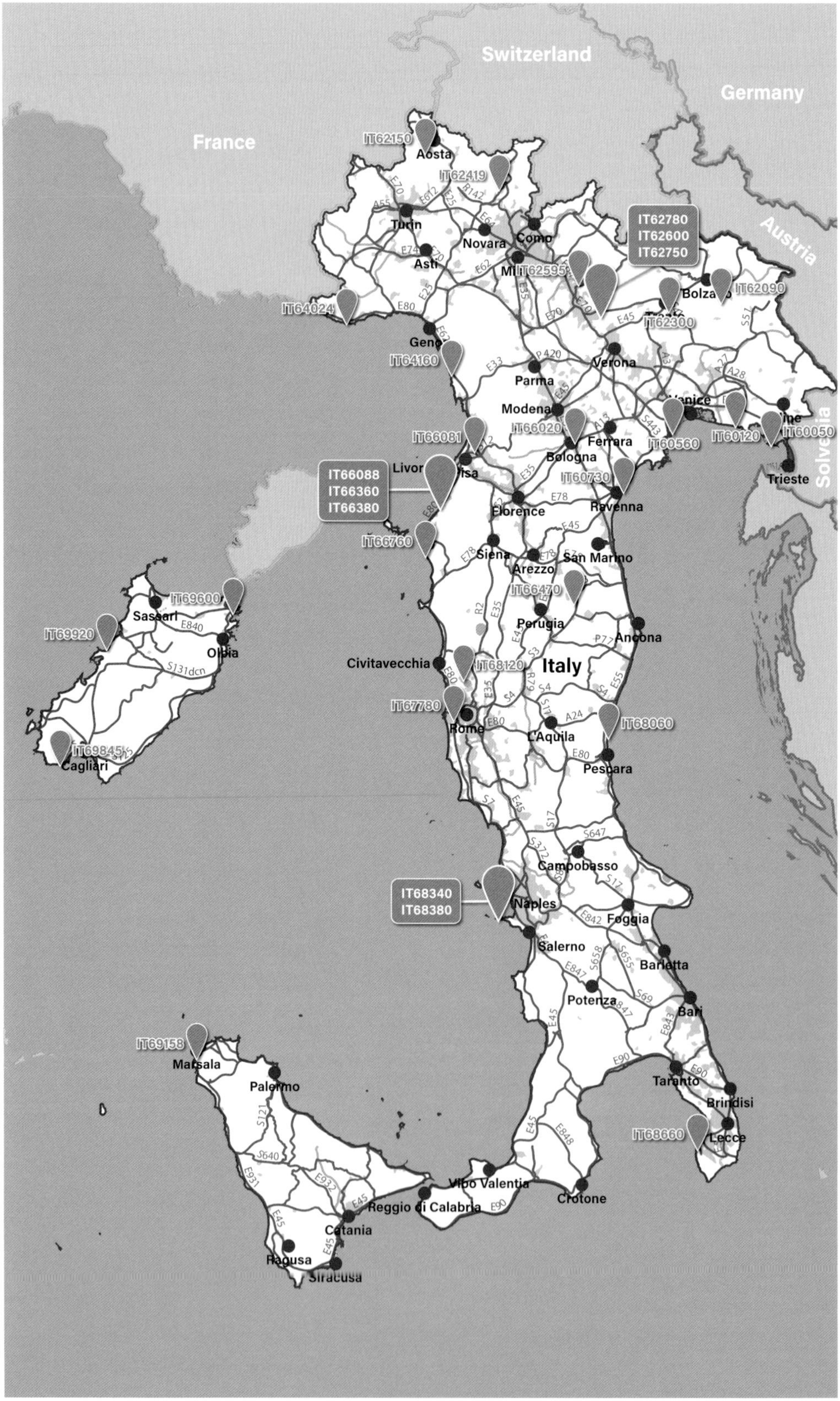
Switzerland
Germany
France
Austria
Solvenia
Italy
IT62150
Aosta
IT62419
Turin
Novara
Como
Asti
IT62780
IT62600
IT62750
IT62595
IT62090
IT62300
IT64024
Genoa
IT64160
Parma
Verona
Modena
IT66020
Ferrara
Bologna
IT60560
IT60120
IT60050
Trieste
IT66081
IT66088
IT66360
IT66380
IT60730
Ravenna
Florence
IT66760
Siena
Arezzo
San Marino
IT66470
Perugia
Ancona
IT69600
Sassari
IT69920
Olbia
Civitavecchia
IT68120
IT67780
Rome
L'Aquila
IT68060
Pescara
IT69845
Cagliari
Campobasso
IT68340
IT68380
Naples
Foggia
Salerno
Barletta
Potenza
Bari
IT69158
Marsala
Palermo
Taranto
Brindisi
IT68660
Lecce
Vibo Valentia
Crotone
Reggio di Calabria
Catania
Ragusa
Siracusa

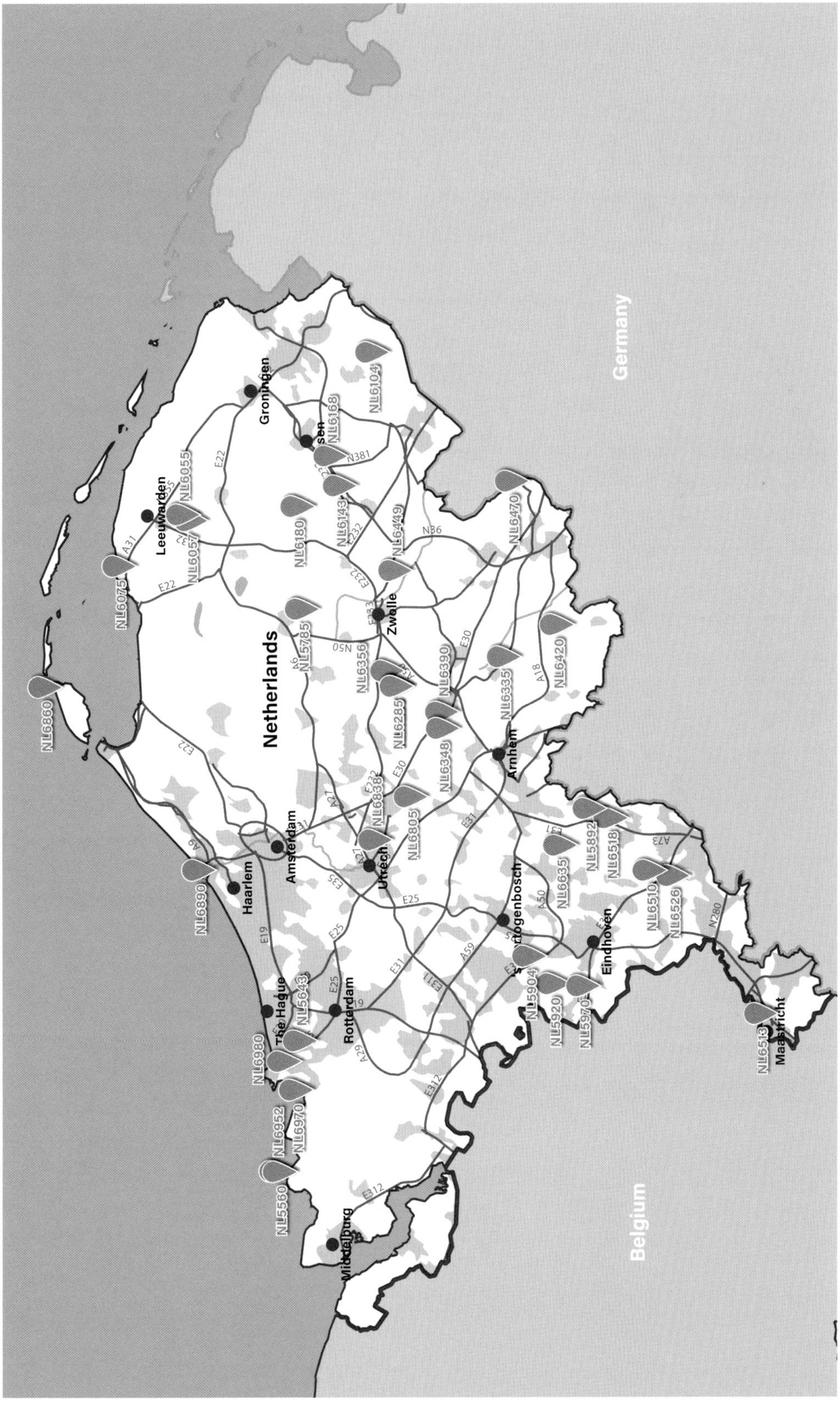
Germany
Belgium
Netherlands
Groningen
Leeuwarden
Zwolle
Arnhem
Amsterdam
Haarlem
Utrecht
The Hague
Rotterdam
Middelburg
Eindhoven
Maastricht
NL6104
NL6168
NL6055
NL6057
NL6075
NL6180
NL6143
NL6449
NL6470
NL6420
NL6335
NL5785
NL6356
NL6390
NL6285
NL6348
NL6860
NL6838
NL6805
NL6890
NL5892
NL6518
NL6635
NL6510
NL6526
NL5904
NL5920
NL5970
NL6513
NL5643
NL6980
NL6952
NL6970
NL5560
E22
A31
N381
N36
E232
N50
A6
E30
A18
E25
E35
E19
A29
E311
E312
A59
A50
E31
A73
N280

Portugal & Spain Map

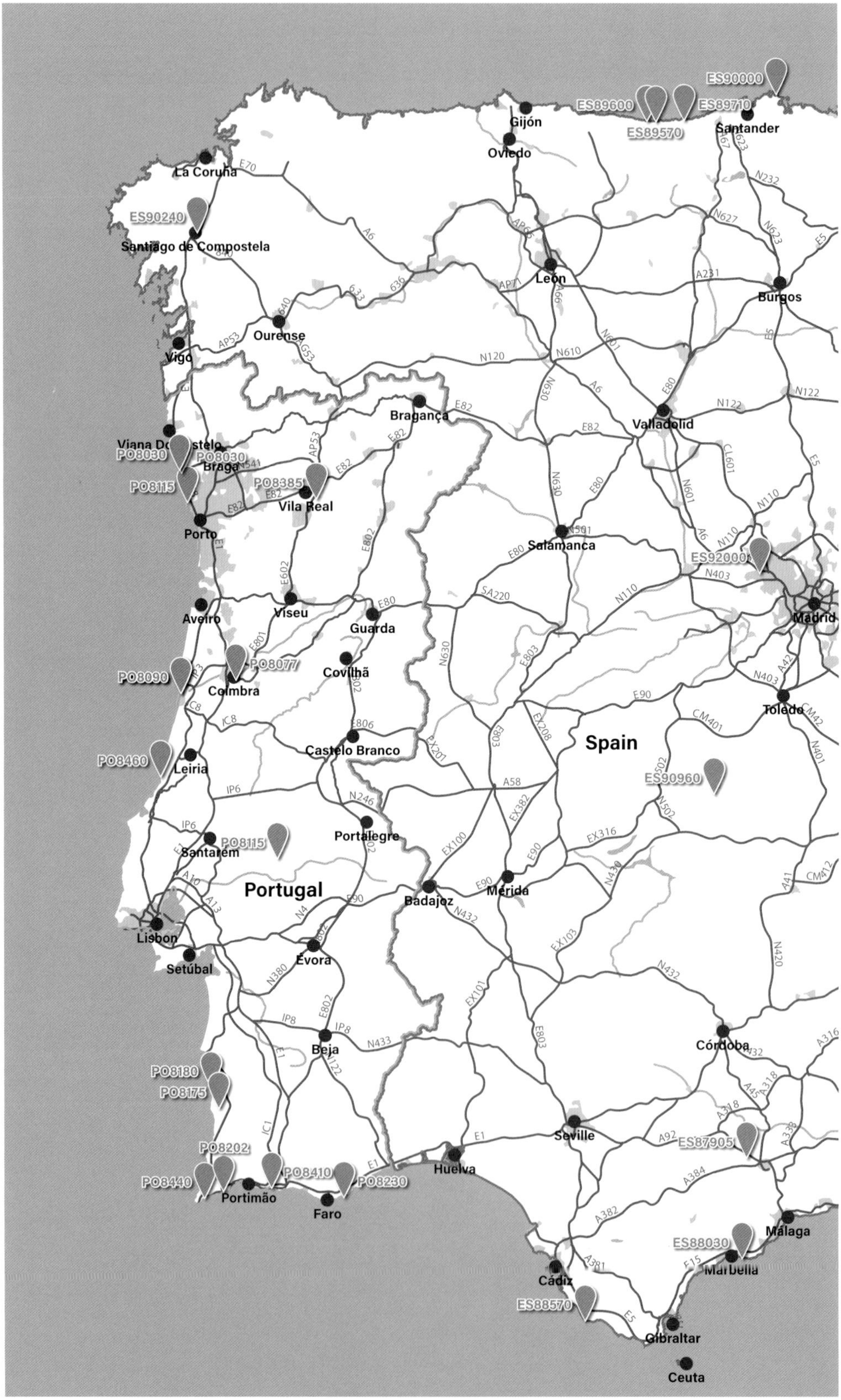

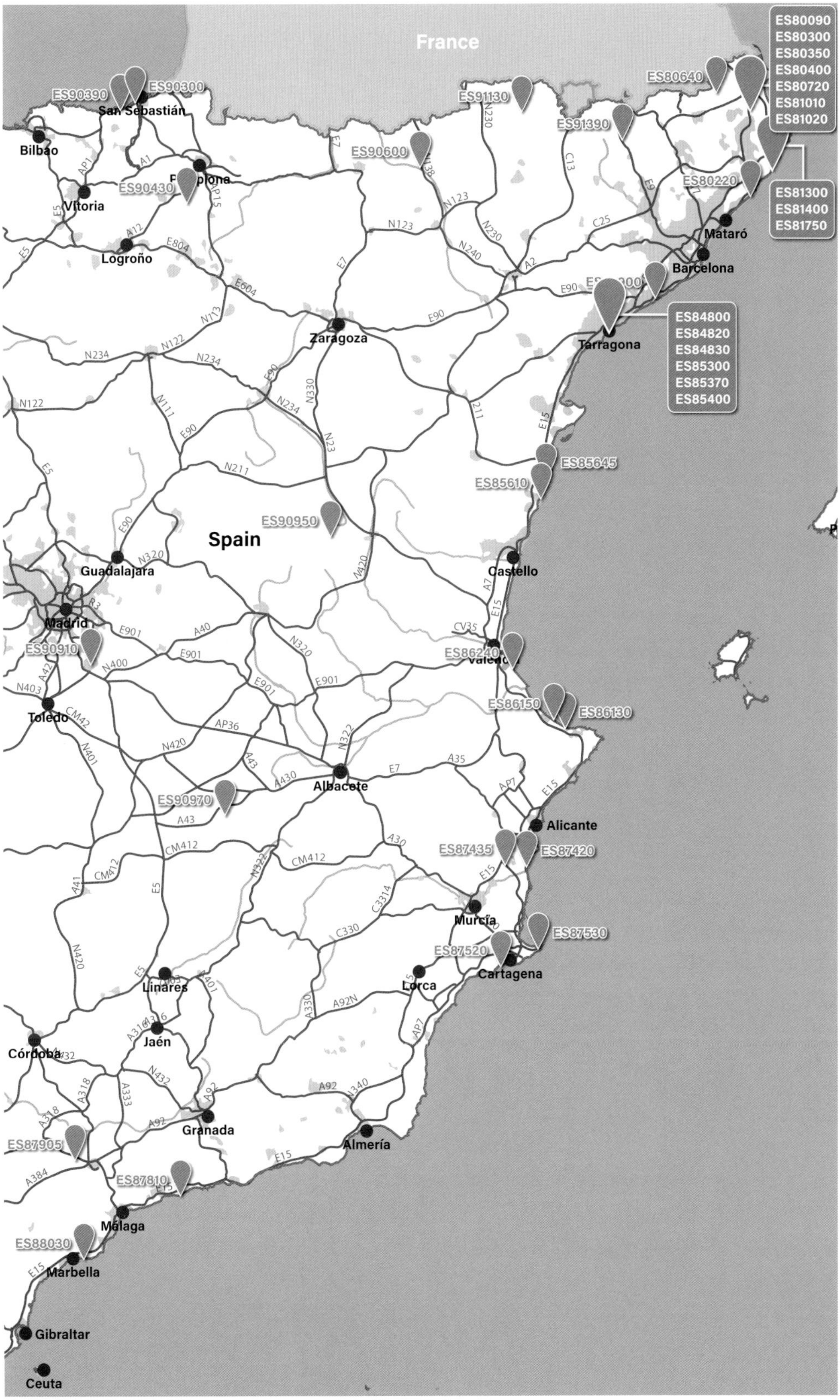
France
Spain
ES80090
ES80300
ES80350
ES80400
ES80720
ES81010
ES81020
ES80640
ES81300
ES81400
ES81750
ES80220
ES91130
ES91390
ES90600
ES90390
ES90300
ES90430
San Sebastián
Bilbao
Vitoria
Logroño
Zaragoza
Mataró
Barcelona
Tarragona
ES84800
ES84820
ES84830
ES85300
ES85370
ES85400
ES85645
ES85610
ES90950
Guadalajara
Madrid
ES90910
Toledo
Castello
ES86240
ES86150
ES86130
Albacete
ES90970
Alicante
ES87435
ES87420
Murcia
ES87530
ES87520
Cartagena
Lorca
Linares
Jaén
Córdoba
Granada
Almería
ES87905
ES87810
Málaga
ES88030
Marbella
Gibraltar
Ceuta

Sweden & Norway Map

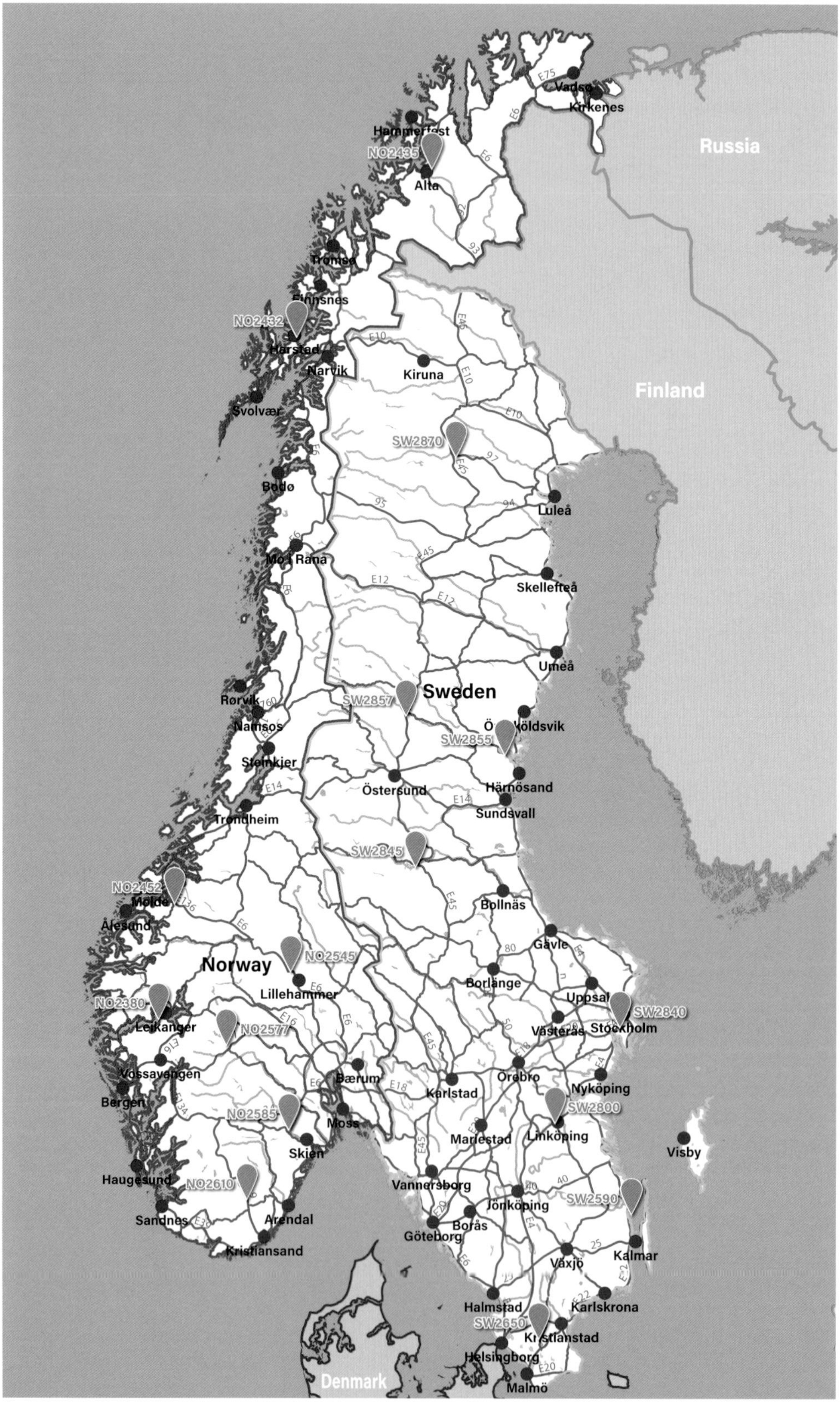

Switzerland Map

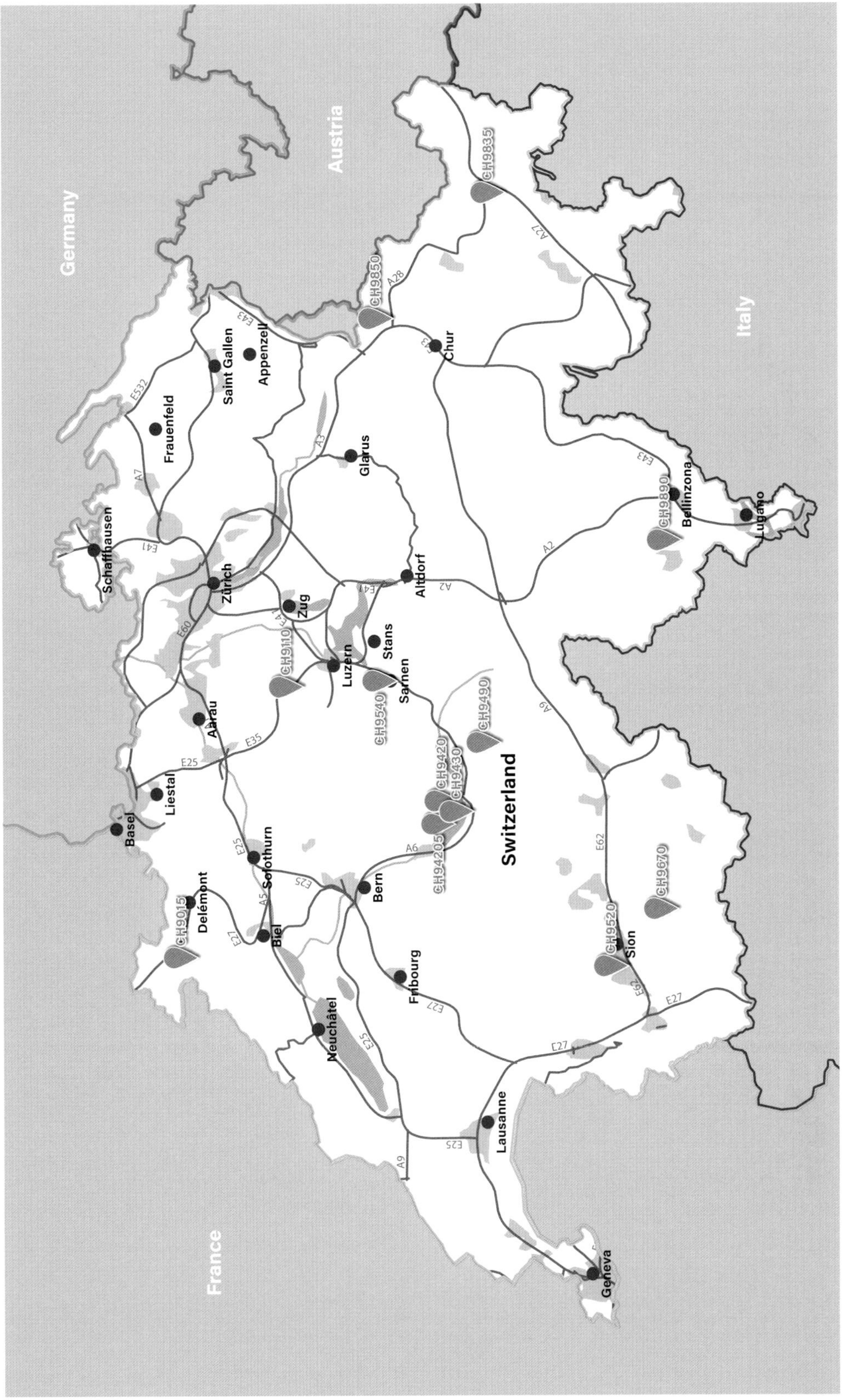

Index By Location

Index By Alan Rogers Code & Name

Contents and Overview Map

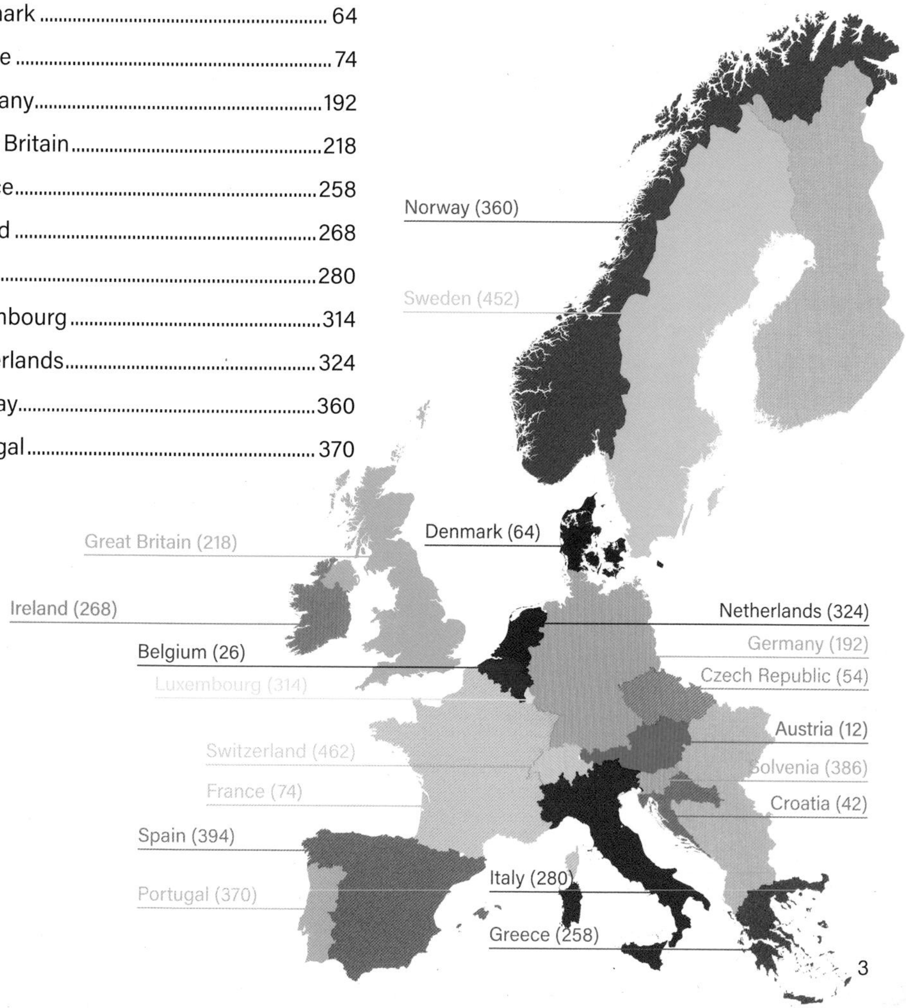
Norway (360)
Sweden (452)
Great Britain (218)
Denmark (64)
Ireland (268)
Netherlands (324)
Belgium (26)
Germany (192)
Luxembourg (314)
Czech Republic (54)
Austria (12)
Switzerland (462)
Solvenia (386)
France (74)
Croatia (42)
Spain (394)
Italy (280)
Portugal (370)
Greece (258)

1968 Alan Rogers launches his first guide. It contained over 50 "really good sites" personally recommended by Alan Rogers himself.

1975 First guide to Britain published.

1985 First guide to France published.

1986 After 18 years of steady development and achievement, Alan Rogers seeks retirement. The company was purchased by Clive & Lois Edwards. Under their direction the company diversified.

1993 Alan Rogers Guides celebrates it's 25th anniversary with the introduction of a new logo.

1998 First guide to rented accommodation in France published.

2001 Mark Hammerton purchases the Alan Rogers Group. He changes the name to Mark Hammerton Travel.

2002 First Dutch language titles launched.

2004 First guides to Italy and Spain published.

2010 First digital guides introducted. Some guides go fully digital including Naturist and Rented Accommodation.

2011 Alan Rogers undergoes a radical rebrand, the current logo introduced.

2012 First guide to glamping introduced.

2013 The Caravan and Motorhome Club acquires the Alan Rogers Travel Group.

2018 Alan Rogers Guides celebrates it's 50th anniversary, releasing a special edition Europe guide on what would have been Rogers' 100th birthday.